WORLD BALANCE SHEET

World Balance Sheet

*A comprehensive,
inventoried examination covering the extent, distribution, and relative depletion of the world's physical resources in relation to their present rate of consumption, their monetary counterpart valuation, and the population, showing comparative changes over a seventy-year period—in double-entry form, revealing where-from and where-to.*

by Robert R. Doane

AUTHOR OF
The Measurement of American Wealth and *The Anatomy of American Wealth*

CO-AUTHOR OF
The American Consumer Market

HARPER & BROTHERS

Library of Congress catalog card number: 56–9085

Contents

v

Preface

THIS WORK, covering the world economy, represents findings that have been assembled and correlated over a prolonged period, including a series of independent investigations. It is the outcome arising from the suggestions and counsel of many experienced minds, including the untiring patience and liberal cooperation of numerous technical specialists as listed under "Acknowledgments" in the Appendix. To the previous exhaustive work of these many recognized authorities in their respective fields this undertaking is deeply indebted. Thus in this sense the present volume is the product of a considerable cooperative effort.

The world scene has changed tragically since this project was first discussed back in 1936. This twenty-year period has covered an eventful span wherein both the logistics underlying the tactics and strategy of the world's politico-economic industrial organizations have undergone considerable change. It is now over twenty years since the principal concept of this work was first projected. Its background stems from the winter of 1936 when Winston Churchill first suggested that it might be well to examine carefully the factual bases and the documentary evidence underlying the mathematical formulae, accounting, and logistic techniques contributing to the principal assumptions as put forth by Karl Marx in his famous *Das Kapital*. Churchill directed his suggestion to Sir Alfred Mond, 1st Baron Melchett and head of England's Imperial Chemical Industries, Ltd., who was at the time actively interested in problems relating to international industrial organizations and labor relations.

A short time later Sir Alfred broached the subject to the late Orlando F. Weber, then chairman *ex officio* of the Allied Chemical and Dye Corporation of New York, who, upon his return to America presented the matter to this author with the advice that, after checking the critical works of Bohm-Bawerk, Carr, Sombart, Spann, and others, its treatment be given some thought along lines similar to the approach envisaged in my *Anatomy of American Wealth* (Harper & Brothers, 1940), then in course of completion. Particular attention was also recommended for a double-entry accounting approach as so admirably outlined by the Bureau of Business Research of the University of Illinois the year before in their *Balance Sheet of the Nation's Economy*, which had been developed from data in my *Measurement of American Wealth* (Harper & Brothers, 1933). Thus was planted the original germinating seed from which has grown this present volume.

At that time arrangements were entered into for making the first phases of the study in the left wing of the British Museum with full accessibility to the same reports and documents with which Marx had spent fifteen years in completing his work. But the outbreak of the war in Europe put an end to these plans.

Nevertheless, by the early winter of 1939 this part of the work was under way, with copies of all essential documents including Confidential Parliamentary Reports being assembled in my own and the Weber Library in New York, along with other invaluable material made available by the Library of Congress in Washington through the diligent search of the late Dr. Andre Bernard, then European research specialist to the Congress.

A year later, Sir John Maynard Keynes, then a member of the British Exchequer's Council, wrote that he would like to see a study made, covering the then principal European economies, similar to my "Anatomy," dealing in physical quantitative terms and their correlative monetary counterparts. Needless to say, this suggestion was incorporated into our work. Yet another two years found us still at our task when the late Floyd L. Carlisle, then chairman of the board of the Consolidated Edison Company of New York, requested that we incorporate certain broad invest-ment studies of the Western European Nations, and assemble such data as might be secured from reliable sources covering their comparative equivalent in the Union of Soviet Socialist Republics. By early September this was included and was well under way at the time of Mr. Carlisle's untimely death in November of that year.

By 1946 a partial world balance sheet was called for by the late Senator Arthur H. Vandenberg, Chairman of the U. S. Senate Foreign Relations Committee, and a summarized partial monetary balance sheet of Western Europe and the United States was supplied. This was followed by a similar request from the late ex-Senator Robert M. LaFollette, Jr., then a member of a special Senate Committee set up to handle the work Vandenberg had called for. By early spring of the follow-ing year, after a conference with Major General William J. Donovan, the author set up an organization to press the work then in hand to early completion. By the end of 1947 the first rough draft of a balance sheet covering thirty-three nations was completed and forwarded to the Senate Foreign Relations Committee. At the request of Dun & Bradstreet a copy of this draft was published in Dun's Review, March 1948, with further copies being inserted in the *Congressional Record* by the Hon. Clinton D. McKinnon of the House Committee on Banking and Currency, and by the Hon. Homer D. Angell of the House Public Works Committee.

The following year, at the invitation of the Foundation for Economic Education, working in collaboration with an advisory committee of which Dr. Fred R. Fair-child, Professor Emeritus of Economics of Yale University, was chairman, and of which Dr. Ludwig von Mises of the Graduate Institute of International Studies, Geneva, Switzerland, Dr. Willford I. King, then Professor of Economics, New York University, and Dr. Leo Wolman of the National Bureau of Economic Re-search, also members, the author engaged in a work which was confined exclusively to that of a balance sheet of the United States.

It is peculiarly difficult to prepare a study of this kind in today's climate of ex-ceptional intellectual turbulance. The reader will readily understand that in this kind of work there can be no alternative other than the faithful reporting of data supplied by the world's various recognized official bodies and the authorized reports of the outstanding nongovernmental and other specialized organizations. This is done not only as a matter of integrity but for legal reasons as well. In a work of this scope and magnitude we are not engaged in controversy with any nation in the world.

We hope the reader will bear with us in also understanding that in dealing with a world balance sheet, particularly with its quantitative side, because of sheer size we are immediately faced with an uncomfortable arithmetic. Many of the world's political subdivisions are small, relative to others, and we have been forced to carry out our over-all totals to enough places in the arithmetic scale to embrace the smaller geographic units within the digital total. For this we humbly apologize to the sophisticated.

There are problems of semantics, of accurate international standard conversion factors of land, quantity, and currency. The terms used by one government must be convertible into terms understood by other governments, and the methods used must also be understood. In matters of transliteration throughout the progress of this work the author is indebted to Gerald Doane McDonald of the New York Public Library, who has also been in charge of the Manuscript Division of the United Nations.

In many respects this survey has been an adventure in the translation of the newly achieved knowledge of the sciences and their meaning in relation to present-day economic statistics. As this is the Energy Age, pregnant with meaning for every inhabitant of the earth, insofar as the world's physical resources are concerned, we have made our feeble attempt by way of the application of this new knowledge in the hope that it may not be too late for man to become the master of science, rather than an overtrustful faith in science becoming the master of man.

In so doing the author has tried to present an impartial integrated world pattern of resources, people, production, trade, money, and consumption, in an attempt to piece together the many hitherto detached fragments never yet presented as a whole. My own command of the various branches of science is probably uneven and defective, so that I can attempt no more than to sketch the general plan of such a world picture, and point out the varying degrees of unity of its parts however imperfect the execution. The composition, unfortunately, is therefore uneven at times, and probably repetitious too, but unavoidable. I trust these defects will be overlooked. Fundamental economic research of this kind is a pedestrian science which has produced few spectacular results. It is the business of finding hitherto unrecognized and unacknowledged facts relating to the physical foundations of the world that underlie, condition, and in the end direct and limit its economic activities. It is slow work, requiring an immense amount of patient collection of reliable data and statistical testing, much of which is time-consuming and expensive. It does not advance by leaps and bounds. It plods.

Again, in this work, we are dealing with the business of the business world, which strives to do the best it can within the limits of its knowledge arising out of the peculiar structure of our planet which, while physically a single and indivisible unit, is divided politically into a number of separate states. All economic activity, domestic as well as international, is the result of the uneven distribution of resources throughout the planet. No single area of the planet has or can produce all the varied resources which could be put to good use by its inhabitants. Hence trade occupies a great role in the life of nations and in the relation between nations. It is regrettable that the average person shrinks away from such problems and dismisses them as "dull."

Economic problems, however, are not really difficult to grasp. The intellectual equipment necessary to grapple with them is child's play compared with that which is requisite to understanding today's electronics and the atom. In fact they are less difficult to understand than they are difficult to settle—the unmanageable character of man being what it is.

When Adam Smith wrote his *Wealth of Nations*, and Karl Marx produced his *Das Kapital*, neither were in possession of more than a fragmentary smattering of the world's physical geographic inventory as we now know it. In the light of today's advanced knowledge there are beginning to appear certain significant facts covering the world's natural resources in relation to the population that would indicate "conservation" to be the outstanding battle-cry for the future, rather than increased unbridled "exploitation." It would therefore seem that on the educational, ethical, moral, religious, economic, and political grounds there can be no further justification for longer withholding this knowledge from the people.

Throughout this work we have been primarily engaged in an examination of these material foundations as a structural whole, as they exist in fact, rather than in any critical examination of the world's institutional superstructure as it exists in theory. In this manner we have been hopeful that a broader basis might be indicated for the establishment of a more comprehensive unified orientation of the principal subject matter of political economy more in line with the other advancing sciences.

In the business world corporations and limited companies play the major role. These corporations are artificial individuals, legal entities, enjoying immortality. They are formed by men and given a legal life to perpetuity, while capital is valued on a basis of thirty years—a generation—with depletion valued on an average basis of fifty years—a half-century—and depreciation, the wearing away of what is produced, at ten years, with labor costs on a year-to-year basis. All this while money values are carried as an assumed constant. What, pray tell, is "scientific" about this kind of calculating arrangement?

As spiritually, historically, and politically man has demonstrated his propensity for myths, fictions, and rationalized hopes, so too, he carries these same tendencies over into his business conduct and calls it economics. For the eternity and the infinite of his religious faiths he has substituted the attributes of the "inexhaustible" to his natural resources, and "life-everlasting" to matter and energy. Apparently it has seemed more comfortable and reassuring that way.

Notwithstanding these characteristics, we are aware that people, while not denying the existence of material things, are well-disposed to a deep innate desire to rise above the restrictive influences of the purely physical world to that more mitigative point permitting its subordinations to the higher realms of the mind and spirit—to which may also be assigned quite definite values. That these values serve as superior motivating and guiding forces of the social life within which frame man must live, there can be no doubt. This human phenomenon is every bit as much a "fact" as are any of the other order of facts encountered in measuring and accounting for the finite world about us. It has been because of these various differences in the beliefs of people that we have included in our world inventory comments on the extent of education and illiteracy, and tabulations of religious affiliations as an equally vital descriptive part of the world's inventory.

Whether the present marks the beginning of an era of socialization on a scale hitherto unknown to mankind, or whether it represents but another passing improvization in an unstable world economy, whatever the case may be, there appears ample evidence that we are face-to-face with the most fundamental root forces with which we have ever yet been confronted, and from which there is no longer any evasion or escape.

Throughout the long and seemingly interminable hours of this work the author has been eminently thankful and especially grateful for the indefatigable helpfulness and invaluable cooperation in the research, preparation of tabular matter and final preparation of the manuscript, to his wife and lifelong companion, Mabel Compton Doane.

Time runs out. Of all the original participants in this work now living—only Sir Winston Churchill and the author remain. Sir Alfred Mond, Sir John Maynard Keynes, Orlando F. Weber, Floyd L. Carlisle, Senator Arthur H. Vandenberg, Dr. Andre Bernard, and ex-Senator Robert M. LaFollette, Jr.—all have passed away, leaving great memories, great achievements, great nobilities of outlook. To all of them this work at long last is now humbly, appreciatively, and respectfully dedicated.

R.R.D.

New York City
October 12, 1956

And better surely it is that we should know all we need to know, and yet think our knowledge imperfect, than that we should think our knowledge perfect, and yet not know the things we need to know.

> —FRANCIS BACON; *Novum Organum, Magna Instrauratio,*
>   Part I, 1620

We must examine and fix what ignorance is—what we are, and can be ignorant of, and thus we are thrown upon an entirely new research.

> —JAMES FREDERICK FERRIER; *Agnoiology, Institutes of*
>   *Metaphysics,* 1854

I

Introduction

There is, probably, no nicer or more difficult task in the statistical line to be exacted of any man than an estimate of the true value of large masses of wealth spread over a wide expanse of territory.

> —HENRY GARNETT, *U. S. Census Office, 1884*

MANY OF THE problems concerning the measurement of national wealth are still existent. While some of these problems may have become more difficult with the mounting scale and complexity of a world economy, nevertheless developments in methods of statistical measure and greater availability of information should open the door for more precise and useful knowledge than ever before.

There exists an unprecedented backlog of needs for more informative wealth and income data. This is particularly true as it relates to a balance sheet treatment disclosing who owns and who owes what. In this respect the National Conference on Research in Income and Wealth has discovered a long list of new uses for such facts relating to wealth and the claims upon it. In other words, there is a growing need to know how the current operations of both the individual national economy and the world economy as a whole are influenced not only by their resources and population but by the composition of their assets and liabilities structure.

1

Applied and practical economics thus bristle with questions for which such information on wealth and claims is needed. In addition to this so-called practical money-count approach, there exists an ever-growing and greater need for a fundamental research that encompasses the basic elements upon which all other analyses ultimately depend. It is with these more elemental "raw" components that this work has been essentially concerned.

The economic goods that make up wealth are quantitative concepts susceptible of more or less accurate measurement, depending upon the choice of the characteristic to be measured. For instance, coal has volume, weight, thermal capacity, utility, and market price, among many other physical, chemical, and economic qualities, each of which may be reduced to a common denominator and measured with varying degrees of satisfactory accuracy. Each of these qualities has economic significance, but the distinctive economic measurement is that of the quantity of utility possessed by the good in question. The foregoing illustration was suggested by the late Dr. Richard T. Ely, former president of the Institute for Economic Research and author of *Outlines of Economics* and many other treatises on the subject. "Utility" is a traditional term used in economics; it means primarily the power to satisfy wants, regardless of the kind of wants, and is therefore the essential common attribute of all goods viewed from the economic standpoint.

Articles of wealth everywhere and anywhere are like free goods in that they possess utility—the power to satisfy wants—but are unlike free goods in that they are scarce. Hence the distinguishing characteristic of an article of wealth is its combined attributes of scarcity and utility. In today's world, when economics is focusing attention upon problems of national prosperity, it is important that we understand clearly its leading concepts—the foremost of which is that of wealth. The term itself denotes the name of a condition of well-being, from its ancestral Saxon term "weal." In its more usual sense wealth is the collective name of a category of goods, but only those goods upon which the satisfaction of desires depends in a special and practical sense.

The simplest and most common approach to the mechanical estimation of the quantity of utility possessed by goods as wealth has been expressed in terms of *price*—the amount of money for which they may be exchanged—and which we call the money-count. The measurement of wealth in terms of money has attained predominance chiefly because of its superior practicability. Better measure is to be desired, in view of some of the limitations of the monetary method, but practical difficulties have tended to stand in the way of such a development.

MANY TRADITIONAL CONCEPTS HAVE OUTLIVED THEIR USEFULNESS

The mounting population of the world in relation to natural resources capable of supporting that population has not only strained our effective tools of measurement but has altered the kind of goods we have to measure. The traditional so-called "free" goods—a list quickly exhausted—when contrasted with the list of human wants, has always been viewed as of relative insignificance. Thus in the past we rarely thought about our wants for *air* and *water* because these elements were available in abundance and without exertion. Today, however, peoples in many parts of the world are discovering that they are not so sure about either "free" good. Witness the mounting "smog" areas and the lowering of the underground water table.

In investigating the world's wealth we are confronted with an assortment of many kinds of wealth—some of the articles being given great value in one area while being looked upon in other sections as of little or no worth. Hence, international comparisons of national wealth and income, in view of the enormous differences among countries in industrial structure, family arrangements, tribal customs, and consumer demand, present formidable difficulties independent of the monetary exchange equivalence factor.

Therefore, in world wealth measurement, the investigator has to be prepared to extemporize, to improvise, and explore, to encounter considerable trial and error. In other words the task sets the pace; he can only compose as he proceeds. The investigator must deal with fundamentals, otherwise he becomes lost in deceptive "representative" statistics.

THE INVENTORY METHOD

At his disposal is the inventory method which aims at a monetary valuation, in the aggregate, of each "form" in which wealth is embodied, without regard to the ownership. This method depends for its success almost entirely upon the existence of statistical material compiled for other purposes, e.g., government taxation figures, import and export statistics, banking figures, expert valuations of mineral resources, and statistical enumeration of objects to which an average value can be applied. In fact there are few classes of statistics that have not been pressed or "coaxed" into service for this method.

Among the various uses to which the figures of national wealth are put, there are the so-called "tests of progress" by way of comparisons between different years; tests of the "distribution of wealth" according to the form or embodiment which wealth takes, i.e., productive goods, lands, and homes, chattels, etc.; and tests as to the "concentration of wealth" covering the various forms of security holdings, bonds, bank deposits, etc.

There are tests covering the relative "prosperity" or resources of the different nations or communities at the same point of time, either as a whole or per head of the population, and also in relation to the national debts and taxation. In addition there are comparisons of wealth and income, and considerations of the distribution of wealth according to individual fortunes for purposes of disclosing changes in that distribution.

PROPAGANDA USES, MISUSES, AND ABUSES OF WEALTH FIGURES

Professor Albert G. Hart, of Columbia University, has pointed out that the time was when wealth estimates were the crown of economic statistics. "In the absence of income measurements they offered the best yardstick against which to measure quantities." In a predominately agricultural society, people, he says, may have thought of their affairs more in terms of wealth than income. In other words, wealth was more a natural focus of attention for the farmer than for the wage earner. Unfortunately, these early wealth estimates were often misused to give a semblance of concreteness to superficial analogies between public and private affairs, for purposes of outright propaganda, or for "business-getting" objectives. To condemn wealth figures, however, because they have been misused at times is to miss entirely the real point of wealth data.

WORLDWIDE NEED FOR A NEW KIND OF WEALTH STATISTIC

The fundamental goal of researches into wealth, national and international, is a critical examination of the foundation material supporting the existing wealth structure, disclosing the *course* along which wealth and its seeking may be taking mankind. It is with this aspect of a world balance that this study is primarily involved. While such an approach may at first seem sober, it can supply a useful picture of realities that have been thus far obscured from view.

TAKING PIE OUT OF THE SKY AND PUTTING IT INTO THE FUTURE

It has become popular for several countries to issue widely publicized studies proclaiming disclosures of what the "future" has to offer mankind. The rose-tinted promises these various statistical contrivances portray are primarily in accord with the current dominant political sentiment and hopes of the business or social interests sponsoring them. Their stereotyped nature, however, rarely edits an all-consuming optimism out of their "findings."

If an undertaking of this kind is dedicated to "man's right to knowledge and the free use thereof" then we should ask and heed the advice of science in all fields relating to man's well-being. A cursory examination shows that society has become far more dependent upon science than ever before. All estimates of future needs indicate that this dependence will continue at an accelerated pace. This rate of dependence sets scientific activity apart as the foremost rapidly expanding sector of the world's social structure.

A single generation has changed our knowledge and has engulfed us in many things incapable of being understood before. Ours is, of course, an era of new experience. Because it is new it may appear dangerous. We cannot close our minds to discovery. We dare not hallow ignorance. Walter Bagehot once remarked, perhaps more in sadness than in mockery, that "one of the greatest pains to human nature is the pain of a new idea."

IMPACT OF THE NEW SCIENTIFIC REVOLUTION

That we are witnessing an unprecedented growth in the scale and intensity of scientific work there can be no doubt. As recently pointed out by the "Committee on the Social Aspects of Science" of the American Association for the Advancement of Science,[1] "scientific research has placed in human hands the power to influence the life of every person, in every part of the earth." But the public interest in, and understanding of, science is not yet commensurate with the importance that science has attained in our social structure. Nor can it be said that society provides good conditions for the proper growth of science. The effort to explain the

[1] Dr. Ward Pigman of the Department of Biochemistry, University of Alabama, chairman; and Dr. Paul B. Sears of Yale University, president of the American Association for the Advancement of Science. (*New York Times,* December 31, 1956, p. 6.)

nature of science and its meaning to the public takes on additional importance as people seem to have implicit faith in the ability of science to make possible almost anything, while at the same time displaying a remarkable reluctance to heed the advice of science.

The frontiers of man's world today are separated by nomenclature and technical knowledge on the one hand, and by ignorance and tradition on the other. The vastness of life, the greatness of the planet earth together with its faults, will, after all prevail—regardless of all attempts at exploitation. Technical specialists write, for the most part, either to themselves or to specialized groups. We live in a time when a treaty between the present and the future is available to us.

Social thinking suffers from a disadvantage as compared with scientific thinking. The effectiveness of today's scientific thinking rests on the work of predecessors on whose shoulders it stands and whose results have been accepted as valid without an independent check. Even Sir Isaac Newton could not have gotten far if he had had to start by inventing the multiplication table. The situation is by no means so favorable for social thinking. Some of the fundamental issues have never been thought through, much less discussed, accepted, and recorded. Many of the most significant and crucial facts now known to be true about the world we live in have not yet been made available to the people.

Hence, in this work, we have dared to explore a new course in our examination of the world's resources. It may not be popular, but it has the authority of the world's foremost men of knowledge behind its findings.

Throughout this work we have been engaged in an examination of the physical foundations of the world as a structural whole rather than in any critical examination of the world's institutional foundations. In this manner we have been hopeful that a broader basis might be outlined for the establishment of a comprehensive and unified orientation of the principal subject matter of economics in line with the other sciences of mankind.

The need for large-scale, long-time scientific provision for the future is admittedly great. The world's resources of land, air, and water have now become so important to man everywhere that the need for more knowledge and study to determine their position and significance in relation to the population has become of paramount concern.

Man's achievements in knowledge, especially in the physical sciences and in the arts of communication, transportation, and mechanical production may have led to an overoptimistic and overconfident feeling that he has "conquered nature." This widespread feeling as to the permanent enslavement of a constant, stable, and inexhaustible earth may be open to question on more than one count. No one "conquers" nature. He works *with* it. He strives to enter into a harmonious relationship with it. The natural processes of the land, air, and water, and their correlative resources, are bigger than man, and a continued imperfect adjustment of man's efforts in relation to those natural forces can end disastrously to both man and his institutions.

In the course of a procedure of this kind it becomes necessary to attack the problem by giving consideration to such independent factors as land, water, minerals, population, etc. These embrace constituent parts of the natural world irrespective of the business processes of capitalism, socialism, or communism. The whole economic process, whatever the system, consists in nothing else but utilizing such objective resources.

For instance: has the increase in population of the world been a *cause* or a *consequence* of economic advance? Or: has its increase tended to exaggerate economic performance? And last: does it menace such performance? In fact, are there *any* menacing factors independent of an economic process?

Since any economic system appropriates all it can to such ends as it may envisage, all is well until its leaders attempt extrapolation. It is here that population, land, and technological progress become troublesome. For it is conceivable that the past performances and achievements of capitalism as well as communism cannot be repeated—say in another twenty-five-, forty-, fifty-, or seventy-year period.

STUMBLING, FRIGHTENED MAN AND MORAL RESPONSIBILITY

We are today passing through an age wherein knowledge and the basis for a better understanding of the world about us, as opposed to traditional faith, are more available and more needed than ever before. Today's storehouse of new knowledge, and its potential for greater intelligence and wisdom, would seem to indicate that to permit mankind to stumble, without realizing the possible consequences, onto a course of action which may end in an irreparable decay of the human race constitutes the gravest moral responsibility any man or group of men can take upon themselves.

A CONSOLIDATED BALANCE SHEET AN IMPOSSIBILITY

If all of the data were available covering every aspect of each of the world's sovereign states and their colonies, with international agreements covering precise date and accounting terminology, endorsed by a corps of certified public accountants operating under universally agreed purchasing-power parity of exchange values —it would still not be feasible to draft a consolidated balance sheet.

A consolidated balance sheet is a convenient device when unified control over a group of subsidiaries or previously independent units is desired. In a political world composed of ninety-five independent sovereign national states and eighty-six non-self-governing territories and dependencies, however, such an accounting device cannot, for many reasons, be pressed into service.

Even if a fictitious world parent-nation were to be assumed, and an attempt made at a consolidation wherein all similar assets and liabilities were combined and from which were excluded all account balances as reflected in colonial or subsidiary relationships, it would render a wholly inadequate idea of what lies beneath the surface. Especially is this true when a substantial portion of a national economy's operation is dependent upon its colonial affiliates.

THE COMPOSITE BALANCE SHEET, ONLY, IS PRACTICAL

Only through the summarization of the compiled available data can an exploratory trial composite balance sheet be obtained: one wherein both the physical assets and the claims against them may be disclosed in the light of the generally known relationships inherent in the functional arrangements of the world exchange economy as presented in round figures—with a grand total showing each class of assets and liabilities. These more complete data covering the world's principal nations are given in the concluding chapter of this work.

COMBINATORIAL ANALYSIS

The nature of worldwide data demands the utilization of that branch of mathematics known as combinatorial analysis. Such an approach seeks to exhibit all the ways in which a given number of things may be associated and mixed together, making as certain as possible that we have not omitted any collection, arrangement, or treatment.

Those working in this field have long recognized that such an approach was in need of cultivation, since it facilitates operations of all kinds, including the fundamental method of investigation involved in the mathematical principle of probabilities. In qualitative scientific work, whether observational or experimental, it is important not only to bring the data into comparable numerical form but also to be able to measure as definitely as possible the validity of the mean results obtained.

In such treatment the principle of *precision measure* may or may not be exactly the same as the classical *probability of error* so much used in the statistical analysis of observational data in economics and sociology. The probability of error is taken by mathematicians to mean *the limits within which it is as likely as not that the truth will fall.* Thus, in the handling of international data we are bound to accept those figures as officially reported, whether or not precision measure or probability of error may be considered as misnomers.

HISTORICAL PERSPECTIVE

The year 1882 has been chosen as a bench-mark period from which to measure world comparative data, because by that year various important scientific bodies had agreed upon international standard units of measure and geographic and geodetic international ellipsoid of reference. Much data of high reliability bearing both on the world's land area and on population had come into being, and the foundations for today's scientific world had been set in place.

The first Boer war had just ended, the Victorian era was in full bloom, the world was momentarily at peace, the Industrial Revolution with its mechanical promise was getting into full swing, and the great period of economic transition was under way. Charles Darwin, Thomas Huxley, Herbert Spencer, John Ruskin, Walter Bagehot, James Bryce, Victor Hugo, Alexander Dumas, Nietzsche, and Karl Marx were still living. It was, with the exception of Marx's *Critique*, a period of great hope and faith in the idea of progress in a world of abundant opportunities, and inexhaustible natural resources.

Since that time quantities of research material have been collected and millions of dollars expended by government agencies, universities, and scientific organizations throughout the world. There are still gaps in the information so badly needed. New methods of making available the material now lodged in forgotten pigeonholes, and the data in new fields, are both needed; for an appraisal of world resources, combined with a statement of their financial position as a whole, should be made available. Until the two are correlated, no over-all balance sheet can have more than superficial meaning. It is to this end that this study has been dedicated.

Private property is an institution which is apt to establish itself in societies in which the single family or household is the normal unit of economic activity . . . But the natural unit of economic activity is now no longer the single family, the single village or the single national state, but the entire living generation of mankind. Since the advent of Industrialism our modern Western economy has transcended the family unit *de facto* and has therefore logically transcended the family institution of private property, . . . and in these circumstances Industrialism has put its formidable "drive" into private property, enhancing the man of property's social power while diminishing his social responsibility, until an institution which may have been beneficent in the pre-Industrial Age has assumed many of the features of a social evil.

—ARNOLD J. TOYNBEE, *A Study of History* (1947)

Western civilization as a whole is still more different, sprawling over whole continents, impinging on all other societies, involving the entire world in its destiny; by comparison the mighty Roman Empire was a piddling local affair. . . . The Roman Empire had nothing like our material resources. Its famed wealth and power were negligible in comparison—the Imperial revenues were a mere fraction of the annual income of United States Steel, or the annual budget of the city of New York. Lacking the basic idea of systematically applied knowledge, the Romans had no real command of their physical environment. . . . Such differences are not necessarily in our favor and by no means guarantee our success. They make nonsense of all neat patterns got by analogy . . . to locate the exact position of our civilization on the downcurve of their historic cycles . . . in the rhythm of disintegrating societies.

—HERBERT J. MULLER, *The Uses of the Past* (1952)

II

Setting

WAR AS A MAJOR activity of mankind has dominated the world economic scene for half the lifetime of half the people now living, and all of the lifetime of the remaining half. It can no longer be overemphasized that wars and the preparation for wars are historical events of the greatest importance and magnitude in human society.

THE PRODUCTION-CONSUMPTION-DESTRUCTION CYCLE

The outright destruction of capital and property in modern warfare is carried forward on a tremendous scale, undreamt of in any previous century. The estimate of Professor E. L. Bogart covering direct and indirect costs of World War I exceeded $394 billion—almost an insignificant sum when compared with similar costs covering World War II. (See Table II–1.) Even these sums do not include the losses to neutral nations. The shift within large areas of the world economy from agriculture to industry, from hand processes to technical processes of the greatest complexity and cost, brought a shift from human independence and self-sufficiency to human dependence, with wars absorbing ever more of society's efforts.

TABLE II–1. GROSS MONETARY COSTS OF WORLD WARS I AND II

	Direct	Indirect	Total
World War I	$ 208,405,851,000	$186,334,000,000	$ 394,739,851,000
World War II	2,084,060,000,000	427,868,000,000	2,511,928,000,000
Total	$2,292,465,851,000	$614,202,000,000	$2,906,667,851,000

SOURCES: World War I: *Direct and Indirect Costs of the Great World War*, E. L. Bogart, Oxford University Press, 1919.

World War II: *Encyclopaedia Britannica*, 1948 ed., Vol. 23, page 343; *Encyclopaedia Britannica Yearbook*, 1948, page 807; Preliminary Report, Temporary Sub-Commission of the Economic Reconstruction of Devastated Areas, United Nations, 1946.

NOTE: The figures include both the Western Allied Nations and the Axis Powers. It has been estimated that, by 1972, accruing costs directly connected with World War II will raise the figure to $4,291,000,000,000. This latter figure is based on the estimated cost for the United States by Robert S. Thomas, Military Historian, War Department, Washington, D.C.

Caution: Owing to economic dislocations and the rapid changes in the value of a common measure, gold, and the still more rapid change of national currencies, no really reliable estimates have thus far been possible.

To this end, business, government, and finance become more or less fused in the large-scale effort to produce the materials of war. A mobilization of scientific and technical resources comes into being, with every encouragement being given to strengthen earnings, raise the value of property, plow back undistributed earnings through padding depreciation, depletion, and cash reserves—thus vastly increasing money profit on investment and creating an atmosphere of general "prosperity"—all of which involves an immense amount of consumption of the irreplaceable raw materials of the earth.

It is worth noting that war involves the complete destruction of those products created for war purposes. Whether such goods be called "noneconomic goods" or by some other designation, it cannot be denied that the huge increase in the national debts of the world is accompanied by no corresponding increase in national assets, and is thus bound to have an ultimate effect upon the total economic goods.

THE NEW DOMINANCE OF CLAIMS

Since war materials are produced primarily for the government, it is necessary for the national economy to provide the government with funds to pay for the goods purchased. It is also necessary to finance the particular business enterprises engaged in the production of these goods. The satisfaction of each of these needs raises many problems, all reflected in the balance sheet structure of the nation's business, banking, and government—particularly as it relates to "claims."

Under such conditions doubts are raised covering future business enterprise—the extent to which business will be taxed, the extent to which it may be regulated and controlled, the extent to which government operation of business may be carried. Against this there lurks a fear of what the late David Friday has called "the curse of peace"—the problem of reconversion of the economy to a peacetime basis. Little doubt should remain that the traditional neglect of the effects of war in the theory of economic development cannot be longer continued.

ENTRANCE OF THE BALANCE SHEET AS A MEASURING TOOL

In anticipation of these and kindred situations, over the past eighteen years several measuring tools have been suggested to avoid the confusion in the general public mind that exists when opinions have to be formulated in the absence of a sufficient basis of relevant facts. One of these suggestions is the monetary balance sheet.

A notable attempt in this direction was made some eighteen years ago, when the Bureau of Business Research, College of Commerce and Business, University of Illinois, published a *pro forma* statement in balance sheet form drawn largely from my earlier work, with the following statement: "A national balance sheet provides an accounting tool especially useful for those interested in the development of economic statistics by governments, private agencies, and individuals. The nearest approximation to such a balance sheet that has come to our attention is that shown in *The Measurement of American Wealth*, Harper & Brothers, 1933." [1]

Ten years later, the late Senator Arthur H. Vandenberg, in a public address said: "Intelligent self-interest immediately requires a sound over-all inventory of our resources to determine the latitudes within which we may consider foreign needs. This comes first, because if America sags the world's hopes sag with her. In my opinion this is the most important examination in many years. We need a total balance sheet." [2]

In the intervening period Governor Francis P. Murphy of New Hampshire made some cogent remarks in a message to the two branches of the legislature:

The very essence of government is the duty of helping its citizens solve and plan their economic problems. In its complete and proper sense all states are great and complicated business enterprises, collecting and spending money for numerous purposes in order that their citizens may the more easily earn their own living. Yet of the business of the states, taken in this broad sense, we know practically nothing. Neither does any government in the world. The fact is, we lack basic facts without which we cannot possibly operate wisely. We do not know the assets or the liabilities of the people as a whole. We have no knowledge of their real wealth. Unless we have that information we shall continue to grope blindly in making our administrative decisions and in preparing our laws. [3]

Another ten years later, the U.S. Department of Commerce stated: "The logical and most useful extension of our national accounting system, would be the construc-

[1] Bureau of Business Research, College of Commerce and Business Administration, University of Illinois, Bulletin No. 25, Vol. XXXIV (November 1936).
[2] Senator Arthur H. Vandenberg, U. S. Senate Foreign Relations Committee, 1946.
[3] Francis P. Murphy, Governor of the state of New Hampshire, January 1937.

tion of a corresponding asset and liability account, in other words a Balance Sheet, as a badly needed accompaniment of the annual national income statement." [4]

Later that same year, at the invitation of the editor of Dun and Bradstreet's monthly publication, the author prepared a summarized comparative balance sheet of the European nations and the United States which was published early the following year.[5]

Following the governor of New Hampshire's call for a state balance sheet, a privately financed commission, with the editorial guidance of Samuel Crowther in collaboration with Franzy Eakin, published their report to the commission, which was regarded as the first attempt to show the operation of a commonwealth in the form of a consolidated balance sheet.[6]

Again, at the national Conference on Research in Income and Wealth, in 1948, papers were submitted, covering the technical problems of construction and the need for a consolidated national balance sheet, by R. W. Goldsmith, A. G. Hart, and R. J. Burroughs.[7]

Insofar as this writer has been able to discover, the above-mentioned seven instances embrace about all that has been offered on this subject, each meeting with only mild general response.

A WORLD AFRAID OF FACTS

Several factors underlie this indifferent interest. The first may be the rather widespread and popularized conception that the comprehension of an entire economy, and particularly a world-scale economy, lies beyond the province and ability of mortal man—a field that more advisedly should be left to the international bankers, the cartelists, statesmen, and God. Accompanying this is the alternative attitude that there is nothing much that anyone can do about the matter, even if it were comprehended.

The second, and perhaps more likely factor, may be an apprehensiveness over the authenticity of the figures, coupled with concern over the advisability of making available *too* complete a picture of the workings and structure of the total economy, for fear that it might serve to expedite the revelation of flaws in the existing dominant theories of political economy. Such matters are considered the prerogatives of private interests, and, like rights, patents, and trade secrets, they constitute a monopoly protection. As long as there are no readily available apparent boundaries to serve as a frame of reference, both the business and political communities of interest have nothing to fear in the verbalization of their views and doctrines, safe in the comfortable feeling that there is no body of knowledge in existence to challenge them.

Again, man's quest for profit, the net product, of all enterprise free or otherwise, operating as it does on the competitive principle, dislikes being disturbed.

---

[4] *Survey of Current Business,* Office of Business Economics of the U. S. Department of Commerce, Washington, July 1947 Supplement.
[5] *The Wealth of Thirty-three Nations,* Robert R. Doane, Dun's Review, March 1948, pp. 21–44.
[6] *What We Earn and What We Owe,* a report by Samuel Crowther to the Commission for the Promotion of the Wealth and Income of the People of New Hampshire, Concord, New Hampshire, December 3, 1939.
[7] *Studies in Income and Wealth,* Vol. 12, Conference on Research in Income and Wealth, National Bureau of Economic Research, New York, 1950.

Then there exist the interminable technical disputes over structure and terminology in the field of accounting itself, undoubtedly spurred by the competitive principle also, but unfortunately serving the interests of those who might want to retard the work.

Accounting, like statistics and law, is a highly technical and in part conventional art. In these fields there are no doubt many cases that are simple and easily understood by laymen. Such cases present no problem. But there are other cases, less numerous but important, which are complex and require the application of special techniques and conventions for proper presentation. The procedures followed in such cases and the significance of the results so far outweigh the controversial conventions opposed to them that nothing should be permitted to withhold them longer from public view.

EXHAUSTING RESOURCES AND NEED FOR THEIR MEASURE

There enter into the present world setting the fundamental measures of the raw material power of the different countries—a problem which may be approached from several different angles, each providing a particular kind of information. We might measure, at least so far as the basic elements and the minerals are concerned, the distribution of the national treasures as they are to be found in the top-soil and the subsoil. Until now, however, two factors have militated against such a procedure: first, our knowledge of the quantity and quality of the earth's crust resources has been generally vague, and second, the problem of the time over which these treasures could be expected to last has been even more indeterminate. All of such data have been woefully inadequate, as most countries engaged in the recent world conflict soon discovered.

Notwithstanding these difficulties, there has been established as an integral part of the United Nations a Social and Economic Council, which has among its aims the development of knowledge and policies directed toward raising the standards of living in all countries and the establishment of an awareness throughout the world of the fundamental economic problems of each country. This council, aided by its statistical organization, has stimulated international economic research and enriched such knowledge to the extent that international comparisons of gross national product, of national income, and of wealth can now become of practical interest and importance.

Every student of current events is aware of the fact that the world's economic affairs are passing through a period of stress and strain. Whether the strain caused by war and postwar adjustment will prove more than this or that system can carry we do not know. No economic system can escape assuming a great variety and indefinite potential of economic wants, an increase in population, a limit to the supply of natural resources, and the necessity of adapting relatively scarce means to the most advantageous ends.

The fact to keep in mind, in today's world setting, is that we are extracting nearly 25 billion tons of irreplaceable raw materials of all kinds from the surface and subsurface of the earth annually, while over the past seventy years man has used up one trillion tons of these materials from what he erroneously considered to be his inexhaustible heritage. This is in addition to the 9 billion tons of geological erosion annually.

THE POPULATION CRISIS—A VITAL PART IN THE PRESENT SETTING

There is no single element in today's setting of more importance than the world population problem. Here man not only comes face to face with the stern realities of his relationship to cultural and religious doctrines, but meets up with the chemical and physical resource problem as well. This involves moral issues of the highest order. The problem is not whether turnips and cabbages can multiply faster than humans, but rather whether the soil, with its nutritive elements, can multiply too, paralleling the fastest probable rate of increase of mankind.

Barely two generations back, there were few countries in which all the land capable of yielding food was so highly cultivated that a larger produce could not be obtained from it. A large portion of the earth's surface remained entirely uncultivated, and it was then commonly thought that any limitation of production or of population from this source was at an indefinite distance, and that ages must elapse before any practical necessity might arise for taking some limiting principle into serious consideration.

That indefinite distance has now apparently reached a termination point. To further ignore a limiting principle may become the most serious error in the whole field and history of political economy. This question today is probably more important and certainly more fundamental than any other, for it involves the whole subject of the maldistribution of wealth, and, unless thoroughly understood, can

TABLE II-2. THE WORLD'S GEOPHYSICAL INVENTORY, 1882–1952

(*In Square Miles*)

	1882	1952	Change
Total superficial area [a]	196,971,984	196,950,284	− 21,700
Total hydrosphere [b]	152,691,700	153,712,989	+1,021,289
Pacific Ocean	63,982,751	63,801,668	− 181,083
Atlantic Ocean	31,528,077	31,830,718	+ 302,641
Indian Ocean	28,355,941	28,356,276	+ 335
Arctic Ocean	3,995,715	5,440,197	+1,444,482
Adjoining seas	10,181,716	10,139,750	− 41,966
Land surface water	8,541,400	8,341,211	− 200,189
Ice-cover on land	6,106,100	5,803,169	− 302,931
Total terresphere (dry land) [c]	44,280,284	43,237,295	−1,042,989
Africa	9,499,768	9,513,093	+ 13,325
America, North	8,013,313	7,742,918	− 270,395
America, South	6,028,505	5,762,166	− 266,339
Asia	15,380,377	14,937,699	− 442,678
Europe	2,292,429	2,248,288	− 44,141
Oceania	3,065,892	3,033,131	− 32,761

[a] Refers to the total mean area of the globe, sometimes called the superficial area, in the sense of pertaining to the superficies or surface.

[b] The hydrosphere includes all of the water on the surface of the globe; not only in the oceans and seas, but also the lakes, rivers, ponds, dams, reservoirs and swamps, both salt, fresh, and frozen. Unfortunately, it has been the custom of official political governmental agencies to report only the oceans and adjoining seas under the designation of "hydrosphere," thus considerable confusion leading to erroneous conclusions have resulted in many misleading figures being currently reported under this heading.

[c] Refers to actual dry land only, after deductions for surface water.

result in something more revolutionary in its consequences than anything now troubling mankind.

On the average the four elements, oxygen, silicon, aluminum, and iron, make up 87 per cent of all known terrestrial matter—including the lithosphere, hydrosphere, and the atmosphere—yet with the exception of oxygen they constitute but an insignificant fraction of the matter so essential for all living things. On the other hand, 54 per cent of the dry matter of man is carbon, the very keystone in the arch of his life. Yet carbon constitutes but eight one-hundredths of one per cent of all terrestrial matter, and of this we are told by authorities that only about one two-hundred-and-fiftieth part is in such form as to be directly usable by plants, animals, and man—with this small store constantly diminishing. Those who, in the face of these facts, advocate that every effort should be made to increase population as a way toward increased riches and the contentment of peoples do so unthinkingly.

The comparative exhibits as disclosed in Tables II–2, II–3, II–4 and II–5, when viewed in relation to the Summary Tables II–6 and II–7 covering changes in world wealth, contain material for sober thought. In later chapters the balance sheet will be shown in more detailed form. It suffices here in broad outline only.

TABLE II–3.   THE WORLD'S GEOPHYSICAL INVENTORY, 1882–1952

(*Volume in Thousands of Cubic Miles*)

	1882	1952	Change
Total planet earth	259,944,034	259,900,741	− 43,293
Total hydrosphere-cover	347,114	349,544	+ 2,430
Under hydrosphere	183,752,387	191,524,890	+7,772,503
Total terresphere (dry land)	75,844,533	68,026,307	−7,818,226
Africa	16,837,486	15,425,318	−1,412,168
America, North	13,879,549	12,345,969	−1,533,580
America, South	10,314,856	9,060,987	−1,253,869
Asia	24,952,851	22,274,380	−2,678,471
Europe	5,081,584	4,562,222	− 519,362
Oceania	4,778,207	4,357,431	− 420,776

SOURCES: 1882 period: The International Geodetic Association, Berlin, Germany. 1952 period: The International Geodetic and Geophysical Union, Savre, France.

TABLE II–4.   THE WORLD'S GEOPHYSICAL INVENTORY, 1882–1952

(*Mass in Trillions of Net Tons*)

	1882	1952	Change
Total planet earth	6,601,298,332	6,594,126,820	− 7,171,512
Total hydrosphere	4,668,635,634	4,872,181,487	+203,545,853
Total terresphere (dry land)	1,932,662,698	1,721,945,333	−210,717,365
Africa	429,051,119	390,881,591	− 38,169,528
America, North	353,677,274	311,672,105	− 42,005,169
America, South	262,842,127	229,018,729	− 33,823,398
Asia	635,846,028	563,076,124	− 72,769,904
Europe	129,488,400	115,370,337	− 14,118,063
Oceania	121,757,750	111,926,447	− 9,831,303

SOURCES: 1882: The International Geodetic Association, Berlin, Germany. 1952: The U. S. Navy Hydrographic Office, Washington, D.C.

(In Quadrillions of I. T. Calories)

	1882	1952	Change
Total planet earth	65,376,618,160,795,200	65,305,594,372,555,200	— 71,023,788,240,000
Total hydrosphere	46,236,299,861,398,502	48,252,136,573,819,450	+2,015,836,712,420,948
Total terresphere	19,140,318,299,396,698	17,053,457,798,735,750	—2,086,860,500,660,948
Africa	4,464,150,662,458,067	3,871,134,920,313,015	— 593,015,742,145,052
America, North	3,205,678,248,789,596	3,086,675,861,571,170	— 119,002,387,218,426
America, South	2,603,083,288,717,951	2,268,109,887,231,855	— 334,973,401,486,096
Asia	6,379,164,720,509,514	5,576,480,700,186,590	— 802,684,020,322,924
Europe	1,282,401,326,059,579	1,142,581,672,515,296	— 139,819,653,544,283
Oceania	1,205,840,052,861,991	1,108,474,756,917,824	— 97,365,295,944,167

SOURCE: I. T. Calories are International Table Calories converted at the accepted values commonly used for the units of energy, with conversion factors taken from tables of the American Petroleum Institute Project at the National Bureau of Standards, Washington, D.C.

Formula: $E = mc^2$. Although this formula, $E = mc^2$ is actually used in a somewhat different connotation, whereby matter is annihilated as it is converted into energy, yet there is a kinship between $E = mc^2$ and $M = e \cdot 3.93$ which expresses an energy-work-heat equivalence independent of the weight of the mass.

See the International Conversion Factors for units of energy as revised March 3, 1945; *Encyclopaedia Britannica*, '48 ed., Vol. 4, Calorimetry, Table II, p. 623.

NOTES: The above inventory represents the first of its kind prepared on a world-wide scale within the frame of reference of today's atomic energy age.

RATIONALE: When considering *mass* it is commonly thought that when we weigh a body or a substance, we are discovering how much matter there is in that body or substance. Specifically speaking, this is not so, for if we take a heavy object suspended from a spring scale and carry it aloft in a high-altitude airplane, the higher we rise, the lighter the object will become. Upon returning to earth, we observe that the weight of the object also returned to its original value. Hence, to the best of our knowledge, the *amount* of material in the object, or substance, did not change during the flight, yet the *weight* did.

We may conclude, therefore, that the weight of a body, regardless of its size and periodic location, is not a true measure of the *amount* of material in it. Hence, to obtain an adequate *unit* to represent the amount of material, we must discover some *property* of the object which depends on its quantity, but not its location or the earth's gravitational pull.

In the light of today's knowledge total mass is no longer one of nature's constants. Nevertheless, Einstein has shown that every form of energy has an equivalent mass. Hence, *mass* can be thought of as potential energy, and in this relationship the observer's measure of the mass of a body may be expressed in terms of energy of one kind or another.

Also, as mass releases its energy, the remaining mass is less than the original. Therefore, if we are engaged in measuring potential energy in relation to an ever-changing mass, then, as the mass decreases, so also does the equivalent available potential energy in one form or another. This is *the principle of the equivalence of mass and energy as used in Atomic theory*.

COMMENT: Schematically, according to Einstein, the process of energy release goes like this: an atom of mass A splits into two atoms of the mass which we call A^a and A^b, and which separate with the release of energy. When these two masses are brought to rest, and are then considered as a unit, together, they are poorer in energy content than was the original atom. In contradiction to the old principle of the conservation of mass, the sum of the mass $A^a + A^b$ is also smaller than the original mass A. In other words, $A = A^a$ and A^b; but $A^a + A^b$ no longer equals A.

15

TABLE II–6. COMPARATIVE CHANGES IN THE COMPOSITE BALANCE SHEET OF THE WORLD, 1882–1952

(In Millions of U. S. Dollars)

	1882	1952	Change	% Change
Assets:				
Private business [a]	534,335	1,698,971	+1,164,636	+ 217.95%
Private banking & finance [b]	272,640	887,627	+ 614,987	+ 225.56
Private households [c]	545,026	1,946,861	+1,401,835	+ 257.20
Private institutions [d]	27,716	189,194	+ 161,478	+ 582.61
Government [e]	69,723	1,648,277	+1,578,554	+ 2,264.03
Total assets [f]	1,449,440	6,370,930	+4,921,490	+ 339.54%
Liabilities:				
Private business	264,031	318,047	+ 54,016	+ 20.45%
Private banking & finance	173,126	773,123	+ 599,997	+ 346.56
Private households	140,914	286,188	+ 145,274	+ 103.09
Private institutions	23,156	58,272	+ 35,116	+ 151.64
Government	13,940	1,926,835	+1,912,895	+13,722.34
Total liabilities [g]	615,167	3,362,465	+2,747,298	+ 446.59%
Net worth:				
Private business	270,304	1,380,924	+1,110,620	+ 410.87%
Private banking & finance	99,514	114,504	+ 14,990	+ 15.06
Private households	404,112	1,660,673	+1,256,561	+ 310.94
Private institutions	4,560	130,922	+ 126,362	+ 2,771.09
Government	55,783	− 278,558	− 334,341	− 599.36
Total net worth [h]	834,273	3,008,465	+2,174,192	+ 260.60%

SOURCES: Data for 1882 have been drawn from Mulhall's *Dictionary of Statistics*, 1883, and revised edition, 1892; McCulloch's *Dictionary of Commerce*; Statistical Abstract of the British Commonwealth of Nations; Statistical Abstract of the United Kingdom; British Board of Trade Reports; Booth's *Digest of the Census*, 1886; U. S. Census Bureau, Estimated Tangible Wealth, 1880 and 1890.

Data for 1952 computed from income reports of the United Nations Statistical Office; special reports of the Conference on Research in Income and Wealth, National Bureau of Economic Research. Reports of the Office of Business Economics, U. S. Department of Commerce. Reports of the British Information Services.

NOTE: All U. S. dollar monetary equivalents have been converted from the buying and selling exchange rates as reported by the International Monetary Fund.

[a] Private business refers to all corporate and non-corporate enterprise; including agriculture, forestry, fisheries, mining and quarrying, manufacturing, construction, trade and commerce, transportation and communication, electric and other utilities, other professions and services.

[b] Private banking and finance relates to all banking, investment, insurance, credit agencies, security and produce exchange brokers, real estate lessors, and other holding companies.

[c] Private households contains all personal and householdings, including real property, chattels, and other forms of property.

[d] Private institutions relates to all non-public schools and colleges, hospitals, burial grounds, churches, clubs and fraternal organizations, charitable and welfare agencies, foundations and other forms of philanthropic property.

[e] Government and public relates to the property holdings of all government divisions and subdivisions, including public institutions, roads, highways, canals, harbors and harbor improvements, gold and silver coin and bullion, military and naval, and other government-operated properties.

[f] Total assets in each division includes currency and deposits, receivables, investments, rights and franchises, inventories, buildings, equipment, and land.

[g] Total liabilities contains notes and accounts receivable, mortgages and long-term debts, other liabilities, capital common and preferred stock, surplus reserves and undivided profits as normally included in the net worth or proprietor's equities section of the balance sheet.

[h] Total net worth represents total tangible physical property including inventories, buildings, equipment, and land.

TABLE II-7. COMPARATIVE CHANGES IN TOTAL ASSETS OF THE WORLD'S BUSINESS & INSTITUTIONAL ECONOMY, 1882–1952

(In Millions of U. S. Dollars)

	1882		1952		Increase	Per Cent Increase	Avg. Ann. Rate
Private business:							
Agriculture	381,515	42.2%	953,346	21.5%	571,831	149.9%	2.1%
Mining & quarrying	5,878	.6	26,300	.6	20,422	347.4	4.9
Industry	94,577	10.5	415,856	9.4	321,279	339.7	4.9
Trade	37,403	4.1	157,795	3.6	120,392	321.9	4.6
Utilities	14,962	1.7	145,674	2.0	130,712	873.6	12.5
Banking	272,640	30.1	887,627	21.4	614,987	225.6	3.2
Total private business	806,975	89.2%	2,586,598	58.5%	1,779,623	220.5%	3.1%
Institutional:							
Private institutions	27,716	3.1%	189,194	4.3%	161,478	582.6%	8.3%
Government, civil	55,778	6.2	652,718	14.7	596,940	1,070.2	15.3
Government, military	13,945	1.5	995,559	22.5	981,614	7,039.2	100.5
Total institutional	97,439	10.8%	1,837,471	41.5%	1,740,032	1,785.8%	25.5%
Total business & institutional	904,414	100.0%	4,424,069	100.0%	3,519,655	389.2%	5.5%
Physical assets in the above:							
Land	310,431	34.3%	434,527	9.8%	124,096	40.0%	.6%
Buildings & equipment	91,770	10.1	1,451,193	32.9%	1,364,423	1,486.8	21.2
Stocks of goods	27,960	3.2	682,616	15.4	654,656	2,341.4	33.4
Total physical assets	430,161	47.6%	2,573,336	58.1%	2,143,175	498.2%	7.1%

SOURCES: See Table II–6, Chapter II.
NOTE: These figures represent approximate magnitudes only.
See Indicated Composite Balance Sheet of the World Economy by Principal Sectors, Chapter X.

a This table is a supplement to Table II–6.

HOW THE WORLD APPEARS TO BE GROWING RICHER

All studies of wealth from 1880 on indicate an agreement that, in monetary terms, the average annual increase in total wealth has approximated 3 per cent. However, there are ample indications, as pointed out by Lord Melchett in 1933, that the world since 1914 has been overspending its income by 7 per cent, and that actual wealth is thus decreasing.

This latter factor we shall examine in our concluding chapters. World statistics to date have been hopelessly inadequate, and those we have had were usually twelve to twenty-four months late and rarely studied by those in authority. Thus many ominous facts have not been recognized as an integral part of the world's setting.

SCIENTIFIC FACTS VERSUS MONEY AS A BASIC METHOD OF MEASUREMENT

The complexities of international trade and banking, aggravated by the inherent political instability of the world, are such that no one group or country can control the system as a whole. Yet it is essential that something should be done to prevent the recurrence of crises if civilization is to survive.

The period from 1886 to 1914 inclusive had only three crises in forty-eight years. This comparative stability coincided with the greatest advance in the conditions of human life that mankind has ever experienced. During this period, by merest accident, the new gold production sustained a sufficient currency to carry the enormous increase in the production of other things. It was easy, in dealing with small quantities and almost locally, to make gold and silver coinage and notes and bills act as a useful and convenient method of exchange. Every day people could see the wealth as expressed in horses and cows, and land and buildings; but as the world's physical wealth increased in other ways, bullion lost its relative importance. The old monetary system became inadequate for the purposes for which it was used and wealth ceased, in the main, to be visible, tangible, and personal, becoming rather a matter of record—a vast system of *claims* to a share in something.

After 1914 the fact that the wealth of the world increased regularly year by year was a fundamental discovery that influenced the world economic outlook and provided the basis for an entirely new conception of money. This increase appeared to be due not only to the development of new countries, and the increase in population, but also to man's inventions and the discovery of new sources of power and materials.

Over the past century the annual average increase in steel has been about 6 per cent, in the chemical industry about 5 per cent, with world pig-iron production averaging 4.2 per cent, and agricultural production, at the world level, barely 1.2 per cent. With this complex of rates, currencies, and crises, the *facts of the scientific world* are the only reliable and absolute facts we have left by which we can now measure both the course and the progress of world wealth. In this connection the reader is referred to the section on "Scientific Land Measurement" in the following chapter on Land.

EARTH MEASUREMENT

The coming International Geophysical Year is not without its significance in the current world setting. Sponsored by the United Nations Educational, Scientific, and Cultural Organization at the suggestion of the International Council of Scientific Unions, it promises to be one of simultaneous worldwide observation in all fields of geophysics. This is to take place in 1957–58, with fifty-five nations participating and now forming committees to carry out the project.

Answers to a number of basic questions will be sought, such as: is the world's atmosphere leaking into outer space? where do cosmic rays come from? More information will be sought on the earth's weight and density. Studies of electric earth currents, and currents generated by chemical activity of ore bodies, and systematic observations of the hydrosphere and the ionosphere are planned. All of these studies will be conducted on the most elaborate and extensive basis undertaken in world history.

The first and somewhat limited effort at worldwide observation was made in 1882–83, with Germany, England, and the United States participating; the next took place fifty years later in 1932–33, with twenty-four nations participating. Both were originally sponsored by the European Geodetic Association, later the International Geodetic Association (*Internationale Erdmessung*), and now the International Geodetic and Geophysical Union.

Much of the material of these two earlier worldwide studies has been used in many of the tabulations and exhibits throughout this book. The reader may thus secure a sort of preview of the scope of this important work, as well as an indication of what it promises by way of filling in many gaps in our present-day knowledge.

This, from all major aspects and in brief, appears to be the present setting— whether or not on a final frontier of bitter fact—as man becomes, or should become, increasingly aware of the limits of his mind, his faith, his earth, and his wars.

All places are in one continuous space, an ultimate environment.
—WILLIAM TORREY HARRIS, *Speculative Philosophy*

We live in an environment of many facets related not as single pieces, but as a mosaic, the pattern of which is not easily discerned at first glance. It must be seen in different lights before we appreciate its true design and real worth. Thus it is easy to look to immediate gain, forgetful of the long-time advantage. But to achieve a lasting economy, man must consider all the effects of his operations on land.
—EDWARD H. GRAHAM, *Natural Principles of Land Use*

Both the march of land occupation and the ensuing national development have been accompanied by a prodigious wastage of the resources with which nature originally stocked the land. What has happened to the bountiful land . . .? The answer lies largely in a false philosophy of plenty, a myth of inexhaustibility, . . . which persists, in some quarters, even at the present time.
—HUGH HAMMOND BENNETT, *Soil Conservation*

III

Land

OF ALL THE categories of mankind's physical possessions, land indisputably occupies a unique and important position. Unfortunately, however, "land" has come to be defined in so many different ways, for particular purposes in specialized fields, that its basic position as the keystone in the arch of civilized life has become obscured.

The classical economists maintained an abstract conception of land that can scarcely be said to correspond with fidelity to fact. Land is, of course, an element independent of man, but man is most assuredly not independent of land. He is a beneficiary of what land and its uses afford, while at the same time he is an agent affecting its relative productiveness. As such, land and what man does with it has come to occupy a key place in the resource hierarchy of today's world. In this sense, the total supply of land, although limited, can no longer be viewed as "fixed" or "unalterable."

LAND IN THE BALANCE SHEET

The chief difficulty, in its economic sense, has centered round whether land is capital, and whether land is a "renewable" or a nonreproducible asset. Throughout the greater part of the world's history, land has been the foremost element of wealth and the chief source of savings and capital accumulation. Land in some form or other plays an important part in the balance sheet of every economy. Nevertheless, in economics it is commonly treated as a separate factor of production, differing from capital in that no increase in the price paid for its use will evoke an increased supply. Here the economists are on firmer ground, as they realize that land contains elements that are used up in the process of production, with both the nutritive elements, mineral deposits, and native forests as examples of this class of exhaustible material.

Land, in its full economic sense, need not be terra firma. Underwater areas, such as oyster beds, and bodies of water where valuable fishing and petroleum rights are involved, may figure as land. It has also been convenient to regard land as synonymous with all that nature supplies, external to man, which is valuable, durable, and appropriable—thus including waterfalls and other sources of water-power. Valuable rights to particular uses of land, such as franchises and the rights of privately owned transportation systems, enter into the matter.

Perhaps nothing has confused mankind more than his various concepts of "capital" as the exclusive product of the human agency, with land being considered as something apart from capital, a point made much of by Marx and most socialist doctrines.

In the writings of the economists land is given the broadest possible meaning, including not only the soil and its undetached products, such as forests and growing crops, but also all of nature's productive forces, rivers, lakes, and mines. Nevertheless, in the balance sheet under present accounting practices, land represents in money terms in the United States barely 13 per cent of the total assets, and in the world as a whole approximately 9 per cent. (See Monetary Valuation Summary Table II–7.)

Perhaps there is no better illustration delineating how far modern man has strayed in his sense of value than to view the changes that have occurred in his valuation of the world's physical assets since 1882. Here we find that, operating under a pecuniary system of economy, the relative values of land and of all the remaining physical assets that man has extracted from land have literally reversed themselves. After isolating the physical assets by classes from the summarized over-all world balance sheet we find the results as shown in Detail III–A.

DETAIL III–A

Per Capita	1882		1952	
Total physical assets	$581.86	100.0%	$1,099.63	100.0%
Total land	505.45	86.9	153.06	13.9
Total all other physical assets	$ 76.41	13.1%	$ 946.57	86.1%

In the course of a year man extracts, crops, and moves a tremendous volume of materials from the land. With the aid of modern technology he can move over ten times as much today as he could seventy years ago. The main point here is that, in what he considers to be "capital formation," capital is viewed as the product of the human agency, with the point of its origin either obscured or overlooked through his faith in an inexhaustible earth and his ability to master it.

If we retranslate the above per-capital monetary figures into physical quantitative terms, we find that the world economy, equipped with its present-day mechanized power tools, consumed an average of 550 billion tons of raw materials, or about 220 tons per capita in 1952, as against 42 tons per capita in 1882. All of this immense production came from the land, its surface and subsurface, in the form of iron, coal, oil, wood, cotton, salt, sulphur, food, etc. In other words, as his total land per capita dwindles, he extracts and removes more per capita from it—in the man-land ratios as shown in Detail III–B.

DETAIL III–B

Per Capita	1882	1952
Total world acres	20	10
Total production, tons	42	220
Total food production, tons	2	1

Thus as man's per-capita acreage of land is cut in half he has multiplied the materials he takes from it by ten, and monetarily by over twelve, as disclosed in the monetary per-capita table.

It is largely due to this apparent abundant productivity of land—the "bounties of nature," as traditionally viewed—that people not directly connected with its production problems look upon it as "cheap" in relation to man's other forms of capital goods.

We find land in all forms provided by nature; however, in economics we are concerned not with its physical supply as such but with its economic supply. In all of the older countries, the toil of ages has become embodied in the present usefulness of land, and inasmuch as no land is economically utilizable which does not represent human labor of some kind, land has come to be looked upon as the result of "stored up effort," and as such, "man-produced."

The cost of bringing agricultural land under the productive control of man is high. It would, of course, take a good-sized volume to describe even briefly the improvements in agriculture over the past centuries. These improvements, while appearing to render the bounties of nature more available, have tended in the long run to lower prices paid to producers. Thus an apparent "surplus" comes into view.

There have been improvements not only in methods of tillage and cultivation, in fertilizers, in insecticides, in plants, and in breeds of livestock but also in accessibility due to the opening up of highways and methods of transportation—all making for a better utilization of the world's land supply. These factors working together have, from a monetary point of view, tended to make the return on investments in landed property low. It is a fact of common observation in some parts of the better developed world that the rate of capitalization, i.e., the ratio of income to selling value, has been lower for land than for most other forms of capital goods.

The mistake here has undoubtedly been that the increased productivity, due to the current improvements in use, has been accepted as evidence of an abundance of land, whereas it has actually been an increase in exploitation. To the "economy of abundance" school of thought, and to those in the United States who are around seventy years of age, this is apt to appear as sufficient evidence that there is no land shortage anywhere in the foreseeable future. In other words, the monetary figures have obscured the fundamental realities.

LAND INVENTORY

As measured in representative monetary terms, land in the farmer's balance sheet approximates 40 per cent of his total assets; for the nonfarm business balance sheet it constitutes a bare 2 per cent. For the world as a whole, for all business including agriculture and the institutional economy, land represents about 9 per cent of total assets. Insofar as land's physical representation is concerned, land occupies approximately 25 per cent of the earth's surface.

For these differences in accounting for land, see Monetary Summary Tables II–6 and II–7, Table III–1 (Land Use), and Table III–2 (Land Inventory). The data in the physical tables have been assembled from the latest world survey of the Food and Agriculture Organization of the United Nations. This coverage is the most complete ever made available, and is believed to be correct within a very narrow margin of error.

In monetary balance sheets, correct determination of inventories involves questions of quantity, quality, ownership, and pricing. Quantities may be determined by physical count, measurement by weighing, accompanied with considerations of quality, and scaling down of values of obsolete and shopworn articles. In Table III–2, it will be noted that these practices as to quality, in terms of quantity, have been adhered to.

LAND PRODUCTION—THE PHYSICAL PROCESS

Denudation, erosion, and the weathering process of disintegration and chemical decomposition have been the predominate natural forces responsible for the present condition of the world's land. This continuous process of continental degradation is known as geological erosion. By contrast, *"accelerated"* erosion is the result of human interference with the natural order, and effects within a brief period the removal of soil created throughout long ages by weathering.

The time element involved in the natural process of geological erosion becomes so shortened by man's interference that impairment or destruction ensues without sufficient intervals for restoration. In other words, human eagerness, through necessity in tilling the land, accelerates the removal process of natural erosion by failing to allow sufficient intervening periods for recovery of the eroded surfaces under the protection of vegetation.

In the building of the world's topsoil, which contains the plant foods, approximately 7000 years—or 1000 years for each inch of plowable 7-inch depth—is the required natural time element. At the present time all geological and pedological surveys indicate that this food-producing topsoil is being depleted at the average rate of $\frac{1}{10}''$ per year, which means, if the process continues unabated, that the next 70 years will see the entire 7 inches of the world's present topsoil lost for

TABLE III-1. CHANGES IN THE WORLD'S LAND-USE BALANCE SHEET, 1882–1952

(In Thousands of Acres)

	1882			1952			Change	
	Acres	%	Total Acres	Acres	%	Total Acres	Acres	% Change
Grand total available land		100.0%	28,339,382		100.0%	27,671,869	− 667,513 d	− 2.4%
Inaccessible forest	12,454,987	43.9		5,835,088	21.1		−6,619,899	− 53.2
Desert & wasteland	2,675,200	9.4		6,436,997	23.3		+3,761,797	+140.6
Built-on a	2,180,644	7.7		4,051,843	14.6		+1,871,199	+ 85.8
Pasture & meadow	3,807,098	13.4		5,404,175	19.5		+1,597,077	+ 41.9
Cropland b	2,036,560	7.2		2,537,589	9.2		+ 501,029	+ 24.6
Accessible forest	427,399	1.5		2,338,957	8.5		+1,911,558	+447.3
Orchards & gardens	104,933	.4		130,694	.5		+ 25,761	+ 24.5
Total accounted for			23,686,821			26,735,343	+3,048,522	+ 12.9
Unused		16.5	4,652,561		3.3	936,526	−3,716,035 e	− 79.9%

SOURCES: Compiled from data of the Food and Agriculture Organization of the United Nations, Vol. IV, Part I; Mulhall's *Dictionary of Statistics,* 1883 ed.; *Encyclopaedia Britannica,* 11th ed., 1911; *Encyclopedia of Social Reform,* Bliss ed., 1908; Statistisches Jarbuch fur das Deutsche Reich, 1906; Yearbook of United States Department of Agriculture, 1905. See *Forest Resources of the World,* Food and Agriculture Organization, Division of Forestry, 1948.

a See Table VII–4, Chapter VII, Consumption

b Quality of cropland

	1882	1952
Good land	85.0%	41.2%
50% top-soil lost	9.9	38.5
Submarginal land	5.1	20.3
Total	100.0%	100.0%

Use of cropland:

	1882	1952
Crop failure	3.0%	7.0%
Temporary fallow	10.0	14.9
Crop harvested	87.0	78.1
Total	100.0%	100.0%

c Decrease in unused land
Where-to:

	1882	1952
Pasture & meadow	1,597,077	
Cropland	501,029	
Orchards & gardens	25,761	
Built-on	1,592,168	
Total		−3,716,035

d Total decrease in land area

	1882	1952
Unused land		−3,716,035
Acc'ted for land		+3,048,522
Total		− 667,513

TABLE III-2. PRELIMINARY INVENTORY OF GRADATION CHANGES IN THE WORLD'S FOOD PRODUCING LAND, 1882–1952

(In Acres)

Grade description	1882		1952		Change	Total
Excellent	760,167,196	12.8%	637,724,158	7.9%	− 122,443,038	− 122,443,038
Good	1,589,273,182	26.7	1,340,027,978	16.6	− 249,245,204	− 249,245,204
Fair	2,536,043,310	42.6	2,195,708,494	27.2	− 340,334,816	− 340,334,816
					− 712,023,058	
Poor	310,427,335	5.2	2,300,650,445	28.5	+1,990,223,110	+1,990,223,110
On way out	752,679,977	12.7	1,598,346,625	19.8	+ 845,666,648	+ 845,666,648
					+2,835,889,758	
All grades	5,948,591,000	100.0%	8,072,457,700	100.0%		+2,123,866,700

(Acres per Capita)

Grade description	1882		1952		Change	Total
Excellent	.5	12.2%	.3	9.4%	− .2	− .2
Good	1.1	26.8	.5	15.6	− .6	− .6
Fair	1.8	43.9	.9	28.1	− .9	− .9
					−1.7	
Poor	.2	4.9	.9	28.1	+ .7	+ .7
On way out	.5	12.2	.6	18.8	+ .1	+ .1
					+ .8	
Total	4.1	100.0%	3.2	100.0%		− .9

SOURCES: Computed from data covering approximately 2 billion acres of agricultural land, or 25 per cent of world total, as prepared under the direction of Dr. Curtis F. Marbut, Bureau of Chemistry of Soils, U. S. Department of Agriculture.

another 7000 years. The rate at which the principal topsoil plant nutrients are being depleted is shown in the accompanying Table III–3.

TABLE III–3. CHANGES IN WORLD INVENTORY OF PRINCIPAL TOP-SOIL PLANT NUTRIENT RESOURCES, 1882–1952

(*In Thousands of Net Tons*)

	1882	1952	Change
Nitrogen	16,712,800	10,682,700	— 6,030,100
Phosphorus	7,713,600	5,789,100	— 1,924,500
Potassium	117,632,400	73,625,500	— 44,006,900
Calcium	117,632,400	61,950,200	— 55,682,200
Magnesium	53,995,200	36,931,300	— 17,063,900
Sulphur	7,713,600	4,121,200	— 3,592,400
Total	321,400,000	193,100,000	— 128,300,000
Organic matter	161,656,126	223,686,994	+ 62,030,868
Total	483,056,126	416,786,994	— 66,269,132
Water	9,245,880,000	11,318,267,000	+2,072,387,000
Grand total	9,728,936,126	11,735,053,994	+2,006,117,868

	(Per Acre)			(Per Capita)		
	1882	1952	Change	1882	1952	Change
Nitrogen	8.2	4.2	— 4.0	11.7	4.3	— 7.4
Phosphorus	3.8	2.3	— 1.5	5.4	2.3	— 3.1
Potassum	57.8	29.0	— 28.8	82.0	29.6	— 52.4
Calcium	57.8	24.4	— 33.4	82.0	24.9	— 57.1
Magnesium	26.5	14.6	— 11.9	37.7	14.8	— 22.9
Sulphur	3.8	1.6	— 2.2	5.4	1.6	— 3.8
Total	157.9	76.1	— 81.8	224.2	77.5	— 146.7
Organic matter	79.4	88.1	+ 8.7	112.7	89.8	— 22.9
Total	237.3	164.2	— 73.1	336.9	167.3	— 169.6
Water	4,540.0	4,460.2	— 79.8	6,448.5	4,543.1	—1,905.4
Grand total	4,777.3	4,624.4	—152.9	6,785.4	4,710.4	—2,075.0

	1882	1952
Total cropland acres	2,036,559,615	2,537,588,715
Total population	1,433,804,000	2,491,280,000

SOURCES: Dr. Curtis F. Marbut, Bureau of Chemistry of Soils, U. S. Department of Agriculture; Dr. Ernest E. DeTurk, professor of soil fertility, University of Illinois.
NOTE: Organic matter is an important source of nitrogen, phosphorus, and sulphur in approximately 36% nitrogen, 60% phosphorus, and 4% sulphur. It is deficient in calcium and magnesium, and contains no potassium.

In petrology, metamorphism and metasomatism are the principal processes by which the fundamental alteration is affecting the composition—mineral and chemical, structural or textural—of the crust of the earth. The entire crust of the earth is subject to these slow alterations. This geological phenomenon, of course, includes the subsurface where the great mineral deposits of the earth are found. Geologists have long been directing their attention to climate and the weathering processes of the past and present, because of their effect not only upon the organic world but chiefly upon the materials that have gone into the making of the crust of the earth—this land that man mines and builds and lives on.

The geologic schedule of building time, and man's annual rate of removal in terms of tons is now running as illustrated in Detail III–C.

DETAIL III–C

	Time Required for Nature to Produce 1 Ton: (Years)	Man's Removal Rate: (Tons Per Year)
Petroleum	250,000,000	535,000,000
Coal	1,000,000,000	1,325,000,000
Iron	2,000,000,000	103,000,000
Lead	4,000,000,000	4,000,000
Topsoil	7,000	6,170,000,000

From this it will be noted that while man is removing petroleum at a current annual rate of 2.1 times faster than it can be produced, and coal at a rate of 1.3 times faster, he is removing the all-important nutrient ingredients from the soil at a rate of over 800,000 times more rapidly than nature can replace them.

When it is further realized that man is losing 40 million acres of land per year to the deserts, 48 million acres to "build-on" areas for living and working purposes, and 10 million acres per year to the seas, it becomes apparent that the world's land inventory is being depleted at an alarming rate.

SCIENTIFIC LAND MEASUREMENT

Agricultural research is largely a public function. Few individuals or private business concerns have the scientific interest, public spirit, money, or personal incentive to do it well. As a private undertaking such research does not pay, principally because the benefits cannot be monopolized but must be shared with the entire community. Publicly conducted, however, it has paid large dividends. Not to carry on such research would mean neglecting one of the world's greatest sources of national wealth. Indeed it is far more fundamental than that, for under the strain of an unprecedented increase of population it becomes a vital matter of caring for life itself, and an all-important element in today's world setting.

National agriculture is not a separate but an integral part of the world's economic system. It affects and is affected by financial, industrial, and social conditions at home and abroad. For these reasons, rather complete agricultural statistics have been kept by the world's leading nations since 1880. However, public aid for agricultural research came slowly before that period, due largely to the seemingly inexhaustible abundance of natural resources which appeared to negate the necessity. Unfortunately this uninformed view still prevails among large segments of the non-farm population.

Although soil science was founded in Russia about 1870, and soil survey work was started in the United States in 1898, it was not until 1939 that the results of a world agricultural census under the leadership of the International Institute of Agriculture in Rome published a part of their summaries, in five volumes, covering thirty-nine of sixty-three countries for the year 1930, and titled the *First World*

Agricultural Census. Meantime preparations were made for the second world census to be taken in 1940–41, but World War II interfered. Hence it was not until 1949 and 1950 that full world data became available through the work of the Food and Agriculture Organization of the United Nations, which took up the work of the original institute.

These classifications of land use and land grades are given in accompanying Tables III–1 and III–2, with the nutrient qualities shown in Table III–3. Here the classifications have been presented in a manner to cause one to think of the facts in such groups, and of the groups in such order, that one may call to mind most quickly and with least difficulty their fundamental relationships.

Insofar as the volume weight of the soil is known, the weight of dry soil per cubic foot, or per acre foot, or of any fractional part, can be computed readily. The average weight of dry soil per acre at plowed section depth (6¾ to 7 inches) is given by agricultural experts as 2 million pounds, or 1000 tons. These weight figures are used in calculating the amount of soil water, the supply of organic matter, and the quantities of plant food elements present.

LAND PRODUCTION—MONETARY MEASUREMENT AND PROCESS

Few people realize what it costs to render land useful. From the standpoint of economics, accessibility is a crucial factor. This means the building of roads and lanes, the clearing of land, erecting of buildings for storage of equipment, stock, and materials, etc., all of which invoke outlays closely related to the ultimate valuation of the land. Time is also required to get the settlers on the land, and still longer time to bring the land into use.

To the economist these are called *ripening costs* of land, and are properly chargeable against the increment in land value resulting from such change in use as has been effected. Obviously the time interval described as a ripening period is not peculiar to capital investments in land alone. Such expenses are incurred in other forms of capital; but in the case of land, they are particularly significant because of the heavy investments and long period of time required to change land from one use to another. Thus, this ripening cost process exists in connection with land to a degree not found in connection with most forms of fixed capital.

In addition to the ripening cost factor there are exhaustion costs, reflecting depletion, which manifest themselves well enough in the changing current market value of the land by way of its productive ability but for which the average farmer rarely provides either a depletion reserve or adequate maintenance outlays. In such cases, where the unseen plant nutrient resources of the land are unknown, the tax appraiser may, for fiscal purposes, be overvaluing the land, or the prospective buyer may place an undervaluation on it. In either case, what has happened usually is that the farm operator, by not including a sufficient charge allowance for the nutrient removal as a cost factor entering into the price of his product, is actually operating at a loss while considering himself to be achieving a profit. In other words, he has been squandering his capital at both his and the government's expense, but to the benefit of the food purchasing consumers.

As an example of this erroneous approach to realistic monetary cost-accounting practices, Detail III–D, taken for the United States for the year 1930, may prove illuminating:

DETAIL III–D

(*In Millions of U. S. Dollars*)

Total cash receipts		$ 9,050
Production outlays:		
Maintenance, depreciation, buildings & equipment	$1,284	
Wages paid farm labor	1,134	
Feed purchased for livestock	791	
Farm property & other taxes	756	
Irrigation charges, grazing fees & other	698	
Interest on farm mortgages	572	
Rent paid nonfarm landlords	522	
Gasoline & petroleum for operating equipment	360	
Seeds, bulbs, & plants purchased	342	
Livestock expenditures	312	
Fertilizer & lime	288	
Total production cash outlays		7,059
Total apparent net return (product net)		$1,991
Net plant food removed from soil @ fertilizer costs [a]		3,002
Actual deficit unprovided for		−$1,011

SOURCES: The U. S. Department of Agriculture, Statistical Yearbook, 1950, p. 648. Hugh Hammond Bennett, *Soil Conservation*, 1939, p. 9.

[a] Contains 92,172,300 tons of plant nutrients washed out of fields, @ $35.70 per ton = $3290, less fertilizer replacement of $288.

It may be observed from this customary method of farm cost-accounting, as practiced by the U. S. Department of Agriculture, that the farmers are the real "exploited classes," both as businessmen and as wage workers—a form of exploitation that has gone on without protest for centuries, unknown and unseen—at the expense of the world's food-producing land, in favor of the nonfarm population.

MINING THE LAND

Farmers are engaged in mining the soil and extracting the minerals essential to the growth of their product. It will be noted from Table III–4a that over one billion tons of vital soil minerals are mined annually by virtue of the production of the world's food, while nearly 5 billion tons of these materials are removed by action of wind and water erosion.

While the mining industry of the world, covering some thirty leading minerals including coal, oil, iron, copper, lead, zinc, tin, manganese, magnesium, potash, phosphate, sulphur, etc., is extracting some 2.5 billion tons of these minerals annually (Table III–11), the world's agriculture is running industry a close second with 8 billion tons annually if one includes crops grown. The agricultural mineral reserves of the world, as shown in Tables III–5 and III–6, are inclusive of organic matter.

Mining is a continual harvest; it is purely extractive. The traditional classical economic theory views mineral land as differing basically from agricultural land, because, as it states, there is no possibility of replacing the materials taken from the earth. Under this theory, agricultural land has been considered capable of being *enriched* by use, under the conditions of modern cultivation—an assumption not borne out by the facts. Nevertheless, the mining industry is favored by most

TABLE III-4. THE WORLD'S AVERAGE ANNUAL PLANT NUTRIENT BALANCE SHEET—1952

(In Net Tons)

The world's annual removal:

	Crop consumption	Animal consumption	Weed & insect consumption	Wind erosion	Water erosion	Radiation absorption [b]	World's total consumption
Nitrogen	35,100,000	16,000,000	4,200,000	27,000,000	101,500,000	300,000	184,100,000
Phosphorus	5,400,000	2,700,000	700,000	4,400,000	15,300,000	-	28,500,000
Potassium	24,400,000	19,800,000	5,200,000	92,800,000	349,600,000	500,000	491,800,000
Calcium	7,600,000	5,300,000	1,400,000	163,100,000	613,400,000	1,800,000	792,600,000
Magnesium	3,800,000	2,700,000	700,000	51,000,000	191,900,000	700,000	250,800,000
Sulphur	3,700,000	2,100,000	600,000	31,500,000	119,800,000	1,300,000	159,000,000
Sub-total	80,000,000	48,600,000	12,800,000	369,800,000	1,391,000,000	4,600,000	1,906,800,000
Organic matter [a]	800,500,000	300,000,000	128,100,000	534,400,000	2,500,000,000	-	4,263,000,000
Grand total [a]	880,500,000	348,600,000	140,900,000	904,200,000	3,891,000,000	4,600,000	6,169,800,000

The world's annual replacement:

	Man-made fertilizers	Nature's put-back [d]	Man-made irrigation	Atmospheric fall-back	Precipitation fall-back	Sub-soil [e] replacement	World's total replacement
Nitrogen	2,200,000	60,200,000	240,000	3,600,000	7,100,000	800,000	74,140,000
Phosphorus	2,200,000	4,700,000	-	600,000	-	400,000	7,900,000
Potassium	2,000,000	11,700,000	4,500,000	12,500,000	11,800,000	5,900,000	48,400,000
Calcium	15,200,000	7,000,000	26,800,000	21,900,000	44,200,000	6,000,000	121,100,000
Magnesium	c	3,500,000	9,000,000	6,800,000	17,600,000	2,700,000	39,600,000
Sulphur	4,900,000	1,700,000	19,660,000	4,300,000	32,300,000	300,000	63,160,000
Sub-total	26,500,000	88,800,000	60,200,000	49,700,000	113,000,000	16,100,000	354,300,000
Organic matter	-	565,100,000	-	71,600,000	-	-	636,700,000
Grand total	26,500,000	653,900,000	60,200,000	121,300,000	113,000,000	16,100,000	991,000,000

(In Net Tons)

The world's annual deficit:

	Crop consumption	Animal consumption	Weed & insect consumption	Wind erosion	Water erosion	Radiation absorption	World's total deficit
Nitrogen	− 32,900,000	+ 44,200,000	− 3,960,000	− 23,400,000	− 94,400,000	+ 500,000	− 109,960,000
Phosphorus	− 3,200,000	+ 2,000,000	− 700,000	− 3,800,000	− 15,300,000	+ 400,000	− 20,600,000
Potassium	− 22,400,000	− 8,100,000	− 700,000	− 80,300,000	− 337,300,000	+ 5,400,000	− 443,400,000
Calcium	+ 7,600,000	+ 1,700,000	+ 25,400,000	− 141,200,000	− 569,200,000	+ 4,200,000	− 671,500,000
Magnesium	− 3,800,000	+ 800,000	+ 8,300,000	− 44,200,000	− 174,300,000	+ 2,000,000	− 211,200,000
Sulphur	+ 1,200,000	− 400,000	+ 19,060,000	− 27,200,000	− 87,500,000	− 1,000,000	− 95,840,000
Sub-total	− 53,500,000	+ 40,200,000	+ 47,400,000	−320,100,000	−1,278,000,000	+11,500,000	−1,552,500,000
Organic matter	−800,500,000	+265,100,000	−128,100,000	−462,800,000	−2,500,000,000	—	−3,626,300,000
Grand total	−854,000,000	+305,300,000	− 80,700,000	−782,900,000	−3,778,000,000	+11,500,000	−5,178,800,000

a Complete analysis undetermined; b Earth's annual loss to outer space, and disintegration in the air; c Included with calcium; d Manures, legumes, and bacteria fixation; e Nutrients derived from soil-growth below 7-inch depth.

TABLE III–4a. THE WORLD'S ANNUAL FOOD RESOURCE BALANCE SHEET, 1952

(In Net Tons)

Total Basic Chemical Nutrients in World's Food-producing Top-Soil   416,786,993,573 [a]

Removal:		
Annual removal by crops	880,500,000	
Annual removal by grazing	348,600,000	
Total removal for food		−1,229,100,000
Removal by crop failure, insects, and wind	1,045,100,000	
Removal by water erosion and leaching	3,891,000,000	
Removal by atmospheric absorption	4,600,000	
Total removal by natural causes		−4,940,700,000
Grand total annual nutrient removal		−6,169,800,000
Replaced:		
Received from animal manures	653,900,000	
Nutrients in annual rainfall and fall-back	234,300,000	
Soil rebuilding from below top-soil	16,100,000	
Total natural soil rebuilding		+ 904,300,000
Irrigation systems	60,200,000	
Commercial chemical fertilizers	26,500,000	
Total replaced by man		+ 86,700,000
Grand total return to soil		+ 991,000,000
Annual average *net* loss		−5,178,800,000

SOURCES: U. S. Department of Agriculture; United Nations Statistical Yearbook, 1952; Food and Agriculture Organization of the United Nations.

[a] It takes on an average of 1,000 years to build 1 inch of top-soil. At present rate the basic soil nutrients will be exhausted in approximately 80 years, or by the year 2032.

TABLE III–5. THE WORLD'S INVENTORY OF TOP-SOIL NUTRIENT RESOURCES, 1882–1952

(In Thousands of Net Tons)

	1882	1952	Change
Total land	483,056,126	416,786,994	−66,269,132
Africa	108,204,572	93,360,287	−14,844,285
America, North	93,712,888	80,856,677	−12,856,211
America, South	57,483,679	49,597,652	− 7,886,027
Asia	115,450,414	99,612,091	−15,838,323
Europe	53,619,229	46,263,356	− 7,355,873
Oceania	54,585,344	47,096,931	− 7,488,413

NOTE: Top-soil nutrients refer to the principal nutrient elements normally found present in plowable top-soil and pasture land at a depth of approximately 6⅔ inches. In addition to oxygen and silicon, these elements are calcium, nitrogen, potassium, phosphorus, magnesium, sulphur, boron, organic matter, and some twenty-five other trace elements significant for plant growth but present in the soil in relatively minute quantities.

These data have been based upon soil analyses and lysimeter studies applied to 365 million acres in harvested crops, and 1 billion acres of pasture of all kinds.

SOURCE: National Resources Board Report on Land Use, Washington, D.C.

TABLE III–6.   CHANGES IN AVERAGE HUMAN CONSUMPTION OF THE WORLD'S
BASIC TOP-SOIL NUTRIENTS, 1882–1952

(*In Net Tons*)

	1882	1952	Change	% Change
Nitrogen	16,140,620	29,103,140	+ 12,962,520	+ 80.3%
Phosphorus	7,308,960	15,874,440	+ 8,565,480	+117.3
Potassium	111,461,640	201,605,388	+ 90,143,748	+ 80.9
Calcium	111,461,640	169,856,508	+ 58,394,868	+ 52.4
Magnesium	51,162,720	101,067,268	+ 49,904,548	+ 97.5
Sulphur	7,004,420	11,641,256	+ 4,636,836	+ 66.2
Total [a]	304,540,000	529,148,000	+224,608,000	+ 73.8%

	1882	1952	Per cent
Reserve supply [b]	483,056,000,000	416,787,000,000	
Exhaustion period [c]	1,586 yrs.	788 yrs.–798 yrs.	−50.3%
Nitrogen	55 "	20 " – 35 "	−63.6
Phosphorus	25 "	11 " – 14 "	−56.0
Potassium	386 "	139 " –247 "	−64.0
Calcium	386 "	117 " –269 "	−69.7
Magnesium	177 "	70 " –107 "	−60.5
Sulphur	25 "	7 " – 18 "	−72.0
Organic matter	532 "	424 " –108 "	−20.3

[a] Computed from data in *The Chemistry of Food and Nutrition*, Dr. Henry C. Sherman, Columbia University, 1927.
[b] See Table III–5. Adapted from data covering approximately 2 billion acres of land, or nearly one-fourth of the world's food-producing acreage, prepared under the direction of Dr. Curtis F. Marbut, Bureau of Chemistry of Soils, U. S. Department of Agriculture.
[c] Number of years until exhaustion period of reserve supply at existing rates of consumption.

governments of the world, and is permitted to write off large amounts of its land value each year as a legal deduction from total cash receipts before computing net income for taxation purposes. In the United States this depletion averages some 15 per cent of total value assigned to land, and in many cases even exceeds the entire value of the land by a considerable amount—whereas in agriculture the average deduction for depletion of farm land resources barely approximates one-tenth of one per cent.

KINDS OF LAND AND HOW MUCH

Over the past half-century the world's land has been traditionally classified, in terms of square miles in area, broadly as *Forest, Grass,* and *Desert* land, and given in round numbers in the atlases and encyclopedias as: forest land, 22 million square miles; grass land, 13 million square miles; and desert land, 17 million square miles; for a total of 52 million square miles.

These classifications have also been broken down, in the same source books, as a total food-producing land area of 50,300,000 square miles, consisting of 26 million square miles of land suitable for grazing and 24,300,000 square miles capable of producing crops.

More recently the popular almanacs give an account of the world's land on a different basis: 33 million square miles of fertile regions; 19 million square miles of steppes; 5 million square miles of deserts—total, 57 million square miles.

CONFUSED REPORTING

As the above three totals are different to a considerable ·extent, there can be little wonder that they should be confusing to the average layman in such matters. Further, no two atlases, encyclopedias, almanacs, or yearbooks give the same total land area of the world in any single year. And the same widely accepted dispensers of popular knowledge disclose an astonishing flexibility in the manner in which they vary their data from year to year, with no two years ever giving the same over-all figures.

This variation has ranged from as high as 52,150,000 square miles for the inhabitable world (Encyclopaedia Britannica Yearbook, 1953, p. 57) to as low as 37,400,000 square miles (The Twentieth Century Fund, *World Population and Production*, 1953, Vol. I, p. 41), both in the same year—a variation of 14,750,000 square miles amounting to a discrepancy exceeding 9 billion acres of land. This is a lot of real estate to account for in any responsible land inventory.

PAY YOUR MONEY AND TAKE YOUR CHOICE

If the reader is willing to accept the 750,000 square mile ice-cap of Greenland and the 6 million square miles of Antarctica as "land," then, according to the following "authorities" there has been a wide variety of changes in the world's land inventory. These discrepancies over a 5-year inclusive period run as tabulated in Detail III–E.

DETAIL III–E

Year	Britannica Yearbook	Information Please Almanac	World Almanac	Statesman's Yearbook
1952	58,209,392	58,151,000	53,202,786	49,709,000
1948	57,566,335	57,215,000	59,407,786	52,472,000
	+643,057	+936,000	−6,205,000	−2,763,000

DIMINISHING CONJECTURE

Both the area and the population of the world as a whole have been the subject of estimates in scientific works for the past three and one-half centuries, and are still considered by many to be matters of rough approximation. Every decade, however, has brought a diminution of the field of conjecture, as some form of civilized administration is extended over the more backward tracts, followed by a survey and a census, thus reducing the area of speculation and narrowing the range of probable error.

PRODIGALITY OF IGNORANCE OF THE WORLD NO LONGER EXCUSABLE

The conception and development of a systematic plan of the earth—its land and its water—and the guiding influence of its environmental factors through the circulation of water and of air on the distribution of plants and animals, and finally on the movements of man, can give to this aspect of the world's wealth a philosophical dignity and a scientific completeness which it has never previously possessed. This should be the starting point for all wealth studies, global and national.

THE GEOGRAPHY OF WEALTH AND THE ATLAS OF IGNORANCE

The foundations for a geography of wealth have been developing through a long series of efforts to cope with accumulations of new facts and new discoveries. So complex a science has demanded the labor of many specialists to advance it by the separate study of its interdependent parts. There is a geographical aspect in all of the sciences which are concerned with the earth, and it follows that some knowledge of each of these sciences is required in dealing understandingly with the principal subject matter of economics—particularly world economic geography and economic theory.

Exact and organized knowledge relating to the distribution of the phenomena of the earth, in terms of its natural resources and their elemental sustaining power, has been slow in developing. Eleven years before Adam Smith published his *Wealth of Nations,* Immanuel Kant was delivering lectures on physical geography[1] which he viewed as the basis not only of history but also of all other departments of knowledge, inclusive of the political and economic. In fact, physical geography has long appealed to thinkers who view knowledge of the world, resulting from fact, experience, and reason rather than traditional unverified "fact," as an educational discipline of primary importance.

It was not, however, until the year 1952, that the office of the geographer of the U. S. Department of State began to make progress on the *Atlas of Ignorance,* designed to point up the lack of systematic data for many parts of the world.

HOW THE LAND IS DISTRIBUTED AMONG THE POLITICAL UNITS OF THE WORLD

Traditionally the earth has been divided into six continents, and sometimes five with Asia and Europe being joined as "Eurasia," according to the knowledge acquired piecemeal during long periods of discovery. Our age and our point of view have marked out the earth's wealth, outside the polar regions, as consisting of some eight principal large political areas:

1. The British World Empire, now called the British Commonwealth of Nations.
2. The European Continent, without England and without Russia, both of which tend to find their economic and political centers of gravity outside Europe.
3. The French Union, composed of France and French Overseas Territories and Associated States.
4. The United States and its possessions and spheres of influence in Panama and on the islands of Cuba, Puerto Rico, Virgin Is., Hawaii, Guam, Samoa, and the Philippines.
5. Soviet Russia, the U.S.S.R. and its spheres of influence in both Europe and Asia.
6. The Asian nations, including China, Mongolia, Tibet, Thailand, Japan, and parts of the Middle and Far East.

[1] University of Konigsburg from 1765 onwards; printed in *Schriften zur Physischen Geographie,* Vol. VI, 1839.

7. **Latin Africa,** that is, the parts of Africa occupied by France, Belgium, Spain, Portugal, and formerly by Italy.

8. **Latin America,** which includes all of South America, excluding the British, American, and Dutch possessions.

In Land Table III–7 and its supplemental Tables III–7a, III–7b and III–7c a more detailed breakdown of the political distribution is given, disclosing changes that have occurred between the years 1882 and 1952. In addition to these major groupings there is now the United Nations and its auxiliary organizations.

TABLE III–7. HOW THE WORLD'S GROSS LAND AREA HAS BEEN DISTRIBUTED AMONG THE NATIONS, 1882–1952

(Inclusive of Home Country and Dependencies, in Thousands of Square Miles)

	1882		1952		Change		% Change	
Russia	8,648	16.35%	8,599	16.67%	−	49	−	.57%
China	5,645	10.67	3,745	7.26	−1,900		−	33.66
England	4,500	8.51	2,526	4.90	−1,974		−	43.87
France	4,279	8.09	4,698	9.11	+	419	+	9.79
Canada	3,654	6.91	3,845	7.45	+	191	+	5.23
United States	3,624	6.85	3,628	7.03	+	4	+	.11
Brazil	3,219	6.09	3,288	6.37	+	69	+	2.14
Australia	2,973	5.62	3,157	6.12	+	184	+	6.19
India	a		1,767	3.43	+1,767			
Pakistan	a		365	.71	+	365		
Germany	1,237	2.43	143	.28	−1,094		−	88.44
Turkey	1,178	2.23	297	.58	−	881	−	74.78
Argentina	1,136	2.15	1,079	2.09	−	57	−	5.02
Denmark	842	1.59	857	1.66	+	15	+	1.78
Portugal	836	1.58	896	1.74	+	60	+	7.18
Netherlands	795	1.50	227	.44	−	568	−	71.45
Mexico	767	1.45	760	1.47	−	7	−	.91
Persia	628	1.19	628	1.22				
Italy	299	.57	117	.23	−	182	−	60.87
Spain	275	.52	331	.64	+	56	+	20.36
Ethiopia	200	.38	409	.79	+	209	+	104.50
Japan	175	.33	142	.28	−	33	−	18.86
Sweden	173	.33	173	.33				
Norway	124	.23	125	.24	+	1	+	.81
New Zealand	105	.20	106	.20	+	1	+	.95
Liberia	35	.07	43	.08	+	8	+	22.86
Greece	25	.05	51	.10	+	26	+	104.00
Belgium	11	.02	917	1.78	+	906	+8,236.36	
Egypt	a		386	.75	+	386		
Union of S. Africa	a		472	.91	+	472		
Libya	b		679	1.32	+	679		
Eire	a		27	.05	+	27		
All other c	7,499	14.18	7,096	13.76	−	403	−	5.37
World total	52,882	100.00%	51,579	100.00%	−1,303		−	2.46%

a India, Pakistan, Egypt, area which is now Union of S. Africa, and Eire included under England in 1882.
b Libya included under Turkey in 1882.
c All other:

Cent. Amer. states	243	.46%	294	.57%	+	51	+	20.99%
Other S. Amer. states	3,168	5.99	2,308	4.47	−	860	−	27.15
Asian states	3,701	7.00	3,825	7.42	+	124	+	3.35
European states	387	.73	669	1.30	+	282	+	72.87
Total all other	7,499	14.18%	7,096	13.76%	−	403	−	5.37%

TABLE III–7a. CENTRAL AMERICAN INDEPENDENT STATES

(*In Thousands of Square Miles*)

	1882	1952	Change
Cuba	43	44	+ 1
Haiti	10	11	+ 1
Dominican Republic	18	19	+ 1
Guatemala	47	42	− 5
El Salvador	7	13	+ 6
Honduras	46	59	+13
Nicaragua	49	57	+ 8
Costa Rica	23	20	− 3
Panama [a]		29	
Total	243	294	+51

SOURCE: *The Encyclopedia of Social Reform*, Bliss edition, 1908, p. 921.

[a] 1882: A department of Colombia which did not become an independent state until 1903. The original area has been given as between 31,500 and 33,800 square miles.

SOUTH AMERICAN INDEPENDENT STATES, EXCLUSIVE OF BRAZIL AND ARGENTINA

(*In Thousands of Square Miles*)

	1882	1952	Change
Bolivia	729	413	−316
Chile	280	286	+ 6
Colombia [a]	505	440	− 65
Ecuador	116	106	− 10
Paraguay	158	157	− 1
Peru	714	482	−232
Uruguay	72	72	
Venezuela	594	352	−242
Total	3,168	2,308	−860

SOURCES: *Encyclopedia of Social Reform*, Bliss ed., 1908, p. 921; *Encyclopaedia Britannica*, 11th ed., Vol. VI, pp. 700–706; and George Edmundson, British representative in the Colombian-Venezuelan boundary arbitrations.

[a] Prior to 1903 the republic of Colombia was divided into nine departments with a combined area of 504,773 square miles, a part of which was in dispute with Costa Rica north of the department of Panama, and Venezuela and Ecuador on the east and south.

TABLE III–7b. INDEPENDENT STATES IN ASIA·

(In Thousands of Square Miles)

	1882	1952	Change
Arabia	1,500	1,023	−477
Iraq (Mesopotamia)	172	168	− 4
Israel [a]		8	+ 8
Lebanon [a]		4	+ 4
Syria [a]		72	+ 72
Yemen [b]		75	+ 75
Afghanistan	250	251	+ 1
Bahrain Is.[f]			
Burma [g]		262	+262
Ceylon [g]		25	+ 25
Formosa (Taiwan)	13	14	+ 1
Indo-China [c]	272	272	
Korea	86	85	− 1
Kuwait	8	8	
Mongolia [d]		624	+624
Muscat & Oman	82	82	
Nepal	54	54	
Philippines	116	116	
Qatar	8	8	
Thailand	236	198	− 38
Trucial Oman	6	6	
Indonesia [e]	881	416	−465
Bhutan	17	19	+ 2
Jordan [a]		35	+ 35
Total	3,701	3,825	+124

SOURCES: *British Imperial Cyclopedia*, 1910; United Nations Yearbook, 1952.

[a] 1882: Israel, Lebanon, Syria and Jordan included under Turkish Empire.

[b] 1882: Yemen included under Arabia.

[c] 1952: Indo-China is now "Indo-Chinese Associated States," including Vietnam, Cambodia, and Laos.

[d] 1882: Mongolian area of 1,368,000 square miles was a dependency of China at this time. *British Imperial Cyclopedia*, 1910, Vol. XI, p. 698.

[e] 1882: This group of islands now called Indonesia was governed by the Kingdom of the Netherlands, and did not become an independent republic until 1949, with New Guinea remaining under Netherlands government.

[f] Less than 1,000 square miles.

[g] 1882: Burma and Ceylon included under England.

TABLE III-7c. INDEPENDENT STATES IN EUROPE

(*In Thousands of Square Miles*)

	1882	1952	Change
Albania [a]		11	+ 11
Andorra [f]			
Austria	116	32	− 84
Bulgaria	38	43	+ 5
Czechoslovakia [b]		49	+ 49
Finland [c]		130	+130
Hungary	115	36	− 79
Iceland	40	40	
Liechtenstein [f]			
Luxembourg	1	1	
Monaco [f]			
Poland [d]		120	+120
Romania	61	92	+ 31
San Marino [f]			
Switzerland	16	16	
Vatican City [f]			
Yugoslavia [e]		99	+ 99
Total	387	669	+282

SOURCES: *The British Imperial Cyclopedia*, 1910; United Nations Yearbook, 1952.

[a] Albania: not established as an independent republic until after World War II; boundaries not demarcated until 1925.
[b] Czechoslovakia: did not become an independent republic until 1918.
[c] Finland: a Grand Duchy of the Russian Empire in 1882, with an area of 125,784 square miles.
[d] Poland: partitioned between Prussia, Austria, and Russia in 1882.
[e] Yugoslavia: not established as an independent state until 1918.
[f] Less than 1,000 square miles.

CHANGES IN THE WORLD'S GROSS LAND INVENTORY

In the accompanying Tables III–8 and III–9 are given changes in the world's gross land area inclusive of inland waters, and in mean elevation above sea-level by principal continental divisions.

As water is fundamentally the natural resource most essential to man's existence on the earth, being unique in that it recurs by precipitation, is pure in each recurrence, and is not conserved by non-use, this primary asset is treated separately in another chapter.

Taking good and bad land together, it has been estimated that four acres are required, directly and indirectly, to sustain one human being. Considering the relation of food resources to population, we are here face-to-face with the so-called law of diminishing returns. This proposition came into prominence over a century ago and is commonly associated with the names of Ricardo and Malthus. The modern formulation as stated by Alfred Marshall is: "Whatever may be the future development of the arts of agriculture, a continued increase in the application of capital and labor to land must ultimately result in a diminution of the extra produce which can be obtained by a given extra amount of capital and labor."

As it will be observed in Land Table III–2, the present world acreage of all grazing land, cropland, and orchards has declined to 3.2 acres per capita, with cropland alone now scarcely at 1.1 acres per capita as against all previous 2.5 acreage

TABLE III–8. THE WORLD'S GROSS "LAND" AREA, 1882–1952

(In Square Miles)

	Gross	Land	Water
1882:			
Africa	11,737,615	9,499,768	2,237,847
America, North	9,670,345	8,013,313	1,657,032
America, South	7,164,511	6,028,505	1,136,006
Asia	17,379,065	15,380,377	1,998,688
Europe	3,530,932	2,292,429	1,238,503
Oceania	3,339,216	3,065,892	273,324
Total	52,821,684	44,280,284	8,541,400
1952:			
Africa	11,695,694	9,513,093	2,182,601
America, North	9,360,888	7,742,918	1,617,970
America, South	6,870,168	5,762,166	1,108,002
Asia	16,891,953	14,937,699	1,954,254
Europe	3,455,938	2,248,288	1,207,650
Oceania	3,303,865	3,033,131	270,734
Total	51,578,506	43,237,295	8,341,211

SOURCES: 1882 period: The International Geodetic Association (Internationale Erdmessung), Berlin, 1886; Frederick Robert Helmert, Ph.D., D. Ing., geodisist, University of Berlin; Colonel Alexander Ross Clarke, R.E., F.R.S., English geodisist. 1952 period: *British Imperial Cyclopedia Atlas; Oxford Advanced Atlas; American Oxford Atlas;* Odham's *New Atlas of the World; Atlas General,* Paris; *Encyclopaedia Britannica World Atlas.*

TABLE III–9. CHANGES IN LAND MEAN ELEVATION ABOVE SEA-LEVEL, 1882–1952

(*In Feet*)

	1882	1952	Change
Where-from:			
Continents			
Africa	2,130	1,900	−230
America, North	2,300	2,000	−300
America, South	1,970	1,800	−170
Asia	3,120	3,000	−120
Europe	1,040	980	− 60
Oceania	1,310	1,000	−310
Mean	1,980	1,780	
			−200

CHANGES IN MEAN DEPTH BELOW SEA-LEVEL, 1882–1952

(*In Feet*)

	1882	1952	Change
Where-to:			
Oceans & seas			
Pacific	13,440	14,048	+608
Indian	12,888	13,002	+114
Atlantic	12,660	12,880	+220
Arctic	3,840	3,953	+113
Adjoining seas	1,919	2,200	+281
Inland basins	1,500	1,550	+ 50
Mean	12,650	12,450	
			+200

SOURCES: Land, 1882: Professor H. Wagner, *Lehrbuch der Geographie*, Leipzig, 1900; Dr. von Tillo, Imperial Russian Geographical Society, St. Petersburg, 1889. 1952: U. S. Geological Survey, Washington, D.C., 1952.

Water, 1882: Otto Krummel, *Handbuch der Oceanographie*, Stuttgart, 1907; Sir John Murray, F.R.G.S., *Geographical Journal*, 1902, and *The Depth of the Oceans*, 1912. 1952: E. Kossinna, *Encyclopaedia Britannica*, 1948 ed., Vol. 16, p. 683; U. S. Hydrographic Office, Washington, D.C.

requirements. It therefore appears that, taking the world as a whole, the point of diminishing returns has already been reached.

MAN-LAND RATIOS

Of all per-capita wealth ratios, the man-land ratio far outranks the others in significance. As Professor Zimmermann pointed out over twenty years ago, three major developments that have largely destroyed the former *practical* meaning of the fixed nature of land. These three changes have been the ascendency of the mineral-using industry, the shift from the self-sufficient local economy to the interregional and then to the interdependent international economy, and the application of machine techniques and power machines not only to mining, manufacturing, and transportation but to forestry and agriculture as well.

This has involved a serious shift in the appraisal of "land" from a two-dimensional agricultural to a three-dimensional mineral basis. This is no longer a matter of word-juggling among theorists, but has become a reality. The cultivatability of the earth, as reflected in the physical limits of food production, is of vital importance, and in the end sets the limits of all production.

As agriculture spread, the world's forests were viewed as the reservoir of potential farm land as well as a source of fuel supply. That the ruthless exploitation of forests over the past century, as the world population more than doubled, did not bring the approaching land crisis into view far earlier than it did is another example of the corollary of ignorance with human action.

THE WORLD'S WOOD

In spite of the fact that his has been called the "age of coal, iron, steam, and electricity," wood still forms an indispensable basis of today's civilization. It has many uses, of which fuel ranks first among the masses of the world's population. Next is as lumber for building and construction; then follows the ever-mounting demand for pulp by the world's printing and general business industries. The furniture industry absorbs great quantities of wood and wood veneers. The demand for railroad ties, telephone and telegraph poles, mine timbers, fence posts, cooperage, and shingles absorbs still more. Even your nicely packaged breakfast food products, as well as sanitary tissues of all kinds, have made increasing demands on the world's forests. In the manufacturing industry, wood has maintained its place as a favored material to the extent of utilizing over 40 per cent of the total raw-timber cut annually. In short, man cannot get along very well without wood.

The world's production and consumption of wood amounts to approximately 70 billion cubic feet at the present time, or an average of 27 cubic feet per capita, as compared with less than half that much seventy years ago. For centuries the people of the world had lived in an environment of timber abundance, so much so that it has only been in recent times that difficulties in timber production have been noticeable. According to the report of the Division of Forestry and Forest Products of the Food and Agriculture Organization of the United Nations, the entire world is now undergoing shortages in forest products. In some regions the deficits are of long standing; in others they date from the outbreak of World War II. Everywhere they retard progress toward improved standards of living.

TIMBER MINING

Forests, unlike mineral mines, have been considered renewable. Being a product of the soil, they have been viewed as capable, like any other crop, of being regrown. Unfortunately, the relation between forest and soil is much closer and deeper, in its long-term results, in forestry than in agriculture. When a forest has been cut down such action is creative of man-made erosion at its worst, with far-reaching physical and economic results.

The disappearance of the world's forests, with the growth of industrialism, has affected both the climate and the animal life of the world, going so far, in the opinion of many competent authorities, as "to have affected the physical deterioration of a large part of the world's population." [2]

The world's forests serve a number of important purposes other than the production of timber, and it is important that these purposes be kept in mind. Forests exercise far-reaching protective influences over both land and water resources. They hold the soil against erosion, equalize stream flow, delay melting of snow, and help to maintain the world's ground-water supplies for wells and springs.

[2] *Encyclopaedia Britannica*, 1948 ed., Vol. 9, p. 500.

THE WORLD'S MINERALS

Until recently it was impossible to secure an inventory of more than a handful of mineral reserves. Even then the figures could only be accepted with a grain of salt, as the crucial factor in all estimates of reserves is the ratio between the rate of use and the rate of discovery. Hence, to place a monetary value on these subsoil resources, for the purpose of drawing up a balance sheet of assets and liabilities, could only rest upon several broad assumptions.

Since 1924, however, considerable data has been developed to a point which permits an inventory of some thirty-four of the world's principal minerals as given

TABLE III–10. PRINCIPAL INDUSTRIAL MINERALS DISTRIBUTION IN TOPMOST
TEN MILES OF EARTH'S CRUST

(*Estimated Reserves Available Under Present Technology—in Short Tons*)

	Pounds per ton	Millions of tons in earth's crust	Available world reserves under present technology
Aluminum	179.2	195,300,000,000,000,000	1,543,000,000 [a]
Iron	110.4	119,300,000,000,000,000	20,900,000,000 [a]
Calcium	80.4	86,800,000,000,000,000	98,100,000,000
Sodium	62.8	67,300,000,000,000,000	76,000,000,000
Potassium	57.3	62,900,000,000,000,000	5,500,000,000 [a]
Magnesium	46.0	49,900,000,000,000,000	56,400,000,000
Titanium	13.8	15,000,000,000,000,000	16,900,000,000
Phosphorus	2.9	3,100,000,000,000,000	28,700,000,000 [a]
Manganese	2.2	2,400,000,000,000,000	1,100,000,000 [a]
Sulphur	1.2	1,200,000,000,000,000	1,400,000,000
Barium	1.1	1,190,000,000,000,000	1,340,000,000
Chromium	.8	900,000,000,000,000	110,000,000 [a]
Carbon	.7	800,000,000,000,000	870,000,000
Zirconium	.6	618,000,000,000,000	698,000,000
Nickel	.4	500,000,000,000,000	539,400,000
Strontium	.42	455,000,000,000,000	300,000,000
Vanadium	.37	400,000,000,000,000	450,000,000
Yttrium	.33	358,000,000,000,000	400,000,000
Copper	.22	239,000,000,000,000	110,230,000 [a]
Antimony	.21	238,000,000,000,000	264,000,000
Cadmium	.21	238,000,000,000,000	263,000,000
Uranium	.18	190,900,000,000,000	215,700,000
Tungsten	.11	119,300,000,000,000	4,409,000 [a]
Lithium	.09	95,500,000,000,000	107,900,000
Zinc	.08	95,400,000,000,000	77,161,000 [a]
Columbium	.07	71,600,000,000,000	80,900,000
Hafnium	.06	71,500,000,000,000	80,000,000
Thorium	.04	47,700,000,000,000	53,900,000
Lead	.04	47,700,000,000,000	44,100,000 [a]
Cobalt	.02	23,900,000,000,000	27,000,000
Silver	.022	23,900,000,000,000	26,900,000
Molybdenum	.010	19,500,000,000,000	22,100,000
Tin	.002	2,200,000,000,000	6,614,000 [a]
Gold	.002	2,200,000,000,000	2,450,000
Total		609,947,300,000,000,000	312,636,764,000

SOURCE: U. S. Geological Survey, *The Composition of the Earth's Crust,* Professional Paper No. 127, 1924.

[a] Elmer Walter Pehrson, Chief Economics and Statistical Division, U. S. Bureau of Mines, 1949.

TABLE III–11. WORLD INDUSTRIAL PRODUCTION
OF PRINCIPAL MINERALS, 1952

	Net tons	Per cent of total
Coal and lignite	1,647,955,000	68.226886%
Petroleum	534,621,000	22.133812
Iron	102,515,000	4.244217
Slate	33,951,000	1.405603
Sodium chloride	29,983,000	1.241324
Phosphate	21,275,000	.880805
Sulphur	10,659,000	.441293
Pyrites	10,472,000	.433551
Bauxite	8,267,000	.342262
Potash	4,169,000	.172601
Copper	2,480,000	.102674
Zinc	2,039,000	.084417
Lead	1,653,000	.068436
Manganese	1,565,000	.064792
Magnesite	1,323,000	.054773
Asbestos	1,174,000	.048605
Chrome	882,000	.036516
Tin	181,000	.007494
Nickel	131,175	.005431
Antimony	41,888	.001734
Tungsten	19,842	.000821
Magnesium	17,968	.000744
Molybdenum	15,620	.000647
Silver	5,842	.000242
Mercury	4,960	.000205
Vanadium	1,862	.000077
Gold	918	.000038
Total	2,415,404,075	100.000000%
Returned to soil as fertilizers:		
Phosphate [a]	5,640,000	
Potash [b]	4,170,000	
Nitrogen [c]	3,940,000	
Total	13,750,000	
Total annual extraction	2,415,404,075	100.0%
Returned to soil	13,750,000	.6%

SOURCES: United Nations Statistical Yearbook; *Yearbook of Food & Agricultural Statistics.*

[a] Covers the P_2O_5 content of superphosphates with ground phosphate rock excluded.
[b] Refers to K_2O content, sulphate potash, and nitrate of soda potash only.
[c] Refers to nitrogen content of commercial fertilizers only.

in the accompanying Table III–10, with Table III–11 giving the current rate of production. Owing to the flexibility in rates of both production and new discoveries, no attempt is here made to give more than a cursory indication of their exhaustion periods, as given tentatively in Table III–12 covering the world's principal fuels.

Although discovery will continue to play an important part in adding to the world's resource availability, the development of new techniques for utilizing such basic resources as the world now has may play a more important part. The chances of finding increased supplies are limited by the fact that most frontiers have already been explored; many of them have by now had their possibilities exhausted. In this respect, however, the possibilities of substitute supplies offer a wide range of opportunities.

TABLE III–12. STATUS OF THE WORLD'S FUEL SUPPLY, 1952

(In Net Tons)

	World reserves	Current rate of consumption	Years	Per cent of total world wealth*
Coal [a]	569,934,000,000	2,211,000,000	258	.9%
Petroleum [b]	85,000,000,000	690,000,000	123	.7
Natural gas [c]	76,500,000,000	814,000,000	84	.1
Fuelwood [d]	75,000,000,000	2,000,000,000	37	.1
Uranium [e]	215,700,000	100,000	no data	1.8
Total	806,649,700,000	5,715,100,000		3.6%

SOURCES: [a] From basic data by Dr. Elmer Walter Pehrson, Chief, Economics and Statistical Division, U. S. Bureau of Mines, adjusted for mining operation losses, fires, and depth limitations under present technology.
[b] Dr. Elmer Walter Pehrson, estimated maximum potential.
[c] L. F. Terry, Gas Age, October 26, 1950, p. 58. Adjusted on same basis as coal. President's Materials Policy Commission, 1952, Vol. III, p. 20.
[d] Forest Resources of the World, 1948, Food and Agriculture Organization of the United Nations, Division of Forestry and Forest Products.
[e] University of Maryland, Atlas of Mineral World Resources, 1950, p. 137. Jesse Johnson, Materials Chief, U. S. Atomic Energy Commission, 1955.
NOTE: Natural gas: Because of difficulties in weighing gases and vapors, it is common practice to measure the volumes of these substances at standard conditions. These conversion techniques are well known to chemists and physicists, with the procedures being that of establishing the molecular weight of gas in grams per liter of volume—regardless of what the gas is. These standards are usually expressed in abbreviated terms, such as: NTP, meaning "Normal Temperature Pressure," and GMV, meaning "Gram Molecular Volume." As it is known that gas will occupy approximately 22.4 liters if measured at NTP, hence molecular weight of gas may be approximated by multiplying the weight of one liter of gas (which is 61.026 cubic inches) by its GMV.
Fuelwood: The conversion factor for fuelwood has entailed converting the timber drain on the basis of the equivalent volume 302 Bd. Ft. = 68 cu. ft., as given by the U. S. Forest Service, Report 2, Table 25, from A Reappraisal of the Forest Situation, 1946, and then applying the average pounds per cubic foot of all woods as secured from the Smithsonian Physical Tables. These factors supply a rough average for the world as a whole, and are not necessarily applicable to any specific subnational area.
Current consumption: From data covering world roundwood forest output furnished by the Food and Agriculture Organization of the United Nations. Fuelwood computed on basis of findings given by Raphael Zon, Forest Resources of the World.

* Per cent of total world wealth as valued in current monetary terms.

THE WORLD'S FUEL SUPPLY

The intensified drives toward a greater worldwide industrialization, the swift upward trend of world population, the increase of per-capita consumption of energy resources at a faster rate than population increase, have created an unprecedented demand on the world's store of fuel materials. As a result the rate of depletion of these natural resources is progressing ten times faster than one hundred years ago.

The coal reserves of the world have been estimated to exceed 5 trillion short tons, of which about half were deemed recoverable with present techniques. These recoverable reserves represent more than 80 per cent of the energy of all recoverable mineral fuel reserves. Beginning with the data collected by the Twelfth International Geological Congress in 1913, there have been a number of attempts to arrive at an estimate of the coal reserves of the world, the last being that prepared by the Economic Development Section of the Division of Economic Stability and Development in the United Nations Department of Economic Affairs in 1950.

These earlier estimates, including that of 1950, were of the opinion that the North American coal resources—particularly those of the United States—would outlast all other countries, with enough to suffice for 2000 years. The general opinion was that Europe was rapidly exhausting its supplies, and that if the then present relative rates of exhaustion continued, complete exhaustion would arrive there long before it threatened Asia and North America.

These estimates were based on a minimum workable thickness of seams, ranging from one to two feet, down to 6000 feet as the maximum workable depth. Since that time, however, it has been found doubtful whether it will ever prove commercially possible to produce coal from a depth greater than 5000 feet. More recent analysis has reduced this happy backlog by as much as 90 per cent, which is the figure given in Table III–12.

URANIUM

Estimates of the world's uranium ore have varied considerably from as much as 8 trillion tons on the basis of one ton of uranium per 250,000 tons of rock in the earth's crust (by Harrison Brown) to 2 trillion tons (by Gale Young of the Metallurgical Laboratory in Chicago) to as little as 500,000 tons of known commercial reserves (as given in the *Atlas of the World's Mineral Resources*, Vol. II, p. 137, University of Maryland, 1952).

As a result opinions differ considerably as to its importance as a potential source of industrial energy. Its production, transportation, and consumption have been under strict government control throughout most of the world. Therefore, published data on uranium reserves have been meager. Professor P. M. S. Blackett, former member of Great Britain's Advisory Committee on Atomic Energy, stated in 1949 that the present known (or at least published) sources of uranium would not be sufficient to make an important contribution to world power resources. On the other hand, the University of Maryland has stated that "it is evident that there is enough uranium to furnish atomic energy for a substantial part of future world energy requirements."

However, despite the optimism of this current counterpart of the "gold-rush" era, the energy present in rich uranium deposits known before the war indicates it to be negligible in comparison with the energy in known coal deposits. Although there is now under way a worldwide "buried treasure" hunt such as has never been seen before, nevertheless it might be unwise to waste this new resource in uses for which more abundant known fuels could suffice.

EXTRAPOLATION EXAMPLES

At present each man, woman, and child now living has available for all the activities associated with and derived from human living, only about 10 acres of land—counting all of the land, good, bad, and indifferent, now on the face of the earth; and of these 10 acres less than one-third, or 3 acres of land per person, are really good for anything in the literal sense of the word.

This, of course, at first appears a meaningless and fantastic average if it is thought of in the sense of forcibly attaching each individual human being to a particular 10 acres of the earth's surface. But it is an average fraught with the deepest meaning in a world view—when it is remembered that in final analysis all the means of human living, agricultural, industrial, commercial, and other, are derived directly or indirectly from the inexpansible earth. Further, if the population and land factors above be extrapolated at their established present rates another 70 years, it will be found that barely 4 acres per person of all kinds of land will be available. Of these scarcely one-fifth of an acre per person will be good for anything to live directly upon—for instance, enough cropland to produce 14 loaves of bread per person per year, or 4 one-hundredths of a loaf per day. In other words, if a loaf were divided into 100 slices, 4 of them would be the daily ration per capita; divided into 25 slices, each individual would daily be granted one sustaining slice. The arithmetic may be difficult, but not so impossible as trying to live on such an allocation would be.

THE VISUALIZATION OF WORLD CONSUMPTION IN "SIZE LANGUAGE"

In man's waking consciousness the eye rules supreme. Spengler pointed out a generation ago that nothing transcends the "lordship of the eye" as an aid to the comprehension of what exists. It is fear of the invisible that has long been the essence of human religiousness, and the imperceptibility of things that has rendered many concepts inaccessible to human reasoning. Economists often speak of things that can be seen with the "naked eye."

It may, therefore, be helpful, in order that the full meaning of world quantitative figures be adequately grasped, if they are converted into the "size language" representing volume to which the eye is accustomed—rather than be allowed to stand in terms of cold figures of avoirdupois weight.

For such visual purposes of comparison we may take the giant Cheops pyramid in Egypt, which originally contained some 5 million tons of hewn stones, or 3,394,307 cubic yards covering 13 acres of land, and which represented, until recently, the largest structure of any kind ever erected by man. By comparison, the total quantity of coal taken from the world's underground stores in the year 1952 would equal 650 Cheop pyramids, covering 456,870 acres of land, and would reach over 6 miles high into the sky. That is quite a pile of coal for a single year's performance. In other words, this mountain of coal would extend the height of Mt. Everest by some 3200 feet.

THE BREAD OF INDUSTRY

Coal has been called the "bread of industry." It has also been called the "creator and preservative of overseas world trade," and in this twofold character it has combined with iron to endow the present massed wealth of the earth with much of its life and energy. Coal has played so manifold a part in the development of the world's present economic foundations that it warrants special consideration. Up to a short time ago the output of coal was the measure of a country's industrialization. Even today, with the world's increase in the use of petroleum, natural gas, and water power, coal accounts for 40 per cent of the world's industrial energy.

Since 1882, the bench-mark base-period of this study, the world's total cumulative output of coal has been 120 billion tons, or an amount equal to 35,000 Cheop pyramids, covering an area of 25 million acres, reaching 28 miles high to a point midway in the stratosphere. And regardless of the fact that the pre-1905 physics textbooks told us that matter and energy were indestructible, we now know that insofar as the present and future inhabitants of this planet earth are concerned, this gigantic quantity of coal has literally "gone up the flue" forever as a source of future combustive material.

According to studies estimating the need for energy in the future, at present established rates of consumption the annual world requirement will approximate in another hundred years 2250 per cent of what it is today. As this is some seventeen times the presently known world reserves, it is clear that a considerable adjustment on the part of man's sources of energy is to be expected within the next two or three generations. If the promise of the world's future industrialized life, as now envisaged by businessmen, is to be achieved, the planet earth is going to have to double its present man-land-carrying capacity.

TABLE III–13. COMPOSITION OF THE CRUST OF THE EARTH

Elements	Symbol	Percentage distribution
Oxygen	O	50.00%
Silicon	Si	25.70
Aluminum	Al	7.30
Iron	Fe	4.20
Calcium	Ca	3.20
Sodium	Na	2.40
Potassium	K	2.30
Magnesium	Mg	2.20
Hydrogen	H	.95
Titanium	Ti	.43
Chlorine	Cl	.21
Carbon	C	.19
Phosphorus	P	.11
Sulphur	S	.11
Barium	Ba	.09
Manganese	Mn	.08
Chromium	Cr	.03
Strontium	Sr	.03
Nitrogen	N	.02
Fluorine	F	.02
Nickel	Ni	.02
Bromine	Br	.01
All other elements		.40
Total		100.00%

SOURCE: Estimates of Professor J. D. Main Smith, University of London, England.

NOTE: "All other elements" constituting some 78 elements of the 100 now definitely known, at least 90 are known to be of sufficient stability to exist in a natural state, while only about 30 elements occur in nature in the free state, with most of them being found in chemical combinations with other elements. It will, therefore, be observed that many of the rare earths, minor metallic minerals and the minor non-metallic minerals embrace but four-tenths of one per cent of the earth's composition.

As the temperature of the earth's crust reaches the boiling point (212° F) at two and one-half miles depth, and the melting point of most metals (1,212° F) at six miles depth, these temperatures tend to restrict the availability of mineral supplies.

TABLE III-14. STRUCTURE OF THE EARTH AND ITS SEPARATE GEOSPHERES

Name of geosphere	Miles height or depth	Miles thick	Temperature °Fahrenheit	Chemical characteristics	Comments
Xosphere Interstellar Space	600		−100°	H_2, He, O_2, N_2	Rarefied gases Cosmic rays Meteorites
Ionosphere	140–158	460		H_2, He, O_2, N_2	Cosmic rays * Appleton layer Rebound short radio waves
Stratosphere	60	158	−140°	H_2, He, O_2, N_2, O_3	Cosmic rays Limit of water vapor * Heaviside layer Rebound radio waves H-bomb penetration
	40		−150°		
Tropopause Troposphere	10	10	−150°	N_2, O_2, A, Ne, Kr, Xe, O_3, CO_2	Cosmic rays Radioactive rays Water vapor, carbon dioxide Dust particles
Biosphere	Land-level 2.2	2.2	−165°	N_2, O_2, A, Ne, Kr, Xe, O_3, CO_2, CO, Rn	Radioactive rays Solar rays, water vapor Carbon monoxide Dust particles Living matter, bacteria
Hydrosphere	Sea-level	2.3	44° 29°	H_2, O_2, Cl, Na, Mg, S	Low radioactivity Water Ice

Atmosphere

Earth's crust zones:

				Composition	Description
Weathering	.5	.5			
Sedimentary		.9	118°	O₂, H₂, Si, Al, C, Cl, CO₂, Fe, Mg, Mn, S, Ca	Increased radioactivity / Bacteria / Lowest limit of oxygen
Rocks	2.5	2.5	212°	Same / Crystalloids	Medium radioactivity / Coal, lowest level
Metamorphic	5.0	4.7	628° / 1,212°	Crystals	Increased radioactivity / Lowest level of oil / Melting point most metals
Granite	9.0	7.9	1,212° / 1,832°	O, Si, Al, K, Na, Fe, Mg, Ca, etc.	Highest radioactivity / Quartz, mica, apetite / Lowest level of iron
Basalt	30.0	14.4	1,832°	Same + Ti, P, S, Cl	Medium radioactivity / Boundary between crystal line and glass
Central core / Center	3,958.8	20.0	3,600° / 9,000°	Native Fe	State of matter—glass / Liquid

(Lithosphere brackets Rocks, Metamorphic, Granite, Basalt)

O_2, H_2, Si, Al, C, Cl, CO_2, Fe, Mg, Mn, S, Ca

SOURCE: Adapted from Dr. A. E. Fersman's *Geochemistry*, Vols. I-II, 1934.
NOTE: * Conducting shell surrounding earth.

TABLE III–15. EXTENT OF WORLD'S LAND AREA SURVEYED AND CENSUS ENUMERATION IN 1882

(*Base-period this study*)

	Per Cent Surveyed	Per Cent Enumerated	Area in Square Miles	Population
Africa	9.9%	22.6%	11,737,615	205,823,000
Americas [a]	50.0	90.9	16,834,856	100,415,000
Asia	56.8	40.6	17,379,065	795,591,000
Europe [a]	97.5	98.7	3,530,932	327,743,000
Oceania	94.6	80.4	3,339,216	4,232,000
	49.6%	58.6%	52,821,684	1,433,804,000

SOURCES: Sir Jervoise Athelstane Baines, President, Royal Statistical Society, 1909–1910.
Ernest Georg Ravenstein, F.R.G.S., *Systematic Atlas*, 1884, *Atlas of the World*, 1911; German cartographer, first recipient of Victoria medal of the Royal Statistical Society, 1902.
Professor Hermann Wagner, German Geographical Institute, *Lehbruch der Geographie*, Leipzig, 1900. Professor of geography at Gottingen.
Alexander Ross Clarke, English Geodesist, *Geodesy*, 1880. Reference Ellipsoids named after him.
Encyclopaedia Britannica, 11th edition, Vol. XXII, p. 92, Table I.

[a] Excluding Polar Regions.

NOTE: The principal land tracts still unsurveyed and unenumerated in 1882, in any strict sense of the word, constitute the following:
Africa; about nine-tenths.
Americas; a considerable portion of Central America, South America and Polar America.
Asia; Turkish Empire, Persia, Afghanistan, Indo-Chinese Peninsula.

TABLE III–15a. EXTENT OF WORLD'S LAND AREA SURVEYED AND CENSUS ENUMERATION IN 1952

	Per Cent Surveyed	Per Cent Enumerated	Area in [a] Square Miles	Population [b]
Africa	56.6%	83.6%	11,695,694	206,559,000
Americas [c]	93.6	100.0	16,231,056	342,306,000
Asia	68.0	54.2	16,891,953	1,354,288,000
Europe [c]	100.0	100.0	3,455,938	574,900,000
Oceania	98.5	98.7	3,303,865	13,227,000
Total	83.3%	87.3%	51,578,506	2,491,280,000

SOURCE: United Nations Statistical Office.

[a] Gross area, including inland water; See Table III–8.
[b] See Table VI–4, Chapter VI.
[c] Excluding Polar Regions.

The atmosphere of our planet is our own individual property, and in no sense part of a universal atmosphere spread all over space. By the Greeks the air was considered to be one of the four elements, and it was not until the middle of the 18th century that Priestly discovered that air was primarily a mixture of oxygen and nitrogen— and that a slight difference in the proportion of either element would be fatal to life as we know it.

—Douglas Archibald, R.M.S.

Since the first atomic-bomb explosion in 1945, certain weather peculiarities have appeared. Tornadoes have multiplied in the United States from 300 in 1951, to 532 in 1953, to 699 in 1954, to over 900 in 1955. Have the bombs caused these aberrations? Man's present knowledge of weather mechanics is too limited to justify a categorical denial.

—Irving Bengelsdorf,
Director Research, General Electric Company, 1956

IV

Air

THE CORRELATIVE EFFECT of the atmosphere upon the world's physical balance sheet has been so determinative, particularly in its influence upon the geographic distribution of the races of mankind and their material resources, that for ultimate economic results it must be given a leading place in any inventory of the world's physical assets and liabilities.

The geographical distribution of the world's vegetation, minerals, wealth, and energy depends on the climate and weather more than any other factor. The atmosphere influences man's activities on land, on sea, and in the air. In fact its influence upon the selective processes of history has been decisive.

Common to all of the people throughout the world is the air and its everpresent companion, the weather. This omnipresent and all-engulfing blanket of matter—the atmosphere—has played and is still playing a large part in the format of the world's land and water, and all other forms of the world's material resources. The inventory of the principal physical components upon which the world is dependent must include it.

Most of us are apt to think of the earth as being composed primarily of land and water, with the air taken for granted. Yet the air is actually an important part

TABLE IV-1.   CHANGES IN THE COMPOSITION OF THE WORLD'S ATMOSPHERE, 1882–1952

(In Millions of Net Tons)

	1882	1952	Change	% Change
Ionosphere:				
Outer layer above stratosphere [a]	547,907,761,556	547,852,976,244	−54,785,312	− 0.01%
Stratosphere of the earth, dry [b]	5,732,253,469	5,811,305,945	+79,052,476	+ 1.4%
Water vapor, other natural matter	59,087,495	59,902,360	+ 814,865	+ 1.4
Dust & bacteria	2,305,987	12,816,990	+10,511,003	+455.8
Grand total	5,793,646,951	5,884,025,295	+90,378,344	+ 1.6%
Principal elements:				
Nitrogen	4,327,851,369	4,387,535,988	+59,684,619	+ 1.4%
Oxygen	1,327,589,903	1,345,898,456	+18,308,553	+ 1.4
Argon	72,799,619	73,803,586	+ 1,003,967	+ 1.4
Carbon dioxide *	2,292,901	2,336,145	+ 43,244	+ 1.9
Xenon	702,791	708,979	+ 6,188	+ .9
Krypton	450,591	453,282	+ 2,691	+ .6
Radon	349,451	348,678	− 773	− .2
Neon	108,285	110,415	+ 2,130	+ 2.0
Ozone *	86,386	87,170	+ 784	+ .9
Helium	22,172	23,245	+ 1,073	+ 4.8
Total principal elements	5,732,253,468	5,811,305,944	+79,052,476	+ 1.4%

Additional matter:			
Water vapor * ᵉ	57,322,534	58,113,059	+ 1.4%
Dust particles, normal * ᶜ	1,719,104	1,742,811	+ 1.4
Bacteria, etc. * ᵈ	45,858	46,490	+ 1.4
Total natural additional matter	59,087,496	59,902,360	+ 1.4%
Man-made:			
Products of combustion * ᵉ	2,292,901	12,794,390	+458.0%
Carbon dioxide ᶠ	13,086	22,601	+ 72.7
Total man-made added matter	2,305,987	12,816,991	+455.8%
Grand total	5,793,646,951	5,884,025,295	+ 1.5%

SOURCES: Douglas Archibald, M.A., Royal Meteorological Society, London; Hurd Curtis Willett, B.S., Massachusetts Institute of Technology; Assistant Meteorologist, U. S. Weather Bureau, Washington, D.C.

ᵃ The outer conducting shell surrounding the earth's atmosphere, immediately above the stratosphere, formed by the ionizing action of the sun's radiation. This weight is not felt at the earth's surface.
ᵇ The primary elements of the air before miscellaneous additive matter, containing the biosphere, troposphere, tropopause, and the stratosphere.
ᶜ Due chiefly to volcanic ash and desert area dust storms.

ᵈ Bacteria and the products of decomposition.
ᶠ The exhalation of man and his domestic animals.
* Non-permanent constiuents of the atmosphere.
ᵉ Smoke and air pollution due to man's activities, industrial and otherwise, including residential heating, motor-car exhaust, structure, and forest fires.

of the solid globe. It is not empty space. It is composed of matter and energy resources in large quantities that occupy space. It is also the trade-route via which the physical planet transacts its day-by-day energy, water, and vitally important chemical trading and exchange. It is a busy natural traffic thoroughfare besides being one of man's great new highways.

Without the atmosphere there could be no life on earth; no animal or plant, bird or fish, tree or blade of grass could exist. There would be no weather, winds, clouds, or rain. The air governs the quality, form, and direction of all terrestrial environment—the whole character of the world as man now perceives it.

As the physical primary elements so essential to life all transpire through the air, the changes in the world's air and water balance sheet, are given, in terms of their major elements and categories, in Tables IV–1 and V–1.

Largely because the air contains no gold, coal, or iron mines to have stimulated applied industrial research, its serious study has been neglected until recently. It is now just emerging from its long stage of myth and speculation into a science of fact and certainty. Living as we do at the bottom of this great ocean of air, like fish at the bottom of the sea, we have been absurdly ignorant of the atmosphere its matter, and phenomena in all but a few miles overhead.

The story of the land and sea is, for the most part, a chapter in ancient history when compared with that of the air. The earth has long served as a symbol of rest stability, and permanence; nevertheless its atmosphere is in ceaseless motion and change, under the influence of the heat of the sun, the cold of outer space, the rotation of the earth, and the changes of the seasons as we move in our orbit round the sun.

All water on or within the earth comes from the atmosphere, resulting from the condensation of water vapor in the form of rain, snow, hail, sleet, dew, and frost The water resources of the world are therefore fundamentally affected by changes in the amount, character, and distribution of this physical evaporation-precipitation exchange system. Considering the importance of water resources to all of man' activities, it is worth noting that, to date, no attempt has yet been made at a systematic study of the fundamental facts concerning these resources, or the extent o their possible conservation and use for the world as a whole.

THE GREAT SOIL AND SEA BUILDER

It is through the agency of the wind, rain, snow, and temperature that the atmosphere has produced and is producing its great geological effects. Through this *weathering* process the land itself—economic man's real estate—has come to be what it is. The atmosphere is the great catalytic builder of all the lands and the seas.

THE WORLD'S GREAT GREENHOUSE

The almost complete opaqueness of the atmosphere to the long-wave radiation moving upward from the surface of the earth, combined with the great transparence of the atmosphere to the short-wave radiation coming from the sun, supplies greenhouse effect of great value to all life on the planet.

It will be noted, in Tables IV–2, IV–3, and consolidated in IV–4, that the sun' short-wave radiation in its course downward is absorbed on the order of 14 unit

TABLE IV-2. THE WORLD'S NORMAL ANNUAL GROSS ENERGY TRAFFIC BETWEEN THE EARTH AND OUTER SPACE THROUGH THE ATMOSPHERE

	Energy units [a]	Trillions of calories (12 ciphers omitted)	Trillions of calories (12 ciphers omitted)
Gross normal annual energy exchange through the atmosphere	254		3,302,000,000,000
Sent downward in short-wave radiation by the sun	133	1,729,000,000,000	
Sent upward in long-wave radiation by the earth	115	1,495,000,000,000	
Sun's short-wave radiation normally in stratosphere	6	78,000,000,000	
Gross total normally passing through atmosphere	254	3,302,000,000,000	
Sun's short-wave radiation absorbed by water-vapor clouds	14	182,000,000,000	
Earth's long-wave radiation absorbed by water-vapor clouds	104	1,352,000,000,000	
Total average radiation normally retained	118		1,534,000,000,000
Gross average radiation normally available for transport	136		1,768,000,000,000
Sent downward to earth's surface, direct	86	1,118,000,000,000	
Sent downward to earth's surface by turbulence	4	52,000,000,000	
Sent upward to outer space	40	520,000,000,000	
Net total normal annual energy exchange	130		1,690,000,000,000
Total normal retained in stratosphere	6		78,000,000,000
	136		

SOURCES: See notes, Table IV-6.

[a] Energy units are employed by meterologists and climatologists for simplicity in calculation. Each energy unit represents 13,000,000,000 trillion calories. Written in full: 13,000,000,000,000,000,000,000. Expressed in words: 13 sextillion.

TABLE IV–3. CONSOLIDATED EARTH-ATMOSPHERE-SUN BALANCE SHEET

	Trillions of calories (12 ciphers omitted)	Energy units	Trillions of calories (12 ciphers omitted)
Total gross normal annual energy exchange		248	3,224,000,000,000
From the sun's short-wave radiation	1,729,000,000,000	133	
From earth's long-wave energy reserve	1,495,000,000,000	115	
	3,224,000,000,000	248	
Sun's short-wave energy absorbed by clouds	182,000,000,000	14	
Earth's long-wave energy absorbed by clouds	1,352,000,000,000	104	
Total absorbed by water-vapor	1,534,000,000,000	118	1,534,000,000,000
Gross energy available			1,690,000,000,000
Sun's short-wave units reflected by clouds	559,000,000,000	43	
Earth's long-wave units direct to outer space	143,000,000,000	11	
Atmospheric turbulence	234,000,000,000	18	
Allowance for 1% abnormal variation [a]	13,000,000,000	1	
	949,000,000,000	73	949,000,000,000
Net loss to outer space by earth and atmosphere		57	741,000,000,000

SOURCES: See notes to Table IV–6.

[a] 1% is carried by meteorologists as 1 unit, or 13 trillion billion calories. Written in full: 13,000,000,000,000,000,000,000,-000. Expressed in words: 13 sextillion.

TABLE IV-4. THE ATMOSPHERE'S NORMAL THERMAL GREENHOUSE ACTION

	Energy units	Calories (Trillions)	Calories (Trillions)
The atmosphere's normal average energy content	136		1,768,000,000,000
Total sun's short-waves sent downward [a]	133	1,729,000,000,000	
Less total earth's long-waves sent upward [b]	115	1,495,000,000,000	
Total normal atmospheric turbulence	18		234,000,000,000
Sun's short-waves absorbed by water-vapor clouds [c]	14	182,000,000,000	
Earth's long-waves absorbed by water-vapor clouds [d]	104	1,352,000,000,000	
Total normal absorption, or earth's greenhouse canopy	118		1,534,000,000,000

SOURCES: See notes to Table IV-6. Dr. Harry Wexler, Chief, Scientific Services Division, U. S. Weather Bureau Washington, D.C.

[a] See Table IV-3, line 2; [b] line 3; [c] line 5; [d] line 6.

only, whereas the earth's upward long-wave radiation is absorbed on the order of 104 units, or nearly 7½ times as great.

This property of the atmosphere, which depends on the characteristic absorption qualities of the water-vapor present, is similar to the action of ordinary window glass used in greenhouses—where the underside is given a light coating of white-wash—permitting greater ease in raising the temperature inside. The luminous rays are let in but are prevented from escape when they have become converted into dark heat. Thus, if there were no atmosphere, the average temperature over the earth's surface would be some 42° Fahrenheit less, or about 18° Fahrenheit instead of the observed 60° Fahrenheit.

SUNSHINE

Less than a two-billionth part of the sun's total annual output of energy falls upon the surface of the earth. Expressed in terms of horse-power this amounts to 25,000 trillion horse-power hours, or more than enough heat and power to supply the entire world's present annual kilowatt-hour needs some 700,000 times over. Expressed in terms of coal, wood, and petroleum fuel-tonnage equivalents this approximates 148 trillion tons per year.

One of the problems now facing the scientific world is the storage of the sun's energy for release and use when needed. It is clear that accurate knowledge of the sun and its energy is entitled to our due respect. All of the physical activities that flourish on the surface of the earth derive their energy directly or indirectly from the radiation of the sun. It is with the *laws* of this continual exchange that the physicists have developed the present general theory of radiation as described in its mathematical meaning in this chapter.

According to W. W. Campbell, Director of the Lick Observatory of the University of California, there are approximately 100 million 250-acre farms in the world, each receiving sun radiation, near the middle of a clear day, at the rate of 1 million horse-power per day. As about 43 per cent of the sun's rays are intercepted by the atmosphere overlying the average farm, we are interested in the average percentage of possible sunshine normally available throughout the world. Since sunshine, temperature, wind, and rainfall are so directly related, a glance at the Detail IV–A may prove of interest.

DETAIL IV–A

	Sunshine (Per Cent)	Temperature (Degree F.)	Wind (Av. M.P.H.)	Rainfall (Inches)
Africa	50	68	6.5	33
America, North	65	59	9.5	25
America, South	50	68	6.2	55
Asia	60	68	6.5	30
Europe	60	68	10.3	23
Oceania	60	60	6.5	20
Average world totals	58	60	7.5	39

RAINFALL

The world's rainfall is proverbially uncertain, but it appears from the most trustworthy records that at any given time and place the total rainfall rarely varies over 1 or 2 per cent.

TABLE IV-5. THE WORLD'S AVERAGE ANNUAL WATER EXCHANGE SYSTEM THROUGH THE ATMOSPHERE

	Cubic miles	Inches	U. S. standard gallons
Evaporation from oceans	92.121	41.3	101,383,854,384,384,000
Evaporation from inland waters	1.321	.6	1,454,968,933,681,600
Evaporation from peripheral land	20.871	29.9	22,861,979,053,056,000
Evaporation from closed basins	2.399	13.0	2,615,786,110,080,000
Total evaporation	116.712	84.8	128,316,588,481,201,600
Precipitation over oceans	86.124	38.5	94,510,409,520,384,000
Precipitation over peripheral land	26.868	38.6	29,497,219,614,720,000
Precipitation over closed basins	2.399	13.0	2,615,786,110,080,000
Total precipitation	115.391	90.1	126,623,415,245,184,000
Net vapor loss			1,693,173,236,017,600
Total evaporation from oceans	92.121	41.3	101,383,854,384,384,000
Ocean vapor carried to land, net	5.613	2.8	5,180,271,627,982,400
Total vapor lost in atmosphere	.630	.4	1,693,173,236,017,600
Total ocean vapor lost	98.364	44.5	6,873,444,864,000,000
Total net precipitation over oceans			94,510,409,520,384,000
Total evaporation from land & inland waters	23.270	42.9	26,932,734,096,817,600
Total received from ocean	5.997	8.7	5,652,142,475,264,000
Less land vapor carried to oceans	.429	.7	471,870,847,281,600
Total net received from oceans	28.838	50.9	5,180,271,627,982,400
Total precipitation received			32,113,005,724,800,000
Less precipitation over inland waters			1,579,621,430,000,000
Total net precipitation on land			30,533,384,294,800,000

SOURCES: *Handbuch der Klimatologie*, Stuttgart ed., 1911; *Ibid.* Vol. I, Part C, Berlin, 1936; Circulation of Water on the Earth's Surface; U. S. Public Health Service, 1928.

In measuring rainfall it will be recalled that 1 inch of rainfall over 1 acre is the equivalent of 113¼ tons, or 27,143 gallons of water, and that enormous quantities of energy are required to elevate the water vapor from the earth's surface before it can be precipitated. It takes from 5 to 10 million horse-power hours to evaporate the water in a single square mile of the average dense cloud, and for every inch of rainfall from 8 to 16 thousand horse-power hours are required before it is precipitated. For the world as a whole, the rain that falls has been aloft as water vapor in the atmosphere for an average of about three weeks.

TABLE IV–6. MAJOR CHANGES IN THE EARTH-ATMOSPHERE-SOLAR EXCHANGE BY CONTINENTS, 1882–1952

(*Water Precipitation reaching Land Surface, in Billions of Gallons*)

	1882	1952	Change	% Change
Africa	8,148,225,000	8,135,653,000	— 12,572,000	— .2%
America, North	6,716,780,000	6,487,019,000	— 229,761,000	—3.3
America, South	4,991,706,000	4,766,704,000	— 225,002,000	—4.5
Asia	12,075,523,000	11,755,481,000	— 320,042,000	—2.6
Europe	2,459,149,000	2,401,272,000	— 57,877,000	—2.4
Oceania	2,312,335,000	2,293,753,000	— 18,582,000	— .8
World total *	36,703,718,000	35,839,882,000	— 863,836,000	—2.4%

* Not adjusted for precipitation over inland waters.

(*Sun's Radiation reaching Land Surface, in Trillions of Calories*)

	1882	1952	Change	% Change
Africa	134,310,000,000	126,893,000,000	— 7,417,000,000	—5.5%
America, North	110,715,000,000	101,179,000,000	— 9,536,000,000	—8.6
America, South	82,280,000,000	74,347,000,000	— 7,933,000,000	—9.6
Asia	199,045,000,000	183,352,000,000	—15,693,000,000	—7.9
Europe	40,535,000,000	37,453,000,000	— 3,082,000,000	—7.6
Oceania	38,115,000,000	35,776,000,000	— 2,339,000,000	—6.1
World total	605,000,000,000	559,000,000,000	—46,000,000,000	—7.6

SOURCES: (Radiation) The basic data for changes in the sun's average annual radiation reaching the earth's surface were obtained from the reports of Dr. S. P. Langley of Mt. Whitney Observatory, in 1893, and published in full in the *Astrophysical Journal,* 1903, Vol. XXVII, p. 2. Dr. Langley's data were later revised downward, in 1900, by Dr. Charles Greeley Abbot, then of Mt. Wilson Observatory, and now of the Astrophysical Observatory, Smithsonian Institution, Washington, D.C. For the 1882 period the Abbot revisions have been employed.
For the 1952 period, the data were based upon the recent findings of Dr. Abbot. Thus the two periods represent the findings, in large measure, of the same man. The fundamental bases for the two periods, as based upon the observed changes in the *solar constant,* which is defined as the amount of radiational energy falling perpendicularly per square centimeter per minute on a surface placed just outside the earth's atmosphere. The relative value of this constant as determined in terms of calories by Dr. Abbot for the two periods is as follows:

1882   2.10 calories = 100.00%
1952   1.94 calories = 92.38%

(Precipitation) British Hydrological Office; U. S. Geological Survey, *Water Supply,* Paper 489; *Utilization of Rainfall,* H. H. Bennett, 1939; *Circulation of Water on the Earth's Surface,* U. S. Public Health Service.
NOTE: It will further be noted that as the world's land area shrinks, and the water area expands, there is a correspondingly smaller land "basin" to absorb the sun's rays, and a larger area for water evaporation from the water surface to occur.

For the world's average annual water exchange system through the atmosphere, see Tables IV–5 and IV–6. Particularly noteworthy is the quantitative decrease in both energy radiation and precipitation reaching the land surface as compared with 70 years ago. This has been due principally to the decrease in land area by erosion rather than to any notable decline in the rate of either radiation or precipitation.

According to the British Air Ministry's Office there are approximately 16 million thunderstorms occurring over the world every year, or nearly 44,000 daily, while the average number of tornadoes totals over 25,000 per year, with hurricanes reaching well over half a thousand.

In tropical hurricanes, sometimes called cyclones and typhoons, the energy supplied by the condensation of the vapor which allows the air to recoup itself for the loss due to expansion has been calculated to reach as much as 473 million horsepower. The air in a hurricane 100 miles in diameter and a mile high weighs as much as 3 billion tons. An enormous amount of energy is required to keep this in motion at from 40 to 50 miles per hour. Such a hurricane is carrying over 700 billion gallons of water at this great speed over the earth's surface. These matters are here mentioned because of the economic effect of wind and rain upon the erosion of the world's land inventory. For purposes of clarification the official designations of water precipitation are given, in the standard units of measure of the U. S. Weather Bureau, in Detail IV–B.

DETAIL IV–B

1 Inch of rainfall:	= Cubic feet =	Tons =	Gallons
Over 1 acre	= 3,630 =	113.25 =	27,143
Over 1 square mile	= 2,323,200 =	72,480.00 =	17,371,520
1 Inch of snowfall:			
Over 1 acre	= 363 =	11.30 =	2,714
Over 1 square mile	= 232,320 =	7,248.00 =	1,737,152

WIND

Wind is the atmosphere in natural motion. The general circulation of the atmosphere and its temperature is ultimately bound up with the general distribution of the rainfall of the world. Wind, itself, has a nomenclature of its own which is frequently misunderstood. For purposes of clarification the official designations, together with their average velocities in miles per hour, are given in Detail IV–C.

DETAIL IV–C

	Mi. per hour
Calm:	Less than 1
Very Light:	1 to 3
Light:	4 to 7
Gentle:	8 to 12
Strong:	25 to 38
Gale:	39 to 54
Whole gale:	55 to 72
Tornado:	72 to 100+
Hurricane (cyclone):	100 to 200+

THE ATMOSPHERE'S PLANT NUTRIENT EXCHANGE

Greater in area than the earth, and greater in circumference by 4000 miles but less in volume by nearly 136 billion cubic miles, the transparent gaseous air is capable of having more stuff packed into it, without affecting its volume, than can ever be packed into the earth.

The atmosphere is, of course, composed primarily of a mixture of gases. The permanent gases near the surface of the earth are mainly nitrogen, oxygen, and argon, which are present in amounts of approximately 78, 21, and 1 per cent by volume respectively. Other constituents amounting to less than $\frac{1}{10}$ of 1 per cent are carbon dioxide, carbon monoxide, hydrogen, neon, helium, krypton, xenon, radon, tritium, and ozone. Until a very few years ago these constituents were thought to remain in approximately the same proportions up to about 180,000 feet, above which there was a slight decrease of the heavier gases relative to the lighter.

In addition to the above, and independent of other gases, there is a considerable amount of water vapor, dust particles, bacteria, products of decomposition, products of combustion, and plant nutrients removed by wind erosion and evaporation. In the popular almanacs these additional products are customarily referred to as being "always small in amount." The fact is that the sum total of these additional products—all land products—at present amount to approximately 15 trillion tons of land matter of all descriptions including basic soil nutrients, and exclusive of water vapor. (See Table IV–1.)

When it is recalled that an average of a thousand tons of dry soil is required to cover a single acre of land to a depth of 7 inches, it takes little mathematical imagination to realize that we have in our atmosphere today the equivalent of 1.5 billion acres of invisible but quite real land material. This is what we mean by the "Invisible Continent." Insofar as this phenomenon relates to the world's land-balance sheet, it will be observed that, as these heavier particles settle back to earth, three-fourths of this annual quantity returns to the oceans and not to the land.

The first investigations of the amount of these solid particles in the atmosphere were those of John Aiken, an English scientist, in 1880. He devised a "dust-counter" and found, through thousands of tests in different parts of the world, that no matter where sampled the air contained a large supply of particles. Later the Owens dust-counter tests confirmed the findings of Aiken.

These dust particles range from 1 to 3 microns in diameter, averaging about three one-hundred-thousandths of an inch (too small to be seen by the naked eye) for a world-over average about 260 particles per cubic centimeter—ranging from 3400 particles at sea level to 26 per cubic centimeter at five miles above sea level. Over large cities the particles range from 80,000 to 210,000 per cubic centimeter of air. They are carried swiftly through the air. A wind of 10 miles per hour will carry them 2780 miles before they reach the earth's surface.

The dust raised from the ground by wind storms can be carried for thousands of miles. In England it has been estimated that as much as 10 million tons has fallen in 2 days. In the United States during the dust storms of 1934 as much as 700 million tons of top-soil material were carried out to sea in less than 4 days. As there are approximately 25,000 tornadoes over the world's land per year, there is afforded ample opportunity for a large volume of such matter to be circulating in the atmosphere at all times. The number of tornadoes in the United States—which has averaged 140 per year over a 36-year period—has increased by 214 per cent, or from 126 in 1945 to 395 in 1953. The recent hydrogen bomb test explosions have individually released 10 times more energy than the most powerful tornado.

The average air-dust scale of origin in round figures stands approximately as shown in Detail IV–D.

DETAIL IV–D

Origin	Tons Annually	% of Total
War and preparation for war	71,000,000,000	33.1
Atmospheric storms	60,000,000,000	28.0
Industrial activities	50,000,000,000	23.3
Agricultural operations	20,000,000,000	9.3
Transportation activities	10,000,000,000	4.7
Volcanic action	3,000,000,000	1.4
Households	200,000,000	.1
Star-dust from outer space	730,000	a
Total	214,200,730,000	100.0

a Less than 1/10 of 1%.

From the above it will be noticed that 70 per cent of the foreign matter sent into the air is due to man's activities. Thus man becomes a meteorological agent.

EASE WITH WHICH THE ATMOSPHERE MAY BE PACKED

The air is easily compressed. The amount of expansion of gases is much greater than the expansion of solids or liquids. The coefficient of expansion is about the same for all gases. Hence, the most striking characteristic of the atmosphere is its tendency to expand. This may be illustrated as follows:

1. If a 10,000 gallon tank is filled with water
   a. The water will assume the shape of the tank.
   b. It will take 10,000 gallons of water to fill the tank.
2. With gas: no matter how small the quantity may be that is put into the 10,000 gallon tank
   a. The gas will fill the tank.
   b. If any gas is drawn off, the remaining gas will still fill the tank.
   c. If any other matter, liquid, vapor, or solid is placed in the tank full of gas, the gas will compress itself and make room for the additional matter without reducing the quantity of gas.

MINING THE AIR

Today man is mining the air on a scale hitherto unimagined. Of the atmosphere's chief chemical ingredients, modern industry makes free use of vast quantities of nitrogen, oxygen, argon, neon, helium, krypton, tritium, and carbon dioxide. The uses to which these elements are now employed by man will be noted in the following:

Nitrogen: Fertilizers, explosives, disinfectants, photography, perfumery, and in manufacturing dyestuffs, nitric acid.

Oxygen: Cutting metals, in medicine, for combustion in fuels, in forming compounds and industrial oxides.

Argon: Filling electric light bulbs.

Neon: In illuminated signs and other bulbs.

Helium: Used extensively for filling balloons and airships.

Krypton: Light bulbs, in tungsten filaments in radios.

Tritium: In hydrogen bombs.

Carbon dioxide: For dry ice and in beverages.

The irreplaceable elements indispensable to all life are now being mined out of the world's atmosphere, by man's industrial operations, at the rate of 3 trillion tons per year. As man digs the earth's mineral wealth out of the ground, he is also digging irretrievable elements out of the air as never before in recorded history. To put it in simpler terms, man is removing these elements from his own atmosphere at a rate 3 per cent faster than they are being produced by the earth's atmosphere-hydrosphere-lithosphere process.

WIND POWER

The story of the world's winds is interesting and important enough to form the subject of a separate volume. The earliest attempts at any rational scheme of accounting for the more obvious features of the general circulation appears to have been made in 1735. The regularity of the "trade winds" was just then beginning to attract the attention of scientists. The term "trade" is used in the otherwise obsolete sense of "course" or "tread"; in the old sense of "path," hence a beaten regular track.

For centuries wind-power was the principal means of sea navigation. Even as late as 1882 slightly over 70 per cent of the world's total sea-going tonnage was wind-propelled. Seventy years later, in 1952, this had dropped to less than 1 per cent. The sailing vessel was always at the mercy of the winds. To make her best speed she could sail only at certain periods of the year, and even then there could be no dependable regularity as to sailing time.

The vast increase in the carrying power of the steamship, coupled with certainty as to the arrival of cargoes, has led to momentous consequences. In the first place, it helped to build up the populations of the newer countries by permitting a large expansion of emigration. As an illustration: during the wind sailing period in the ten years 1825–34, the average annual number of immigrants received by the United States was 32,000. In the last decade before World War II, it was 1,012,000.

A considerable portion of the total mechanical energy for agriculture and other work has been developed by making use of the wind as free "fuel." In Denmark, the Netherlands, and parts of Israel windmills now provide nearly 50 per cent of all the power used annually.

Wind is an inexhaustible source of energy, although only winds of moderate velocity blowing close to the land surface have as yet been harnessed safely. Velocities under 20 miles per hour are useless, while those above 30 miles per hour are dangerous and unmanageable. In Rutland, Vermont, an aerogenerator, operated by the Central Vermont Public Service Corporation, has been in practical use for several years. This wind-power generator has been able to deliver more than 1000 kilowatts, developing over 13,000 horsepower-hours. However, of the 2 trillion horsepower-hours per year available from the world's surface winds, scarcely $\frac{1}{10}$ of 1 per cent is now being utilized.

AIR HIGHWAYS

At present no place in the world is more than twenty-four hours away. Nations, jungles, polar wastes have shrunk to neighborhoods. The mystery of distant lands is as lost as are the world's frontiers. Mountains, oceans, icefields are no longer barriers to transportation. Travel and trade is now measured by hours and minutes rather than in hundreds and thousands of miles. Our geographical concepts have been vastly revised as man's Air Age comes to maturity. "Pepsi-Cola welcomes you to China" in *neon* now greets the traveler from anywhere.

In 1919 there were scarcely 200 miles of air routes in operation throughout the world. Twenty years later, in 1939, this figure had grown to nearly 500,000 miles, and by 1952 it had reached well over a million miles—with nearly 1 trillion miles flown. Thus, in three decades, or one generation, air transportation routes have spread over every continent, bridged every ocean and, in fact, girdled the globe itself. In the modern history of transportation only the growth of the world's mileage of improved highways caused by the development of the automobile can be compared with this achievement.

The total world capital investment in the air, military, civil, and industrial, is about 5 trillion dollars.

HOW HIGH IS THE SKY?

The height of our atmosphere has never been measured as we measure distance on the earth's surface, for the simple reason that thus far man has never been able to reach the "top." Indeed, it would be difficult to determine precisely where the top is, even if we could approach it, since the air would shade off so gradually into outer space that we should with difficulty discover the place where we could say "thus far and no farther." We have, however, arrived at considerable knowledge as to the probable height to which the air exists in such quantity as to possess weight and volume.

At the beginning of the Christian era the earth's blanket of air was thought to be 5 miles high. By 1900 it was thought to be possibly as high as 50 miles. Now, in 1954, it is thought to be somewhere around 600 miles where we reach the limits of its insulating blanket covering the earth.

The atmosphere constitutes an insulating layer between the earth and the conducting layer in the high ionosphere, which is the outer envelope of our atmosphere. The lower atmosphere, called the troposphere, ranging from 5 to 8 miles high and amounting to about one-half the total weight, is a poor conductor and thus serves to protect the earth's surface from the constant bombardment of particles and ions from outer space.

Since this air-to-earth current flows continuously unless disturbed by volcanic or man-made atomic and hydrogen bomb explosions, electrically speaking some form of direct current generator must exist for maintaining the potential difference between the ionosphere and the earth. The nature and the location of this "generator" is still one of the great unsolved mysteries of our time.

THE AIR'S FLUCTUATING LAYERS

The ionosphere or outer protective air layer ranges from 60 to 600 miles in thickness, depending upon the season and proximity to the equator or the polar regions. Star-dust from outer space falls through this layer on down through the stratosphere and troposphere to earth at the rate of 730,000 tons per year. As this action takes place the area is broken down into electrified or ionized layers produced by the ionizing action of the sun's radiation. This means changes in the number of electrons lost or gained by the atoms. These layers are sometimes called the Appleton or F-layer, some 140 miles above the earth's surface, and the Heaviside or E-layer, about 60 miles above. These two layers are important to radio communication.

RADIO BOUNCING BOARDS AND FLYING SAUCERS

The Appleton and Heaviside layers—F and E—are named after their discoverers, William Henry Appleton and Oliver Heaviside, best known for their studies in transient electrical phenomena and propagation of waves in telegraphy and radio. The *short* radio waves rebound from the F-layer while the *long* radio waves rebound from the E-layer.

Immense explosive showers of ionized atomic fragments, one mile across, each thought to be caused by a single atomic "bullet," were first discovered in the earth's atmosphere in 1949—just five years ago, and five years after the ushering in of the atomic age. Whether this was mere coincidence we do not know. Nevertheless, it was by way of a V–2 rocket exploration of the upper atmosphere that this discovery was made. These showers, coupled with the immense amount of ionized dust particles that have been sent into the atmosphere's higher regions by atomic experiments following 1945 to date and the high probability of their creating clouds of polarized dust particles account for the more than usually widespread reports of "unidentified moving objects" in the skies.

DESERT WEATHER AND SMOG CONTROL EXPERIMENTS

It has recently been brought before the attention of the American Meteorological Society that giant windmills can be constructed and operated effectively for the control of the weather over desert and semi-arid regions so that useful crops may be grown in the now wasted areas that comprise such a large part of the world's land surface. These huge windmills, 150 feet above ground, would be used to create artificial "thermal updrafts," or vertical streams of warm air, drawing air from a radius of five miles at the rate of 65 to 90 miles per hour. The result would be a funnel of fast moving air similar to that found in tornadoes, with the updraft being regulated by changing the angle at which the blades operate, or by varying the power of the suggested 500 horse-power motor and rotating the shaft.

It has been claimed that use of the same windmills could be made to relieve such problems as smog by destroying the atmospheric "inversion" which occurs when temperature increases with height, rather than falling off at higher levels as is the usual case. Such warmer air, at high levels, blankets the air below, and prevents its escape. The dissipation of the inverted layer, it is suggested, would release the air below and thus relieve the smog.

THE MODERN SIGNIFICANCE OF THE ATMOSPHERE AND GEOLOGIC TIME

Geologic time is long. No geologist today thinks that the evolutionary growth of the earth and its life could have taken place in less than 4 billion years. This means a succession of changing periods, throughout which the constant shrinking of the earth has led to an instability of its surface that has brought about vast periodic changes, not only in the space relations of land and water but in the shapes and heights of the land as well. There are *intermediate tranquil periods* and *critical periods*. It is through one of these later intermediate periods, when the face of the earth appears so scenically grand, beautiful, and permanent to man, that we are passing today.

We are living at a time when the earth has marked climatic differences, varying between icy polar climates and hot moist or dry tropical conditions. This has not always been the case, for, as geologic time goes, not long ago the temperature of the earth was colder than it is now.

The atmospheric blanket that surrounds the earth, with its carbon dioxide and water vapor, is the great climatic regulator. Due to the increasing abundance of both through the centuries, especially of water vapor, there has resulted a thickened and heavier blanket that not only holds in more of the earth's warmth, but takes up greater amounts of the sun's radiation. At present this atmosphere appears to be gaining in weight at the rate of some 1 trillion 300 billion tons per year, or an increase in total weight of some 90 trillion tons over the past 70 years—a large part of which has been due to man's activities. See Table IV–1 page 54 above.

Both in his mining and his use of the air as a highway, man, through extraction from and pollution of the atmosphere, has launched into the newer and as yet uncharted realm of the active meteorological agent. He is now adding poisonous ingredients to the air at an unprecedented rate in excess of 100 billion tons per year, through industrial combustion, carbon monoxide, and atomic and hydrogen radiation. He does not yet know what the full consequences may be. Hence, more than ever before, the world's atmosphere itself becomes a crucial factor in mankind's environment, for here we find an ecological element as yet uncharted.

Due to the valuable mineral deposits of the earth, the pre-Cambrian or Archeozoic geologic age is of great economic importance. It was during this period, dating back between 1 to 4 billion years ago, that most of today's principal minerals were formed. The greatest gold, iron, nickel, and copper mines of the world are all due to the metamorphic geologic change that took place during that ancient period —quite some time before the emergence of man. (See minerals, Chapter III.) A great variety of non-metallic products, such as graphite, corundum, mica, talc, feldspar, marble, and other modern-day indispensable industrial materials were formed then. The mineral production, throughout the world, from materials formed in this period is ever-increasing as our knowledge of these ancient complex deposits is advancing.

Back in this far distant time, the earth's land surface was some 160 per cent greater than it is today, while the oceans and seas of the world were 50 per cent less. The land masses were high and the oceans were shallow in those early days

TABLE IV-7. THE WORLD'S AVERAGE ANNUAL ATMOSPHERIC PLANT NUTRIENT EXCHANGE BALANCE SHEET—1952

(In Net Tons)

	Wind erosion	Water erosion	Radiation absorption [b]	World's total atmospheric removal	% of total
Atmospheric annual removal:					
Nitrogen	27,000,000	101,500,000	300,000	128,800,000	2.7%
Phosphorus	4,400,000	15,300,000	–	19,700,000	.4
Potassium	92,800,000	349,100,000	500,000	442,400,000	9.2
Calcium	163,100,000	613,400,000	1,800,000	778,300,000	16.2
Magnesium	51,000,000	191,900,000	700,000	243,600,000	5.1
Sulphur	31,500,000	119,800,000	1,300,000	152,600,000	3.2
Sub-total	369,800,000	1,391,000,000	4,600,000	1,765,400,000	36.8
Organic matter [a]	534,400,000	2,500,000,000	–	3,034,400,000	63.2
Grand total [a]	904,200,000	3,891,000,000	4,600,000	4,799,800,000	100.0%

	Atmospheric fall-back	Precipitation fall-back	Sub-soil replacement [c]	World's total atmospheric replacement	% of total
Atmospheric annual replacement:					
Nitrogen	3,600,000	7,100,000	800,000	11,500,000	4.6%
Phosphorus	600,000	–	400,000	1,000,000	.4
Potassium	12,500,000	11,800,000	5,900,000	30,200,000	12.1
Calcium	21,900,000	44,200,000	6,000,000	72,100,000	28.8
Magnesium	6,800,000	17,600,000	2,700,000	27,100,000	10.8
Sulphur	4,300,000	32,300,000	300,000	36,900,000	14.7
Sub-total	49,700,000	113,000,000	16,100,000	178,800,000	71.4
Organic matter	71,600,000	–	–	71,600,000	28.6
Grand total	121,300,000	113,000,000	16,100,000	250,400,000	100.0%

(*In Net Tons*)

	Wind erosion	Water erosion	Radiation absorption	World's total atmospheric deficit	% of total
World's annual deficit due to atmospheric action:					
Nitrogen	— 23,400,000	— 94,400,000	+ 500,000	— 117,300,000	— 2.6%
Phosphorus	— 3,800,000	— 15,300,000	+ 400,000	— 18,700,000	— .4
Potassium	— 80,300,000	— 337,300,000	+ 5,400,000	— 412,200,000	— 9.1
Calcium	— 141,200,000	— 569,200,000	+ 4,200,000	— 706,200,000	— 15.5
Magnesium	— 44,200,000	— 174,300,000	+ 2,000,000	— 216,500,000	— 4.8
Sulphur	— 27,200,000	— 87,500,000	— 1,000,000	— 115,700,000	— 2.5
Sub-total	— 320,100,000	— 1,278,000,000	+ 11,500,000	— 1,586,600,000	— 34.9
Organic matter	— 462,800,000	— 2,500,000,000	—	— 2,962,800,000	— 65.1
Grand total	— 782,900,000	— 3,778,000,000	+ 11,500,000	— 4,549,400,000	— 100.0%

ᵃ Complete analysis undetermined. ᵇ Earth's annual loss to outer space, and disintegration in the air. ᶜ Nutrients derived from soil-growth 7-inch depth.

of the planet's life. Ever since that time of great internal molecular rearrangements, the earth has been losing volume, and dissipating its inherited and derived energy to outer space—as its lands have shrunk in area at the expense of the ever-expanding seas.

During the earth's adolescence, there was far more nitrogen and very little oxygen in the atmosphere as compared with today, and far less carbon dioxide—one of the fundamental materials at the basis of all life. In the present atmosphere there are about three volumes of this gas to 10,000 of air, and there is much more in living things than there is in the atmosphere. (See Table IV-7.) On the other hand, 25 to 30 times more carbon dioxide is present in the oceans than in the air, while the still vaster volumes locked up in the sedimentary rocks and in the fuels and carbonaceous deposits have been computed to be on the order of 30,000 times greater than the volume in the present atmosphere.

These elemental facts are brought forward because of their fundamental importance to life and the activities of plants. Should this life increase but *once again* over its present magnitude, all of the carbon dioxide of the atmosphere would be in the living things, and if that were ever to occur, death would come to all. Therefore, life and all of its abundance—no matter how optimistically planned or hoped for—at any time cannot escape finding itself conditioned by the amount of this small quantity of gas present in our air.

SIGNIFICANT RESEARCH

The classical work on the composition of the atmosphere by Baron Rayleigh and Sir William Ramsay, titled *The Gases of the Atmosphere* and published in 1896, remained little more than an academic curiosity to most people until 1945, when the giant gas diffusion plant of the United States atomic bomb project went into operation at Oak Ridge, Tennessee.

Prior to this work the atmosphere was generally looked upon as not being composed of matter, as having no weight—hence the saying "light as air"—and as representing primarily a great unsolved puzzle to the layman due to the erratic character of the weather. As such it is still the most widely discussed topic in the world.

Up to 1882, through the work of Cavendish, the atmosphere was thought to contain but two elements—nitrogen 79.167% and oxygen 20.833%—and even this was popularly viewed as doubtful. By 1900 the known elements in the air had increased to four, while it was not until 1910 that the present complement of eleven had been identified as permanent constituents of the air. Of these, entirely unknown 70 years ago, we owe six to the findings of Ramsay and Rayleigh. Their investigations have led to significant consequences. Prior to the work of Rayleigh, 1896, the density of gases was not known. And it was Ramsay who discovered in 1903 that helium was the product of radium disintegration, thus leading to the transmutation theory and its important consequences.

MAN-MADE MINIATURE SUNS

The basic concept behind the creation of the H-bomb came from the discovery that solar energy, which we are so dependent upon, is derived from the *fusion* of hydrogen nuclei to form those of helium. It was not until the A-bomb was produced that the scientists could believe they might create a miniature sun.

The union of hydrogen and helium takes place at about 100 million degrees centigrade, and until 1945 there were no such temperatures capable of being created on earth. Further, the natural sun's process of conversion of hydrogen into helium requires some 6 million years and the presence of carbon as a cementing agent.

Notwithstanding these hitherto unattainable accomplishments, it was discovered that the element beryllium, when exposed to radium, could "trigger" the product of uranium, with a tremendous volume of energy in the form of light and heat, to 150 million degrees centigrade in one-billionth of a second. Such a spectacular change is called *nuclear fission,* as distinguished from *nuclear fusion.*

POWER AND THE CHEMISTRY OF THE AIR

We live in a world in which power is going to waste all the time, whether we use it or not. This waste occurs in the form of sunlight, winds, tides, waterfalls, and the inefficiencies of man's ability to make use of the principles of combustion. We are also living in a period of greater technological civilization than has existed in the past, and, if current events are a reliable indication, greater than can be expected to exist in the future.

As a result of these factors, regardless of the fact that gasoline can be made from coal, that alcohol can be produced from crops, and that vast quantities of power can be produced from our new knowledge of the atomic processes, all of these resources are running lower and lower with each successive year. Even the "wonders" of "electronics," fascinating as they are and promising as they at first appear, are not without their limits.

Actually, we are interested not just in energy generally, but in energy that we can put to work on the basis of what, when, where, and how we want it to work. The sunlight of the air falling over the ground at better than one horse-power per square yard will not help a farmer move a rock, pull a plow, or thresh his crop, unless he can acquire the equipment with which to put this solar energy to work. Much the same is true of the other "free" energy sources. They are generally not worth the present monetary investment required to put them to work. At least this appears to be true within the framework of a large part of the world's present institutional set-up.

THE WEIGHT OF THE AIR—IN THEORY AND IN FACT

In any inventory of physical resources the weight of the atmosphere cannot be ignored. This has been described to us in the past in so many different confusing ways as to lead most of us to give the matter up entirely. But in this age of atomics and spatial rocket excursions, this matter may be of considerable importance.

No less an authority than Sir John Herschel estimated the entire weight of the air resting upon the surface of the earth, in 1866, as amounting to $11\frac{2}{3}$ trillion pounds, or some 5.8 billion tons. At that time the atmosphere had not been envisaged as much over 5 miles high, which was the height of what was then termed the homogeneous atmosphere. While most recent popularized estimates have placed the figure at some 5 quadrillion tons, or one-million times that of the nineteenth-century figure, nevertheless it may prove worth while to examine the matter further.

Back in 1643 some Florentine gardeners found that they were unable to pump water higher than 33 feet. This led a pupil of Galileo, Evangelista Torricelli, in the same year, to devise the *mercurial barometer*, based upon the principle that a mercury pump would raise mercury to a height of about 30 inches—which exactly balanced the 33 feet of water of the gardeners. This method of measuring air pressure was presumably sufficient to measure the limits of the atmosphere.

Although over 300 years have elapsed since the time of Torricelli, and great advances in the accurate measurement of atmospheric gases have occurred as recently as between 1896 and 1910, the best atmosphere measures one can find in the encyclopedias and popular almanacs still adhere to the seventeenth-century method.

Because air is elastic, and in common with all gases and fluids not only presses downwards but equally upwards and in all directions, we must not confuse *pressure* with *weight*. To say that barometric pressure is caused by the gravitational attraction of the earth is one thing. To say that atmospheric pressure is caused by the same gravitational forces on all of the atmosphere's gaseous molecules above the point of measurement is a decidedly different thing.

In the turbulence of the atmosphere above the earth the air masses and their relative different compositions, due to their nature, electromagnetic forces, varying temperatures, and moisture, vary considerably in total weight as measured by earth-surface standards.

The composition of the air as shown in Table IV–1 has been given in the terms with which the older physics was familiar. The measure of the same atmosphere in terms of the more recent knowledge is given in Table IV–7.

ATMOSPHERIC HURRICANES AND ATOMIC BOMB EXPLOSIONS

The unusual violence of tornadoes and hurricanes during recent years has engendered public search for reasons. The popular view has centered around the possibility that the large number of atomic bomb explosions, filling the air with radioactive particles, may have affected the atmosphere in an unpredictable fashion, thus accounting for heavy rainfall in some sections and tornadoes in others.

Inquiries on the effects of atomic explosions and atomic particles on the weather were asked for by members of the House of Representatives and the Senate, but the majority of the members of the Armed Services Committee and the Atomic Energy Committee considered the matter out of their jurisdiction.

The Atomic Energy Commission denied that there could be any connection between the bombs and tornadoes. Dr. Harry Wexler of the staff of the U. S. Weather Bureau stated reassuringly that "the energy released by such atomic explosions is rather small compared with the energy released by nature's storms." He stated that a big hurricane, which can last for several days, can liberate energy at the rate of 5 to 10 Hiroshima-type bombs per second.

It will be noted that he confined his comparisons to energy alone, omitting the factors of heat and radioactive reactions in the upper layers of the atmosphere. As there are three types of atom bombs in existence, and several types of tornadoes and hurricanes, a comparison of all types is here given in the order shown in Table IV–8.

It will be noted that the ionization effect, which is the change in the electric charge of the molecules in the atmosphere due to atomic radioactive particles blown into the higher parts of the atmosphere, has not been discussed by officials of either the Atomic Energy Commission, the Department of Defense, or the U. S. Weather Bureau. In this respect, it has been known since 1947 that the entire range of the presently known elements, in both the atmosphere and on the crust of the earth, can be made artificially radioactive, with rates of decay extending from 5 days to over 5000 years.

TABLE IV–8. NATURAL AND ARTIFICIAL ATMOSPHERIC DISTURBANCES

A. Energy Comparisons

Atomic bomb types:	Horsepower developed	Natural storm types:	Horsepower developed	Height in air	
				Bombs	Storms
Hiroshima type	147,500,000	Tornado	30,000,000	8 miles	1 mile
Improved type	1,475,000,000	Cyclone	430,000,000	20 miles	3 miles
Hydrogen type	22,128,000,000	Hurricane	815,000,000	50 miles	5 miles

B. Heat and Time Comparisons

Atomic bomb types:	Degrees Centigrade	Time	Natural storms:	Heat	Time
Hiroshima type	100,000,000°	One-millionth of a second	Tornado	100°	1 day
Improved type	150,000,000°	One-millionth of a second	Cyclone	200°	3 days
Hydrogen type	180,000,000°	One-millionth of a second	Hurricane	300°	5 days

C. Pre-atomic and Post-atomic Era Comparisons of Tornadoes in the United States

Periods:		Average annual number	Total property loss	Average annual property loss
Post-atomic era, 1945–1953	9 years	221	$889,623,228	$98,000,000
Pre-atomic period, 1916–1945	30 years	138	336,427,052	11,000,000
		+83	+$553,196,176	+$87,000,000
		+60%	+164%	+790%

SOURCES: U. S. Weather Bureau, Washington, D.C.; Bulletins of Atomic Scientists, Federation of American Scientists; Reports of the Atomic Energy Commission; Prof. David Dietz, Western Reserve University, Cleveland, Ohio.

In the United States, throughout the entire thirty-year period prior to mid-1945, no single year on record reported more than 173 tornadoes. After 1945, six successive years averaged 264 tornadoes each, with 1951 reporting 300, and 1953 reporting 395. It is probably too early to determine whether these comparisons are merely a statistical coincidence. Nevertheless, according to the record, there has been a marked increase in both the number and the severity of such storms since the atomic experiments.

RADIOACTIVE BOMBARDMENT OF THE ATMOSPHERE

It has long been known that the cosmic ray primary particles which strike the earth's atmosphere from outer space give rise to a wide variety of other particles and radiations. Nuclei with atomic numbers as high as 50 have been found to be present in this primary radiation. Natural forces striking the top of the world's atmosphere cause this bombardment.

Since 1945 man has entered this high-energy particle field, and bombards the atmosphere from its underside with atomic numbers ranging as high as 98. The ultimate effect of this now complete "encirclement" of the atmosphere with highly charged radioactive materials is, of course, unknown.

As officially reported, at present some seven countries of the world are now engaged in the production of radioactive materials. These countries are the United States, Canada, United Kingdom, France, Russia, Norway, and the Netherlands.

ATMOSPHERIC DISTURBANCES IN THE LABORATORY OF THE AIR

Within the past 70 years the major earthborne disturbances of the world's atmosphere were until recently caused by volcanic action. The greatest was the eruption of Krakatoa in the Netherlands Indies in August 1883. It has been computed by competent authorities that a vast column of stones, dust, and ashes projected from the volcano and shot up into the air for a distance of more than 20 miles, with finer dust particles reaching into the higher layers of the atmosphere.

These dust particles were diffused over a large part of the surface of the earth, and were said to have taken 2 years to settle down completely. It will be recalled that dust particles play a highly important role as a constituent part of the earth's atmosphere. First, they are the nuclei round which the water vapor forms into rain drops; second, they serve to shield the earth's surface from the dangerous invisible ultraviolet cosmic rays from outer space; third, they are the basis for the "greenhouse" effect that stabilizes the earth's temperature; and last, they protect life on our planet from the layer of ozone that occupies a region between 15 and 30 miles above the earth's surface, which stops about 3 per cent of the yellow-green light rays coming from the sun.

Ozone is popularly thought of as an invigorating fresh air element. It is a compound having 3 atoms of oxygen to the molecule (O_3), and pure ozone is in fact a deadly poisonous gas that exists in sensitive balance high in the atmosphere. Scientists have been studying the amount of ozone in the atmosphere carefully for the past 50 years, and have found that it also serves to stop some of the infra-red long-wave heat radiation coming from the earth. This ozone layer, if brought down to the surface at the world's average 60-degree temperature, would make a sheet only about one-tenth of an inch thick, yet any rip in this tissue-thin sheet would have deadly consequences for all living things.

In this connection it may be interesting to recall that Dr. Gerald Wendt, at the General Electric Science Forum in 1946, disclosed that the U. S. Chemical Warfare Service had developed roughly an ounce of a crystalline toxin that was described as such a deadly and powerful poison that it could kill every living person in the United States and Canada silently and swiftly, once released in the air. The cost of this development was only $50 million, extremely cheap as compared with the cost of the atomic bomb.

THE HEAT BALANCE OF THE ATMOSPHERE

Every meteorologist is aware of the importance of the delicate heat-balance mechanism of the air, and of the part this balance plays in both rainfall and wind currents. There are only two forces which initiate movement in the resting atmosphere. One of these is the force of gravity, which acts to accelerate each particle of air downward. The other is the internal pressure of the air gases which acts equally in all directions.

The hydrostatic equation expresses the state of exact balance in the atmosphere between these two forces—the force of gravity acting *downward*, and the pressure gradient force acting *upward*. When this condition is not satisfied, downward acceleration of the atmosphere has been observed in what are called *thermal convective* displacements of air. Thus the primary drive of all atmospheric wind systems is found in such thermally direct circulation, although there does exist thermally indirect, or forced, circulation independent of the general circulation which operates between the equatorial heat source and the polar cold source.

These independent forced natural thermal convectives have been due to volcanic action with hot blasts forced into the air from depths as great as 30 miles—the maximum depth to which it has been calculated sufficient heat to melt granite might occur. As this heat is known to be 1000 degrees centigrade, as against the new man-made atomic heat blasts which are a hundred thousand times greater, it would seem ridiculous for anyone to think that such enormous sudden heat convective forces would not produce a reactive effect upon the natural heat balance of the world's atmosphere.

Unfortunately, meteorologists, climatologists, and thermonuclear physicists employed by the various government services are not always in agreement as to the approximate height of the ozonosphere, the amount, area, and time of radioactive "fall-out," and the effects of man-made atmospheric disturbances upon climatic conditions. In this connection it is interesting that the astrophysicists, who have been studying the atmosphere for over 50 consecutive years, are not in agreement with the Atomic Energy Commission's nuclear physicists and weather men, who have been studying their explosive effect for barely 10 years. For example, the AEC places the ozonosphere a full 10 miles higher in the atmosphere than do the Smithsonian Institution's astrophysicists.

Recent bomb blast experiments have reached 50 miles into the atmosphere, 30 miles higher than Krakatoa, the world's greatest "natural" explosion, or into the stratosphere some 10 miles above the ozonosphere. This is according to the Atomic Commission's own report. Unfortunately, again, it is not known whether such reports are exaggerations or whether they have been wilfully *minimized*. Suffice it to say that Sir Winston Churchill told the House of Commons that an "undue number" of atomic and hydrogen bomb explosions might have serious effects on the earth's atmosphere for about 5000 years. He stated that his advice had come from a scientist, and that he was not making a facetious remark.

The sources of Churchill's information could have been Dr. Hans Bethe, formerly director of theoretical physics at Los Alamos Laboratories, and Dr. Leo Szilard, professor of biophysics at the University of Chicago. In 1950 Dr. Bethe stated that "H-bomb neutrons are produced in large numbers, and as these neutrons go into the atmosphere they produce radioactive carbon 14, which is well known to science. This isotope of carbon has a life of five thousand years. Hence, if H-bombs are exploded in some number, the air will be poisoned by this carbon 14 for five thousand years."

Dr. Szilard stated that most of the naturally occurring elements in the atmosphere become radioactive when they absorb neutrons. In this connection Dr. Szilard further stated that he had made a calculation based upon the following assumption:

if a radioactive element were produced which would live five years, and if this element were released into the air, during the following years it would gradually settle out and cover the whole earth with radioactive dust. According to Dr. Szilard, about 500 tons of heavy hydrogen producing 50 tons of such neutrons would be sufficient to kill every living thing on earth.

While the relationship of volcanization to atmospheric conditions and the weather processes and conditions has by no means been settled conclusively by scientists, nevertheless the volcanic action is admittedly due to the escape under pressure of heated material through channels of weakness in the earth's crust, although the

TABLE IV-9. PRINCIPAL ELEMENTS OF THE ATMOSPHERE

Element	Symbol	Atomic number	Atomic weight	Number of protons [c]	Number of neutrons	Number of isotopes	Year discovered
Nitrogen	N	7	14.008	7	7	2	1772
Oxygen	O	8	16.000	8	8	3	1774
Argon	A	18	39.944	18	22	5	1894
Carbon dioxide	CO_2	26 [a]	48.010	22	26	8	
Neon	Ne	10	20.183	10	10	3	1898
Krypton	Kr	36	83.800	36	48	6	1898
Helium	He	2	4.003	2	2	2	1898
Xenon	Xe	54	173.040	54	119	9	1898
Ozone	O_3	24 [b]	39.000	24	15	9	
Hydrogen	H	1	1.008	1	0	3	1766
Radon	Rn	86	222.000	86	136	3	1910

PRINCIPAL RADIOACTIVE ELEMENTS IN THE EARTH'S CRUST

Element	Symbol	Atomic number	Atomic weight	Number of protons [c]	Number of neutrons	Number of isotopes	Year discovered
Actinium	Ac	89	227.00	89	138	2	1899
Americium	Am	95	241.00	95	146	8	1944
Astatine	As	85	210.00	85	125	2	1940
Berkelium	Bk	97	243.00	97	146	2	1940
Californium	Cf	98	244.00	98	146	2	1950
Curium	Cm	96	242.00	96	146	6	1944
Francium	Fr	87	223.00	87	136	2	1939
Neptunium	Np	93	239.00	87	146	10	1940
Plutonium	Pu	94	238.00	94	144	11	1940
Promethium	Pm	61	147.00	61	86	5	1945
Technetium	Tc	43	98.00	43	55	10	1937
Thorium	Th	90	232.12	90	142	6	1828
Radium	Ra	88	226.05	88	138	4	1898
Uranium	U	92	238.08	92	146	3	1789
Polonium	Po	84	210.00	84	126	7	1898

SOURCES: Atmosphere: W. J. Humphrey's *Physics of the Air*; Napier Shaw, *Manual of Meteorology*; Sydney Chapman, Imperial College of Science and Technology, London; *Encyclopaedia Britannica*, '48 ed., Vol. 2, p. 640.

Chemical element description: Prof. Phillip S. Chen, Atlantic Union College, S. Lancaster, Mass.; *Journal of the American Chemical Society*.

Radioactive elements: James Chadwick, University of Liverpool, *Radiation from Radioactive Substances*; Glenn T. Seaborg, University of California; Ernest Rutherford, University of Cambridge, England; Linus C. Pauling, California Institute of Technology.

[a] $C = O_2 = 16$.   [b] $O_3 = 24$.   [c] There is an equal number of electrons in all elements.

immediate contributing factor that "pulls the trigger," so to speak, is still unknown. The analogy between this unresolved question, and that of the relationship between atomic explosion and atmospheric change seems evident.

In the average school and college laboratory experiments may occasionally go wrong. The damage is localized, the lesson learned and soon forgotten. But when all outdoors becomes the experimental laboratory—with politicians and military men tampering with the world's only atmosphere—one mistake may prove to be man's greatest.

The "calculated risk," based upon the so-called mathematical "law of probability" and founded on the principles of chance, is of course a military and a businessman's prerogative. It is the relation of probability, not certainty, that obtains between most of man's premises and conclusions. Though most human judgments may be based upon probability rather than certainty, careful thought is rarely given to the mechanics of this method of reasoning.

Actuarial science, based on the probabilities indicated by recorded observed facts, where biological life expectancy can be calculated within a frame of reasonable certainty, is quite a different thing. It is based on already known provable factors, and through its operation large life insurance companies have grown and prospered.

We are able to predict the motions of planets millions of miles off in space. Anyone can predict that the sun will rise in the morning, but one cannot predict the result of tossing a penny other than the certainty that it will obey the force of gravity and fall. Whether it falls "heads" or "tails" is the chance element. Events in this category we ascribe to chance and let it go at that. Yet chance is merely a euphemism for ignorance. To say that an event is determined by chance is to say that we do not know how it is determined.

One of these principles is based on knowing, the other is based upon not knowing. The future fate of mankind may depend upon which principle the present world leadership follows.

All the rivers run into the sea, yet the sea is not full; unto the place
from whence the rivers came thither they return again.
—ECCLESIASTES 1:7

Of all the necessities of man, water is the most vital and, therefore,
a fitting subject for major research. But the facts are often clouded
with fiction. Nearly half of all water reaching the ocean makes its
trip underground. Modern industry needs water in vast quantities. It
uses water for steam generation, for washing, cooling and conveying,
and as an actual ingredient in manufactured products. In 1950 industry in the United States used about 120 billion tons of water—
almost 50 times the weight of all other industrial materials. In the
last 20 years the nation has increased its withdrawals of underground water over 300 per cent . . . The expectation is that by
1975, industry may require 2½ times as much . . . but even if all
possibilities of more efficient utilization are realized, supplying industrial water in 1975 still will constitute a major problem.
—THE PRESIDENT'S MATERIALS POLICY COMMISSION, 1952

V

Water

WATER RANKS NEXT to the air in its unique influence on the world's physical
resources. And like the air, water has been so much taken for granted that up until
recently it has been difficult to develop a clear appraisal of its nature and true significance. Unfortunately, the fact of its indispensability to life has not been equally
realized in all parts of the world.

Considering water's decisive importance to so many phases of agricultural, industrial, domestic, and cultural life, it is worth noting that as yet no attempt has
been made to present an adequate description of the basic facts concerning water
resources or the extent of their possible conservation, development, and use for
the world as a whole.

POPULAR DECEPTION RELATING TO WATER
RESOURCES

While pointing out the importance of water as a necessary constituent in the
cells of all animal and vegetable tissues and in the crystals of many minerals, the
average popular encyclopedia invariably refers to water as *"one of the most abundant and widely distributed substances on the surface of the earth."*

TABLE V-1. SIGNIFICANT CHANGES IN FUNDAMENTAL RELATIONSHIPS

(Volume in Cubic Miles)

	1882		1952		Change	% Change
Total planet earth	259,944,036,000	100.0%	259,900,741,000	100.0%	— 43,295,000	— .01%
Land above sea-level	75,844,533,000	29.2	68,026,307,000	26.2	—7,818,226,000	—10.30
Air	39,511,493,000	15.2	39,504,913,000	15.2	— 6,580,000	— .01
Water	347,283,000	.1	346,241,000	.1	— 1,042,000	— .30

(Cubic Miles per Capita)

	1882		1952		Change	% Change
Total planet earth	181.3	100.0%	104.3	100.00%	—77.0	—42.5%
Land above sea-level	52.9	29.2	27.3	26.17	—25.6	—48.4
Air	27.6	15.1	15.9	15.24	—11.7	—42.4
Water	.2	.1	.1	.09	— .1	—50.0

SOURCES: 1882: Internationale Erdmessung (International Earth Measurement), Potsdam, 1886; The International Geodetic Association, Potsdam, 1886; Sir John Murray, F.R.G.S., London; Colonel A. R. Clarke, F.R.G.S., London. 1952: The International Geodetic and Geophysical Union, Savre, France.

NOTE: Data for the atmospheric envelope surrounding the earth have been computed from meteorological findings placing the outmost fringe of the ionosphere around 600 miles in height.
^a Land above sea-level.

When viewed from the standpoint of surface only, as shown in Table II–2, water occupies over 78 per cent of the total earth's surface, and over 22 per cent of the total land surface of the globe (referring to land area covered by frozen water or interior water). Notwithstanding this superficial fact, even when taking the world's underground water into account, it will be observed from the total volume relationships, as shown in Table V–1, that water constitutes but one-tenth of 1 per cent of the entire volume of the earth. Since water constitutes nearly 75 per cent by volume of all living things, including man, this latter fact becomes of considerable significance.

Table V–1a.   INTERIOR LAND WATER AREA, IN SQUARE MILES, 1952

	Rivers & streams	Lakes & ponds	Dams & reservoirs	Swamps	Canals & irrigation channels	Total	% of total
Africa	571,194	110,250	12,767	1,108,390	380,000	2,182,601	26.2%
America, North	160,998	205,956	135,366	311,650	804,000	1,617,970	19.4
America, South	259,206	286,944	118,332	343,520	100,000	1,108,002	13.3
Asia	314,997	229,105	98,402	609,750	702,000	1,954,254	23.4
Europe	153,998	179,564	137,988	298,100	438,000	1,207,650	14.5
Oceania	42,000	13,606	6,228	78,900	130,000	270,734	3.2
Total	1,502,393	1,025,425	509,083	2,750,310	2,554,000	8,341,211	100.0%

SOURCES: National Geographic Society, Washington, D.C.; Bureau of Reclamation, U. S. Department of Interior; Corps of Engineers, U. S. Department of the Army; *British Imperial Cyclopedia Atlas; Oxford Advanced Atlas; American Oxford Atlas;* Odhams *New Atlas of the World; Encyclopaedia Britannica World Atlas.*

Furthermore, since the world's fresh water supply, both underground and at ground surface, is decreasing at a rate far in excess of the world's land acreage losses, it would seem to become a matter of serious concern. As may be noted from the data in Table V–1b, the world is now consuming nearly 2 quadrillion gallons more water than is annually replaced by rainfall—a rate nearly 35 times faster than natural replacement.

Over large parts of the world, water is the beginning and end not only of agriculture but of industry as well. In the latter case vast quantities of water are required in the production of iron and steel as well as in the paper and textile industries. As shown in Table V–4, for every ton of iron and steel produced annually some 22 tons of water are required, and for every ton of newsprint produced an additional 265 tons of water are used. Approximately 25 per cent of all electric energy generated is derived from water-power.

Many popular misconceptions concerning water as a resource are due to the relative importance of water-power in the general scheme of the world's power economy. Here many well-meaning people seem to think of water as being not only in abundance but also a free gift of nature, whereas water is no more a free gift than is coal or oil or any other mineral or food. As a matter of fact, in the *Atlas of the Mineral Resources of the World* published by the United States Geological Survey in 1921, water is treated as a mineral, while at the same time most treatises dealing with the chemistry of food and nutrition treat water as a food.

The paucity of water is today the most striking characteristic of large areas of the world where the intelligent use of the available supply is essential to sustain any permanent economic development.

TABLE V-1b. UNDERGROUND WATER SUPPLY, SURFACE WATER SUPPLY, AND AVERAGE RAINFALL ON LAND, 1952

(*In Billions of Gallons*)

	Underground table [a]	Surface [b]	Rainfall [c]	Total available water	% of total	Annual consumption in excess of rainfall [d]	% of total
Africa	43,342,238	18,791,942	8,386,532	70,520,712	22.0%	106,943	5.6%
America, North	34,559,230	20,671,136	5,089,263	60,319,629	18.8	637,840	33.4
America, South	25,394,351	15,785,231	8,207,333	49,386,915	15.4	423,954	22.2
Asia	63,198,741	27,812,074	11,002,844	102,013,659	31.8	255,900	13.4
Europe	12,318,331	7,140,938	1,720,314	21,179,583	6.6	362,843	19.0
Oceania	12,122,079	3,758,388	1,433,596	17,314,063	5.4	122,222	6.4
Total	190,934,970	93,959,709	35,839,882	320,734,561	100.0%	1,909,702	100.0%

SOURCES: *Underground table:* O. E. Meinzer, *Outline of Ground-Water Hydrology;* Nathan Clifford Grover, Chief Hydraulic Engineer (retired), U. S. Geological Survey; Herbert Lapworth, President, Institute of Water Engineers; Baldwin Wiseman, *The Flow of Underground Water; Encyclopaedia Britannica,* 48 ed., Vol. 23, pp. 495–497; See also notes to Table V–3. *Surface Water:* See notes to Table V–1a. *Rainfall:* See notes to Table V–3.

[a] Underground water table: geological estimates of underground water are usually given in terms of cubic miles to a depth of 100 feet. Here the data have been converted into standard U. S. gallons.
[b] Surface water: in terms of approximate quantity as related to total surface water as given in Table V–1a above. Surface water is frequently referred to as "run-off" or "gravitational" water.

[c] Rainfall: refers to the total precipitation, including rain, snow, sleet, hail, dew, and frost. The data given here are to be distinguished from those given in Table V–6 and Table V–2b as the above figures include total precipitation over both drainage and closed basins, as given in Table V–2a.
[d] Consumption: computed from data as given under "where-to," Section B, in Water Table V–2.

WATER TABLE V-2. THE WORLD'S HYDROLOGIC CYCLE, 1882–1952

(*Averages in Billions of Gallons*)

	1882	1952	Change
Average annual precipitation	36,703,718	35,839,882	− 863,836
Inland natural surface water	95,887,086	93,551,669	−2,335,417
Man-made reservoirs & dams	327,656	408,040	+ 80,384
Underground water table	195,517,409	190,934,970	−4,582,439
Total land water supply	291,732,151	284,894,679	−6,837,472
Where-to:			
Natural:			
Absorption by natural vegetation	12,846,301	12,543,958	− 302,343
Surface evaporation	11,246,628	10,981,499	− 265,129
Run-off	11,011,115	10,751,965	− 259,150
Held in top-soil	1,101,112	1,075,196	− 25,916
Wild-life use	365,737	308,636	− 57,101
Total annual use	36,570,893	35,661,254	− 909,639
Mankind:			
Industrial use	72,604	935,430	+ 862,826
Agricultural use	237,562	639,100	+ 401,538
Trade & commercial use	18,500	383,300	+ 364,800
Public protection & general use	9,900	80,300	+ 70,400
Domestic household use	9,600	50,200	+ 40,600
Total man's use	348,166	2,088,330	+1,740,164
Grand total water use	36,919,059	37,749,584	+ 830,525
Annual run-off to:			
Atlantic Ocean	3,402,435	3,322,357	− 80,078
Arctic Ocean	2,488,512	2,419,192	− 69,320
Pacific Ocean	1,761,778	1,731,066	− 30,712
Indian Ocean	1,717,734	1,677,307	− 40,427
Adjoining seas	1,640,656	1,602,043	− 38,613
Total	11,011,115	10,751,965	− 259,150

NOTE: For sources and method see footnotes to Tables V-1a, V-1b, and V-3, and Tables V-6, V-2b and V-2a.

TABLE V–2a. DISTRIBUTION OF TOTAL AVERAGE ANNUAL RAINFALL, 1952

(Quantity, in Billions of Gallons)

	Net rainfall on closed basins [a]	Net rainfall on drainage basins [b]	Net rainfall on total dry land [c]	Rainfall on surface water [d]	Total rainfall [e]
Africa	2,094,328	5,050,484	7,144,812	1,241,720	8,386,532
America, North	355,233	3,980,508	4,335,741	753,522	5,089,263
America, South	85,552	6,906,593	6,992,145	1,215,188	8,207,333
Asia	3,283,495	6,090,254	9,373,749	1,629,095	11,002,844
Europe	355,218	1,110,384	1,465,602	254,712	1,720,314
Oceania	1,091,681	129,554	1,221,235	212,361	1,433,596
Total	7,265,507	23,267,777	30,533,284	5,306,598	35,839,882

(Area, in Square Miles)

Africa	3,634,737	5,878,356	9,513,093	2,182,601	11,695,694
America, North	605,790	7,137,128	7,742,918	1,617,970	9,360,888
America, South	145,389	5,616,777	5,762,166	1,108,002	6,870,168
Asia	5,282,485	9,655,214	14,937,699	1,954,254	16,891,953
Europe	751,179	1,497,109	2,248,288	1,207,650	3,455,938
Oceania	1,696,211	1,336,920	3,033,131	270,734	3,303,865
Total	12,115,791	31,121,504	43,237,295	8,341,211	51,578,506

[a] Land area without drainage outflow to oceans. Adapted from findings of Alexander Supan. *Grundzüge der Physischen Erdkunde*, 5th ed.
[b] Land area with run-off to oceans.
[c] Total land area minus surface water.
[d] Total surface water on land.
[e] Gross total area including surface water.

TABLE V-2b. CHANGES IN THE WORLD'S AVAILABLE GRAVITATIONAL WATER, 1882–1952

(Millions of U. S. Gallons)

	1882	1952	70-year change
Total net precipitation on land	31,266,185,165	30,533,384,294	− 732,800,871
Less the soil's capacity to hold water	10,422,091,721	10,177,124,432	− 244,967,289
Equals total run-off and absorption	20,844,093,444	20,356,259,862	− 487,833,582
Less run-off	5,211,023,250	7,643,329,580	+2,432,306,330
Equals total interception by plants & animals	15,633,070,194	12,712,930,282	−2,920,139,912
Less absorption & interception by animals & man	352,348,495	1,312,686,438	+ 960,337,943
Quantity available for absorption by vegetation	15,280,721,699	11,400,243,844	−3,880,477,855

CHANGES IN THE WORLD'S GRAVITATIONAL WATER SUPPLY BY MAJOR CONTINENTS

	(Area in 1000's Square Miles)			(Millions of U. S. Gallons)		
	1882	1952		1882	1952	70-year change
Africa	11,738	11,696	− 42	7,159,956,365	7,144,811,856	− 15,144,509
America, North	9,670	9,361	− 309	4,471,064,455	4,335,740,528	− 135,323,927
America, South	7,165	6,870	− 295	7,285,021,105	6,992,144,936	− 292,876,169
Asia	17,379	16,892	− 487	9,629,984,980	9,373,748,888	− 256,236,092
Europe	3,531	3,456	− 75	1,500,776,880	1,465,602,432	− 35,174,448
Oceania	3,339	3,304	− 35	1,219,381,380	1,221,335,654	+ 1,954,274
World total	52,822	51,579	−1,243	31,266,185,165	30,533,384,294	− 732,800,871

NOTE: Gravitational water is defined as the difference between precipitation and the soil's capacity to hold and absorb water.

TABLE V-3. COMPARATIVE INVENTORY OF THE WORLD'S WATER SUPPLY, 1882–1952

(*In Billions of Gallons*)

	1882	1952	Change
Average water in oceans & seas:			
Atlantic	110,178,472	111,863,475	+1,685,003
Arctic	80,583,608	81,816,000	+1,232,392
Pacific	57,050,342	57,922,834	+ 872,492
Indian	55,624,083	56,474,764	+ 850,681
Adjoining seas	53,128,130	53,940,645	+ 812,515
Total	356,564,635	362,017,718	+5,453,083
Average water in underground table:			
Africa	43,600,382	43,342,238	− 258,144
America, North	35,779,686	34,559,230	−1,220,456
America, South	26,590,368	25,394,351	−1,196,017
Asia	64,325,226	63,198,741	−1,126,485
Europe	12,810,974	12,318,331	− 492,643
Oceania	12,410,773	12,122,079	− 288,694
Total	195,517,409	190,934,970	−4,582,439
Average surface water run-off:			
Africa	19,242,948	18,791,942	− 451,006
America, North	21,167,743	20,671,136	− 496,607
America, South	16,164,077	15,785,231	− 378,846
Asia	28,479,564	27,812,074	− 667,490
Europe	7,312,320	7,140,938	− 171,382
Oceania	3,848,090	3,758,388	− 89,702
Total	96,214,742	93,959,709	−2,255,033
Average annual rainfall:			
Africa	8,580,031	8,386,532	− 193,499
America, North	5,244,753	5,089,263	− 155,490
America, South	8,321,360	8,207,333	− 114,027
Asia	11,286,183	11,002,844	− 283,339
Europe	1,783,374	1,720,314	− 63,060
Oceania	1,488,017	1,433,596	− 54,421
Total	36,703,718	35,839,882	− 863,836

SOURCES: Sir John Murray, F.R.S., *British Geographical Journal*, 1902; Alexander Supan, Petermann's Mitteilungen, XXXV, 1889; Hermann Wagner, Gerland's *Beitrage zur Geophysik*, ii, 1895. Professor C. Lapworth, British Association Report, Edinburgh, 1892; *Encyclopaedia Britannica*, 11th ed., Vol. XIX, p. 974, and Vol. XI, p. 630; *Encyclopaedia Britannica*, 1948, ed., Vol. 16, p. 683; Hugh Robert Mill, editor, *British Rainfall* and *Meteorological Magazine*; Hugh Hammond Bennett, "Run-off and the Utilization of Rainfall," 1939; C. F. Tolman, "Ground Water," 1937; F. H. Newell, "Water Resources," 1920; Erich W. Zimmermann, "World Resources," 1933.

NOTE: All water data computed on basis of a five-year average, with 1880–1884 = 100 for 1882 period, and 1950–1954 = 100 for 1952 period. All data of this kind represent approximations in relative magnitudes only, and are not to be taken as precise as the fluctuations from year to year vary between 1 and 2 per cent.

TABLE V–4. CHANGES IN TONS OF WATER CONSUMED PER TON OF PRODUCT PRODUCED IN THE U.S.A., 1882–1952

(In Thousands of Net Tons)

	1882		1952		Changes	
	Product	Water	Product	Water	Product	Water
Hay	41,487	373,383	94,914	854,422	+ 53,427	+ 481,039
Wheat	15,126	263,192	38,743	674,200	+ 23,617	+ 411,008
Oats	27,414	340,391	38,048	472,434	+ 10,634	+ 132,043
Corn	56,596	181,107	115,736	375,321	+ 59,140	+ 194,214
Other [a]	39,515	325,419	80,730	667,762	+ 41,215	+ 342,343
Total	180,138	1,483,492	368,171	3,044,139	+ 188,033	+ 1,560,647
Steel	1,737	468,990	105,200	28,403,958	+ 103,463	+ 27,934,968
Iron	4,623	416,070	72,449	10,495,450	+ 67,826	+ 10,079,380
Paper	909	241,794	24,413	6,493,858	+ 23,504	+ 6,252,064
Petroleum	5,337	97,667	344,574	6,316,041	+ 339,237	+ 6,218,374
Other [b]	165,663	7,689,479	2,213,364	86,290,693	+ 2,047,701	+ 78,601,214
Total	178,269	8,914,000	2,760,000	138,000,000	+ 2,581,731	+ 129,086,000
Grand total	358,407	10,397,492	3,128,171	141,044,139	+ 2,769,764	+ 130,646,647
Percentages:						
Hay	11.6%	3.7%	3.0%	.6%	+ 128.8%	+ 128.8%
Wheat	4.2	2.5	1.3	.5	+ 156.1	+ 156.2
Oats	7.7	3.3	1.2	.3	+ 38.8	+ 38.8
Corn	15.8	1.7	3.7	.3	+ 104.5	+ 107.2
Other	11.0	3.1	2.6	.5	+ 104.3	+ 105.2
Total	50.3	14.3	11.8	2.2	+ 104.4	+ 105.2
Steel	.5	4.5	3.4	20.1	+ 5,956.4	+ 5,956.4
Iron	1.3	4.0	2.3	7.4	+ 1,467.0	+ 2,422.5
Paper	.2	2.3	.8	4.6	+ 2,585.8	+ 2,583.5
Petroleum	1.5	.9	11.0	4.5	+ 6,356.3	+ 6,366.9
Other	46.2	74.0	70.7	61.2	+ 1,236.1	+ 1,022.2
Total	49.7	85.7	88.2	97.8	+ 1,448.2	+ 1,448.1
Grand total	100.0%	100.0%	100.0%	100.0%	+ 772.8%	+ 1,256.5%

SOURCES: Canadian Experiment Station, Dr. S. Barnes, Swift Current, Saskatchewan, 1932; Historical Statistics of the United States, 1789–1945, U. S. Dept. of Commerce, 1949; The President's Materials Policy Commission, Vol. V, Washington, D.C., 1952.
[a] Contains all other grains, vegetables, fruits, nuts, and animal products.
[b] Contains coal, stone, clay, sand, gravel, slate, cement, and all other mineral products. See Raw Materials in Appendix.

88

Water is indispensable to virtually all methods of power generation. As boiler water it is used in steam generating power. Internal combustion engines depend on water to prevent over-heating. Water finds extensive use in industry and science as a solvent and a catalyst. In fact, expressed in tons there is far more water used every year than the tonnage of all the products of the earth combined.

WATER A CRITICAL ELEMENT IN THE WORLD RESOURCE PATTERN

Water, as a commodity, must be had regardless of value. In some cases because of its rarity, in others because of its relative abundance, water does not readily fit into the present world economic system. Where water is scarce enough to jeopardize the well-being of the community, its control becomes a matter of public concern. Where water is abundant, it remains a free good and therefore does not become a commodity to which property rights are applied.

The processes of urbanization and industrialization have been replete with the complex problems of water supply. People can live without formal shelter or clothing for months, as was demonstrated during the recent world war. People can live without food for days. But to live without water can only be figured in terms of a very few days, and under certain conditions, a few hours.

The southwestern portion of North America, an area exceeding 2 million square miles, is today facing the stern problem of a shortage of water. In much of this area nothing was done in time to regulate the flow of the ground water, nor to replace it as it was used. Much of the water that originally percolated into the soil was permitted to run off in damaging floods. Forests were felled, large-scale grazing was intensified, with no thought given to the effects upon water supply.

LAND MANAGEMENT, WATER SUPPLY, AND FAITH IN "PERMANENT" WATER

It is axiomatic that any type of land management that provides for a maximum percolation and infiltration of precipitation is highly desirable. The prevention of too rapid run-off is mandatory, for the maintenance of a large ground water supply is essential to all human welfare. All competent authorities are now agreed that there is no such thing as "permanent" inland ground water in the world, although for centuries the geographers have, as a matter of convenience or lack of knowledge at the time, so suggested. This fact is representative of another of those "artifices," far from scientific, employed in past generations which, when carried forward indiscriminately, come to confuse, confound, and deceive mankind.

As an example, one area in the United States, consisting of 200,000 acres, scarcely 40 years ago had 1000 flowing wells with a lift of only 35 feet, which were pumping from the ground 5 times the amount used 40 years previously, with the water table dropping 5 feet per year. Forty years later, by 1952, the pumping lift was 165 feet, and irrigation had become a precarious and costly operation. With the decline in the water level, artesian wells gradually played out; the last one closed in 1930 when 2000 pumps were then pulling water from the valley.

Technicians familiar with the situation warned the public of the disastrous result of their continued heavy use of the underground water supply, which many had thought to be inexhaustible. When they were first warned, a $4 million water conservation plan was voted down by a 7 to 1 vote; yet in the following years more than $16 million were spent for new wells and more powerful pumping equipment. They still thought they could get the water that was not there.

WATER MEASUREMENT

Since 1905 the science of water measurement has advanced to a point where the actual volume of water can for the first time be measured within an error range of 1 per cent. Formerly, measurement of the volume of water flowing in rivers and canals was obtained by checking the speed of objects floating with the stream. In the past 30 years current meters have replaced the floats in numerous parts of the world, and thus a quite accurate measurement is now secured.

Up to 1934 no attempt had yet been made to present a comprehensive description and total data relating to the fundamental facts concerning the water resources of the world. This is particularly true of the distribution of the world's annual rainfall, sometimes referred to as the "effective precipitation," and the resulting annual water "yield." (See Table V–5.)

TABLE V–5. COMPARATIVE PROFIT & LOSS AVERAGE ANNUAL WORLD RAINFALL STATEMENT, 1882–1952

(In Billions of Gallons)

	1882		1952	
Gross rainfall received		36,703,718		35,839,882
Surface evaporation	13,470,265		13,153,237	
Vegetation transpiration	3,361,143		3,281,918	
Less evaporation & transpiration		16,831,408		16,435,155
Net rainfall realized		19,872,310		19,404,727
Absorbed by vegetation	4,897,193		6,191,334	
Percolation into underground	3,964,002		3,070,707	
Flow into reservoirs	163,828		336,225	
Less above catchment		9,025,023		9,598,266
Gross run-off		10,847,287		9,806,461
Less underground discharge		4,404,446		3,208,992
Total annual rainfall loss		6,442,841		6,597,469

SOURCES: National Resources Board Report, December, 1934.
The President's Materials Policy Commission Selected Reports, Volumes I and V, 1952.
NOTE: On the basis of the generally accepted principles of practical business accounting, it is only the net rainfall realized and the amount available for absorption, infiltration, and reservoirs that constitutes the annual "yield" in the sense of a harvest of the precipitation. The remaining run-off which carries with it immense quantities of top-soil and top-soil plant nutrients is a loss and can in no sense be designated as a yield save only in its negative sense as forfeit.
Close examination of this form of presentation of the hydrologic cycle discloses a depletion of the underground water table to be progressing at a rate one-third more rapidly than it is being replenished.
It is important to realize the fact that underground water supplies are subject to depletion just as definitely as any other natural resource. Land erosion tends to prevent the accumulation of the underground water table by interfering with the normal process of intake and percolation.

TABLE V-6. PRECIPITATION AND THE HYDROLOGIC CYCLE

Evaporation

Where-from:	U. S. standard gallons
Oceans and seas	101,383,854,384,384,000
Inland streams, rivers, lakes, reservoirs	1,454,968,933,681,600
Transpiration of vegetation [a]	6,906,385,419,862,000
Land surface	18,571,379,742,674,000
Total	128,316,588,480,601,600

Precipitation

Where-to:	
Oceans and seas	94,510,409,520,384,000
Inland streams, rivers, lakes, reservoirs	1,579,621,430,000,000
Intercepted by vegetation	12,003,809,912,926,400
Absorbed by top-soil	7,492,555,054,533,000
Infiltration to underground water table	426,627,752,727,000
Lost to atmosphere	1,693,173,236,017,600
Run-off to oceans and seas	7,643,329,580,440,000
Ground water discharge to oceans, seas, and man	1,273,888,758,156,000
Total	126,623,415,245,184,000

Gravitational water [b]

Total net precipitation on land	30,533,384,294,800,000
Less the soil's capacity to hold water	10,177,124,431,900,000
Equals total run-off and absorption	20,356,259,862,900,000
Less run-off	7,643,329,580,440,000
Equals total interception by plants and animals	12,712,930,282,460,000
Less absorption by animals and man	1,312,686,438,211,000
Quantity available for absorption by vegetation	11,400,243,844,249,000

SOURCES: The British Hydrological Office, the National Resources Board Report of 1934; U. S. Geological Survey, *Water Supply*, Paper 489; *Infiltration in Relation to Run-off and the Utilization of Rainfall*, H. H. Bennett, 1939.

[a] The quantities of water vapor transpired by vegetation-covered areas of the earth's surface are often of sufficient magnitude to have important effects on meteorological conditions.
[b] Refers to peripheral land with drainage basins to the seas only.

Even today, knowledge of the factors of the supply and utilization of water is pitifully inadequate. Relatively little is known of the details of the hydrologic cycle, whereby the sun daily extracts some 84 trillion gallons of pure water from the oceans and seas and distributes it over the land mass of the world. We know little about the physical factors by which the sun's energy transforms salty ocean water into fresh vapor. We know only the barest details of the routes these clouds of vapor take in their complex travels over the earth. We only vaguely understand the process by which moisture condenses into raindrops that fall back upon the earth. The remaining elements of the cycle are as little known.

In Water Table V-2 will be noted changes in the hydrologic cycle, in relation to the world's water supply, that have occurred over the past 70 years, and in Table V-6 will be observed the complete hydrologic cycle in itself on a basis of where-from and where-to. There is much more still to be learned about infiltration of water into the earth, surface run-off, vegetation transpiration, ground water discharge and recharge, salt water intrusion into streams and underground channels, and many other physical processes affecting the world's water supply.

THE UNIQUENESS OF WATER

It has been said that water was endowed with certain qualities for the express purpose of maintaining an environment fit for life. It is a fact that life, in any form of which we have the slightest inkling, is possible in its continuous evolutionary form only at temperatures between the freezing and boiling points of water—zero and 100 degrees centigrade. At no other temperatures can oxygen, nitrogen, carbon, hydrogen, and sometimes sulphur and phosphorus unite into the highly complex molecules of protoplasm. Such molecules are the only ones that can create new molecules of their own kind. The very continuity of life is dependent upon this fundamental fact.

WATER, THE GREAT TEMPERATURE REGULATOR

The uniformity of temperature which the earth has maintained for over a thousand million years has been due to certain as yet dependable qualities of water. The slow rate at which water becomes either warm or cool, and its high demands for latent heat when it passes from ice to water or from water to vapor, account for this consistency of temperature. Latent heat is energy that can be absorbed without causing any change of temperature. When water is evaporated, no matter what the temperature, it uses up far more heat than would be needed to raise the temperature of the same amount of water 1 degree Fahrenheit.

Thus an abundance of water tends to prevent the temperature from falling below freezing or rising above the evaporation point. In this way water is the remarkable force that holds the temperature of the world within the narrow zone where life as we know it is possible.

WATER, ONE OF THE GREAT MEASURING-RODS OF SCIENCE

Along with the speed of light, water is one of the great constants of science, a standard unit of measure that has made possible man's advance of knowledge of the physical world. Water is the standard for the concrete representation of certain physical units, such as the litre and the calorie, and a standard of comparison for certain physical properties, such as specific gravity, relative viscosity, etc.

The reason for this is that most liquids contract as they become colder. They contract still more on solidifying, so that the solids sink; in other words, they gain weight. But as water cools it contracts only until a temperature of 39 degrees Fahrenheit is reached; then it expands. If it continued to contract like other substances, ice would accumulate at the bottom of bodies of water which freeze in winter. Ponds, lakes, and the oceans from the middle latitudes poleward would consist of masses of solid ice topped with a layer of cold water in the summer. And the ice from the glacial period would still be clogging the ocean depths far toward the equator. Then the ocean currents could not carry tropical warmth poleward as they now do.

THE EFFECTIVENESS OF EXTREMELY SMALL AMOUNTS OF WATER

The range of average temperature of the universe as a whole, as measured on the Fahrenheit scale, is equivalent to 270°—or from 100° below zero to 170° above. The fact that life has persisted from pre-Cambrian times onward, with no interruption so far as paleontologists have been able to determine, makes us certain that with minor exceptions temperatures beyond these limits have not occurred on the earth for a billion years.

Only a few years with temperatures either above or below this range would destroy all life on earth. Therefore this prolonged uniformity of temperature becomes of critical importance, particularly from the standpoint of the world's chemistry.

Water in minute amounts is essential for the majority of all chemical reactions. For example; unless a little water is present, chlorine and sodium will not combine into common salt, even if the sodium is heated to the melting point. Nor will absolutely dry air and coal—even if red hot—burn with a flame and form carbon dioxide. Only minute amounts of water are needed to cause innumerable important actions of this kind. The whole field of organic chemistry is dependent upon the temperature phenomena made possible by the presence of water. Even the gases of the atmosphere, as noted in the previous chapter, would not react as they do without water.

DANGERS INHERENT IN THE CONTAMINATION OF THE WORLD'S WATER SUPPLY

Of all the natural stores of water in the world the oceans and the seas are the most abundant—minute as they actually are in relation to the entire mass and volume of the earth. And from them, all other water is derived.

Water contains some 40 per cent of all the known elements, as shown in Table V-7 and in addition to its natural components, water is highly liable to contamination through either accidental influences of foreign matter, or man's pollution due to industrial practices, or man's war activities—the most dangerous of all.

Not only do the oceans absorb the gases of the atmosphere, such as oxygen, hydrogen, nitrogen, and carbon dioxide, but the atmosphere itself absorbs elements from the oceans. Largely because of these fundamental facts the atomic and hydrogen bomb tests in the world's basic water supply may be viewed as being of considerable world-wide concern.

THE PART PLAYED BY WATER IN BUILDING AND RESHAPING THE EARTH

All igneous rocks have solidified from a state of liquidity, technically referred to as *magma*. Magma is a complex silicate solution carrying gases, the most important of which is water. This magmatic reservoir in the bowels of the earth has been estimated to constitute approximately 5 to 6 per cent of the mass, with crystalline rocks seldom showing a water content in excess of 2 per cent. Here we have direct confirmation that the water content of the original magma before

TABLE V-7. PRINCIPAL COMPOSITION OF WATER

(By Volume)

		Per cent
1	Hydrogen	61.720147%
2	Oxygen	32.083750
3	Sodium	1.850000
4	Calcium	1.650000
5	Phosphorus	1.070000
6	Magnesium	.600000
7	Silicon	.300000
8	Sulphur	.300000
9	Nitrogen	.300000
10	Calcium	.060000
11	Potassium	.025000
12	Manganese	.014000
13	Fluorine	.006000
14	Barium	.005000
15	Aluminum	.004000
16	Strontium	.004000
17	Carbon dioxide	.003000
18	Bromine	.002000
19	Boron	.002000
20	Chlorine	.000400
21	Zinc	.000300
22	Titanium	.000200
23	Copper	.000100
24	Iodine	.000040
25	Lead	.000020
26	Nickel	.000020
27	Uranium	.000010
28	Lithium	.000010
29	Cobalt	.000002
	Trace elements: [a]	.000001
30	Molybdenum ⎤	
31	Silver ⎬	
32	Gold ⎦	
	All other	
	Total	100.000000%

SOURCES: Adapted from James Alexande: Beattie, Massachusetts Institute of Technology *Encyclopaedia Britannica*, 1948 ed., Vol. 23, pag 407.

NOTE: In addition to hydrogen and oxyger water, on an average, contains the following:

	Per cent	Element.
Dissolved substances	3.500000%	
Other absorbed elements	2.696103	
	6.196103	=30
Hydrogen	61.720147	= 1
Oxygen	32.083750	= 1
Total	100.000000%	=32

In further addition, according to the degree o pollution, bacteria are also present.

[a] Trace elements: molybdenum, silver, gold an all other.

crystallization was greater than the rock formed from it. When this is worked ou on the basis of the entire mass of the earth it will be found to constitute but 0.0⁴ per cent of the total—an amount far less than that shown in Table V-1. Analyse: of the clouds of steam given off by active volcanoes has further corroborated thi: evidence.

In the above processes water has served and still continues to serve as an elemen of great importance in land-building. As an oxidizing, dissolving, and carryin agent, water is both a friend and foe of mankind, a friend in that it acts as a metamorphic agent in carrying chemical elements to the sub-soil upon which the top-soil depends for its replenishment of essential soil nutrients, and a foe in tha it is constantly wearing down the land, carrying it away and redepositing it b erosion.

Inland bodies of water are also a source of minerals, such as peat, salt, potash and many medicinal minerals. Bog iron is often deposited at the bottom of swamps The first iron foundry established in America by the New England settlers, ir 1643, secured its ore from the neighboring bogs. Swamps also furnish peat, anc most of the world's coal appears to have been formed in ancient swamps which were then part of the earth's inland waters. To sum up, water is an agent of metamorphism and by its movement land is being constantly worn down, carried away, and redeposited.

All springs, wells, and geysers are supplied by underground water which is caused either by the downward seepage of rain water or the forcing upward of the magnetic water (juvenile water) originating in the molten rock of the earth's interior. This magnetic water is not limitless. Cavities in the firmest rocks cannot hold water at depths of greater than six miles, with the world average for steaming geysers approximately less than one-third of a mile.

GRAVITATIONAL WATER

The water of one-half of the people of the world is supplied from ground water through wells. Yet less is actually known about the quantity and the rate of infiltration, its rate of discharge, and its storage capacity than of any other of man's vital physical resources.

The whole matter of the hydrologic cycle is here particularly obscure. That proportion of the total annual precipitation that is finally disposed of by run-off, evaporation, transpiration, percolation, and absorption is still a matter of rough guessing. Nevertheless, sufficient studies have been made in various parts of the world, and enough evidence on dwindling underground water supplies is now available to enable the construction of a reasonably intelligent guess.

As will be observed in Table V–2, of the water that falls as rain, one part is the run-off (water that reaches the rivers without having penetrated the surface soil) ; a second part is returned to the atmosphere by *evaporation*; while a third part infiltrates into the soil and underlying rocks by percolation. Under the influence of gravity the percolating water penetrates into the earth's crust, first through the superficial weathered and disintegrating layers—the agricultural top-soil—and then on through the more solid rocks by way of the fractures of jointing and faulting, to the planes of bedding of the pore-spaces between their constituent minerals.

At a variable depth below the surface there is a connected body of water, which more or less permanently fills all openings. The surface of this body of water is called the *level of the ground water* or the *water table,* which is the *belt of saturation.* This belt of saturation consists of that part which has a means of horizontal escape called the *zone of discharge.* This zone of discharge lies between the water-table and sea-level.

It was estimated by the U. S. Geological Survey in 1951 that from 35 to 40 per cent of the total stream flow has passed through the porous earth mantle, thus coming from this discharge source and clearly demonstrating the importance of sub-surface ground water in the over-all supply, especially in maintaining stream discharge during periods of low rainfall.

Nearly another 40 per cent, constituting re-use and re-circulation, aids in maintaining this average stream flow. This is particularly important to agricultural irrigation and, to a lesser extent, to the industrial and municipal water economy. Thus, the data as shown in Water Table V–2, resembles to some extent the monetary income flow of the world business economy wherein the "flow" figures represent essentially both income and outgo simultaneously.

Here, however, the analogy breaks down, for outlay and expenditure create income in the monetary economy, whereas the expenditure of nature too frequently means the exhaustion of capital resources rather than their formation. In other words, in the world's water economy man is living off his capital, however deceptively phrased its exploitation may be.

In studies of water supply and use, after allowance deduction from the annual rainfall for return to the atmosphere through evaporation and transpiration of vegetation, it has been customary to refer to the remainder, which is gravitational water, as "run-off," "fly-off," and sometimes as the annual water "yield," with this latter designation possessing a somewhat deceptive connotation.

TABLE V–8. THE WORLD'S DAILY WATER SUPPLY AND DEMAND, 1882–1952–2022 [a]

(*In Billions of Gallons*)

	1882		1952		2022 [a]
Average annual precipitation		100,558		98,191	95,835
Consumed by nature	99,720		97,702		95,748
Consumed by man	965		4,153		10,810
Total consumption		100,685		101,855	106,558
Deficit		−127		−3,664	−10,723
Man's consumption		965		4,153	10,810
From lakes and streams		795		3,422	8,907
From underground table		170		731	1,903

SOURCES: Computed from data of the President's Materials Policy Commission Report, 1952.

[a] Projected to the year 2022 on basis of present rates of consumption and population increase.

However, if the generally accepted monetary accounting practice be applied to the world's annual water economy account as shown in the accompanying Table V–8, which has been drawn from the basic data in Water Table V–2, it will be noted that the annual rainfall account actually discloses a water deficit rather than a yield, for both periods. This deficit discloses an alarming increase over the earlier period while at the same time the water surplus account discloses a marked decline.

Little ground-water remains permanently beneath the land surface. Sooner or later, after descending to greater or lesser depths, it returns to the surface at a lower level than where it entered, coming out in the form of springs and joining the run-off of streams to the rivers. The movement of ground-water is comparatively slow while percolating among the particles of rock waste or through the pores and crevices of rocks.

FLOODS

Floods exact a tremendous toll in human life, disruption of business, and destruction of property. For the world as a whole, in money terms, their average destruction approximates $1.7 billion annually, or nearly $120 billion over the past 70 years.

It is extremely difficult to ascertain all of the consequences of flood disasters, and impossible to put an accurate monetary value on the losses. Property damage caused by floods can be appraised; but loss of life, human suffering, and the other effects on the lives of people cannot be evaluated in terms of money.

WATER, THE GREAT FEEDING AGENT

It is sometimes forgotten, when discussing questions of food problems, that the food materials of all living organisms, including the human being, are prepared originally from inorganic substances in exactly the same way, by the same mechanisms of the chlorophyll apparatus of the vegetable kingdom.

All living substance is fundamentally the same, though differentiated both anatomically and physiologically in many ways. The difference between the nutritive processes of the animal and the plant are not therefore fundamental, as they were formerly held to be. The general vegetable protoplasm has not the capacity of being nourished by inorganic substances denied to the living substance of animals. The cell walls of plants render the entry of such solid material into the organism impossible. The *food must enter in solution* in order to pass the walls.

The explanation of the apparent difference of food supply is simple. The fact of plant absorption does not render these substances food; they are taken in not as food, but as raw materials, raw elements, which are then fabricated into food from the inorganic, gaseous, and liquid matter which they absorb. Thus, water plays its vitally important part at the root basis of all life.

Because of this basic fact, the necessity for water in the transformation of the principal elements by plants into the world's food supply, we have a complex resource which is limited and subject to exhaustion. It is only prudence to develop, utilize, and care for it.

IRRIGATION

The part played by irrigation in man's long history has been both a noble and a tragic one. Man's early struggle for survival in the Eastern Hemisphere invariably took the form of the necessary conquest of water supply for an ever-thirsty land.

The artificial application of water to land in order to promote vegetation has been a need long known to man. History has recorded such practice dating back

TABLE V-9. CHANGES IN THE WORLD'S LAND AREA UNDER IRRIGATION, 1882–1952

(*In Acres*)

	1882	1952	Change	% Change
Africa	5,750,000	13,808,000	+ 8,058,000	+140.1%
America, North	14,425,000	36,281,000	+ 21,856,000	+151.5
America, South	4,233,000	8,935,000	+ 4,702,000	+111.1
Asia	57,892,000	190,064,000	+132,172,000	+228.3
Europe	8,498,000	20,035,000	+ 11,537,000	+135.8
Oceania	714,000	1,624,000	+ 910,000	+127.5
Total	91,512,000	270,747,000	+179,235,000	+195.8%

SOURCES: Sir W. Willocks, *Egyptian Irrigation,* 1899; Sir C. C. Scott-Moncrieff, *Irrigation in Europe,* 1868; F. H. Newell, *Irrigation,* 1902; William E. Smythe, *The Conquest of Arid America,* 1902; Guy Elliott Mitchell, *Encyclopedia of Social Reform,* Bliss ed., 1908; Nathan Clifford Grover, Chief Hydraulic Engineer (retired); U. S. Geological Survey, Washington, D.C.; *Encyclopaedia Britannica,* 1948 ed., Vol. 17, p. 862.

as early as 2000 B.C. It was known to the Assyrians, Babylonians, Moslems, Egyptians, Chinese, and Spanish at the dawn of civilization.

Even American irrigation is so old that its history fades into dim tradition. There is evidence that, centuries before the Norsemen landed upon the shores of America, a dense population lived in the hot valleys of the far southwest. From solid rocks, with primitive tools, they had cut canals along the mountain sides and had erected dams on the edges of river canyons; in the ruins of these many miles of canals and ditches may almost be read the story of another Egypt.

In the early settlement of California by the Spaniards, the padres introduced irrigation. A network of irrigation canals and ditches to help produce crops from a parched soil was utilized as late as 1882. This development was also coincident with the invasion of Utah by the Mormons, who practiced irrigation with great success.

Although the problem of water shortage was showing itself by 1882 in America, it was not until 1898 that a National Irrigation Association was formed. It waged an aggressive campaign to educate the people to the great benefits which the country as a whole could realize from government assistance to irrigation projects. Unfortunately, the eastern part of the country, knowing little about the subject, viewed such projects as an invasion of private enterprise and a dangerous resort to paternalistic schemes involving state socialism.

Western man, more intent on a swift monetary exploitation of the Western Hemisphere's natural resources, has been unusually slow in realizing both the necessity for and the benefits from a more rational comprehension of the ground water problem. The fact that irrigation and proper drainage involve effort and funds, together with the emotional effect of accusations of "state socialism," has helped to put a check on the extension of irrigation in some areas of the world, although its need is pressing.

WATER, PUBLIC UTILITIES, AND FREE COMPETITIVE ENTERPRISE

The greatest impetus to the expansion of agriculture, industry, and public utilities came with the industrial revolution and its attendant mechanical inventions. The factory system so stimulated production that ever-expanding markets became the limiting factor in economic evolution.

Although Malthus had been right in his famous thesis, nevertheless, the opportunities for exploiting the new world with the aid of man's newly-found tools made his warning seem pointless. As William Vogt in his *Road to Survival* has pointed out, "the new lands—including Africa and Australia, as well as the Americas—provided the fuel to keep the population fires burning." Urban centers grew as never before, creating a new need for systems of water-supply, sanitation, transport, and finally power.

In this respect the philosophy of Adam Smith's *laissez faire* did not lend any rationale for the extension of such public functions as the mounting problem of water supply was even then demanding. In spite of the fact that the individual user of water in urban centers had discovered almost a century before Smith that he could no longer depend for his supply upon his own well or upon competing sources, and although these rapid changes were intensifying needs, the tendency was to give greater scope in all other directions to private enterprise.

The evils in a system which left the supply of man's basic economic needs to a private industry insufficiently regulated by government early became too flagrant to be overlooked. Beginning around 1840 the revolt against *laissez-faire* doctrines caused an enlargement of the scope of government action.

TABLE V–10. CHANGES IN THE WORLD'S WATER-POWER DEVELOPMENT, 1882–1952

(Horse-power)

	1882	1952	Change	% Change
Africa	38,000	241,000	+ 203,000	+ 534.2%
America, North	5,378,000	32,484,000	+ 27,106,000	+ 504.0
America, South	278,000	1,980,000	+ 1,702,000	+ 612.2
Asia	1,215,000	12,266,000	+ 11,051,000	+ 909.5
Europe	5,581,000	32,464,000	+ 26,883,000	+ 481.7
Oceania	166,000	2,218,000	+ 2,052,000	+1,236.1
Total	12,656,000	81,653,000	+ 68,997,000	+ 545.2%

CHANGES IN THE WORLD'S POTENTIAL WATER-POWER, 1882–1952

(Horse-power)

	1882	1952	Change	% Change
Africa	247,000,000	190,000,000	− 84,000,000	− 34.0%
America, North	84,000,000	66,000,000	− 18,000,000	− 21.4
America, South	67,000,000	54,000,000	− 13,000,000	− 19.4
Asia	87,000,000	69,000,000	− 18,000,000	− 20.7
Europe	74,000,000	57,000,000	− 17,000,000	− 23.0
Oceania	20,000,000	17,000,000	− 3,000,000	− 15.0
Total	579,000,000	453,000,000	−153,000,000	− 21.8%

SOURCES: U. S. Geological Survey, Washington, D.C., 1921; Dr. Erich W. Zimmermann, *World Resources and Industries*, 1933; *Encyclopaedia Britannica*, 1948 ed., Vol. 17, page 861.
NOTE: The total estimated potential horse-power is probably of less value than the information bearing on its geographical distribution. It should further be noted that all water-power essentially is derived from the continental gravitational run-off.

The older utility services were continued for the most part as a *public* enterprise, while the newer services were supplied by private initiative under some form of public supervision and assistance. Thus emerged the modern notion of a public utility, distinct from other activities and distinct from both governmental services and strictly private business. Today it is becoming advisable to recognize that water, air, and some land cannot be regarded as purely private property detached from a public interest. Whatever the legal rights, no owner has the moral right to waste a critical natural resource or to put it to uses which are harmful to the wider public interest.

THE CRUCIAL PLACE OF WATER IN THE WORLD BALANCE SHEET

When one thinks of world wealth in relation to a world balance sheet, exclusive of intangible assets, he is not apt to think of water as of more than minor significance. Nevertheless, the total world investment in water amounts to a staggering sum. The investment in dams, reservoirs, irrigation, and drainage, water

power, and municipal water supply systems approximates some $320 billion, or
an amount three and one-half times the total value of all the farm land and buildings in the United States. Nor does this include the investment in canals, river
channeling, and water transportation, to say nothing of the additional annual cost
of floods due to lack of adequate foresight and planning.

Consideration has to be given to the problem of equities in water, water rights,
the doctrine of riparian rights (that land owners upstream should not take water
in such a way as to interfere with the downstream neighbor's use of the stream),
and interstate and international compacts—all of which must be balanced against
each other if effective results are to be obtained.

Hence, the use and control of the water resources of the world presents a be-
wildering array of problems, some technological, some social, and all economic,
in which, without an adequate inventory and guiding principle, it is easy to
lose one's way. The vastness of the world, the wide range of climate, rainfall,
and topography, the abrupt seasonal changes affecting most of the world's water-
sheds, all tend to make the formulation of a constructive water policy difficult.

The relation of the water resources of the world to the pressing problems of
creating the conditions for a stable and secure cultural life is fundamental. To
recognize the critical place of water and to promote its greatest usefulness are
objectives worthy of the highest intelligence and energies. These matters are essential and nothing short of clear-cut national and international policy can deal effectively, justly, and democratically with them.

TABLE V–11.   CHANGES IN TOTAL WATER USE IN THE UNITED STATES,
1882–1952

(In Millions of Tons)

	1882	1952	Change	% Change
Where-to:				
Domestic & municipal	7,764,953	22,313,084	+ 14,548,131	+ 187.4%
Industrial	6,933,959	106,676,288	+ 99,742,329	+1,438.5%
Agricultural	53,968,668	116,562,998	+ 62,594,330	+ 116.0
Total	68,667,580	245,552,370	+176,884,790	+ 257.6
Where-from:				
Wells	41,200,536	37,686,065	− 3,514,471	− 8.6
Lakes & streams	26,969,842	187,978,993	+161,009,151	+ 597.0
Sea water	497,202	19,887,312	+ 19,390,110	+3,900.0
Total	68,667,580	245,552,370	+176,884,790	+ 257.6
Total precipitation	408,760,315	366,272,684	− 42,487,631	− 10.4
Less return to atmosphere	286,132,221	262,617,514	− 23,514,707	− 8.2
Fresh-water "yield"	122,628,094	103,655,170	− 18,972,924	− 15.5
Annual consumption	68,667,580	245,552,370	+176,884,790	+ 257.6
+ or − yield	+ 53,960,514	−141,897,200		
Population, U. S. A.	56,156,000	156,986,000	+100,830,000	+ 179.6%

SOURCES: U. S. Geological Survey, *Water Resources Review*, 1949; *Estimated Use of
Water in the United States,* Circular 115, 1951; The President's Materials Policy Commission
Report, Volumes I and V, 1952.

First among the materials required (to be studied) by the statesman is population: he will consider what should be the number and character of the citizens, and then what should be the size and character of the country.

To the size of states there is a limit, as there is to other things, plants, animals, implements; for none of these retain their natural power when they are too large or too small.

—ARISTOTLE; *The Politics*, Book VII, Ch. 4

There is always a political excuse for "the People." Take, for instance the matter of population increase, if we think of the utility of the community as regards prestige and military power, we will find it advisable to increase population to the very high limit beyond which the nation would be impoverished and it's stock decay.

Thus we have to see in what proportion the various social classes profit by the increase in prestige and military power, and in what different proportion they pay for it with their particular sacrifices.

—VILFREDO PARETO; *The Mind and Society*, Vol. IV

VI

People

THE WORLD'S PEOPLE and the existing population balance are of fundamental importance in a world inventory. In fact, it is out of the relationship of people to their resources, natural and cultural, that all values in the great ledger of the world are primarily formed.

The population of an area refers to the total number of human beings existing within the area at a given time; the "peopling" of the area takes into consideration the influence of the various existing forces, migratory and cultural, of which that number is the result. The ecologist studies the rise and decline of population, the environment, and the mechanisms that actuate these rises and declines. Statesmen, military men, and industrialists are interested in the growth of the human population because they make long-range plans on the basis of predicted future population.

Civilization has been defined as "a function of numbers in contact." The word "people," as a general term designating the humankind that goes to make up civilization, did not come into wide use until the sixteenth century—scarcely 400 years, or 13 generations, ago. Prior to that time it was the "populace" or the "multitude." A few years back, it was the "masses." Although none of these terms is scientific, nevertheless Guizot, who wrote his *History of Civilization* in 1828, would have regarded "numbers in contact" as a scientific definition, and as such, too narrow and therefore less accurate than the fundamental idea contained in the term, namely, progress and development, the idea of people marching onward— not to change their place, but to change their condition—by ameliorating and perfecting the relations of men among themselves. To Guizot the idea of the human species as a mere ant-hill, a society in which all that is required is order and physical happiness, in which the greater the amount of labor and the more equitable the division of the fruits of labor, the more surely is the object attained—this was a repugnant and too narrow definition of human destiny.

Needless to say, Guizot was not an ecologist. Neither were his contemporaries; they lived in a period of ever-renewing frontiers, in a world which they were convinced possessed inexhaustible resources, wherein the foremost objectives were the perfection of man's better nature and the regeneration of moral man. Not altogether an erroneous approach, provided it could be achieved. Here, Guizot's definition may itself have been a bit too narrow.

THE ARITHMETIC OF NATURE

Human ecology is a difficult subject to define. This is largely because it lies on the borderline of so many other subjects, and because comparatively little work has thus far been done on it, so that its exact scope and limits still remain to be established. Ecology is concerned with an attempt to reduce and coordinate into the same systematic scheme the existing information—which is enormous, but scattered—on the numbers of all forms of life in relation to environment, with a view to solving some of the urgent practical problems cropping up everywhere as a result of man's becoming "civilized" and interfering with the animal and plant life as well as with the geological and meteorological phenomena around him.

In spite of the general lack of precise quantitative data about the actual numbers of animal life in a given area, there are several important principles which have been discovered about numbers of animals. For instance, one acre of arable soil has been estimated to contain over 2 million springtails and about 800,000 earthworms. Any species of animal and plant life is, in nine cases out of ten, endowed with powers of multiplication which are enormously greater than can be realized in practice. If a species over-increases it runs the danger of over-eating its food supply. At the same time, if it does not produce a large number of extra individuals in each generation it will be in danger of extinction through the operation of checks other than starvation—such as disease, storms, fire, drought, enemies, and other phenomena of environment.

Soil microbiology discloses innumerable micro-organisms living and contributing a highly important function toward the relative fertility of the world's soil— especially insofar as the bacteria and the nitrogen cycle is concerned. The organic matter present in the soil, as well as that added by crop plants, animals, and by the micro-organisms themselves, all serve as a direct source of food and energy.

In terms of numbers, as well as in terms of biochemical changes produced, bacteria are the most important micro-organisms in the soil's population. It is known that the soil usually supports a bacterial population from 1 million to 50 million per gram, or a minimum of approximately 800 trillion per acre of topsoil, in contrast to molds and other fungi which seldom exceed 500,000 to 1 million per gram of soil, and to the algae or protozoa in the soil at a relatively smaller number.

Based upon these facts, even though they appear somewhat obscure, a factorial number sine-curve in terms of relative magnitudes can be constructed disclosing the relational animal and plant life populations on the planet earth, as shown in Table VI–1. The growth curves of all life populations, including the human, are similar in design.

TABLE VI–1. AVERAGE ANIMAL AND PLANT LIFE POPULATIONS ON THE PLANET EARTH, 1952

(In Relative Order of Magnitudes)

		% of total
Human beings	2,500,000,000	$.82 \times 10^{-24}$ [a]
Domestic pets	2,600,000,000	$.89 \times 10^{-24}$
Food & work animals	4,400,000,000	$.149 \times 10^{-24}$
Water animal life ±	580,000,000,000,000	$.19 \times 10^{-18}$
Wild animal life ±	1,667,000,000,000,000	$.56 \times 10^{-18}$
Worms & termites ±	92,428,683,600,000,000,000,000,000,000	.003
Insects ±	3,416,341,600,000,000,000,000,000,000,000	.115
Protozoa & algae ±	70,781,761,494,767,278,000,000,000,000,000	2.391
Land plants ±	721,368,396,106,333,000,000,000,000,000,000	24.364
Bacteria ±2,	165,105,198,325,000,000,000,000,000,000,000	73.126
Total ±	2,960,764,126,209,700,280,247,009,500,000,000	100.000%

SOURCES: Human beings: Statistical Office of the United Nations, 1954; Domestic pets: Computed from U. S. Census Bureau Study, 1930; Food & Work animals: F. A. O. Report, 1950; Water animal life: Gilbert Morgan Smith, professor of botany, Stanford University, 1947; Wild animal life: U. S. Biological Survey, 1939; Francis Harper, research associate, American Committee for International Wildlife Preservation, 1948; Worms & termites: Clarence Hamilton Kennedy, department of zoology, Ohio State University, 1948; Insects: S. G. Paine, professor of bacteriology, Imperial College of Science and Technology, London, 1948; Protozoa and algae: Lorande Loss Woodruff, department of protozoology, Yale University, 1948; Land plants: William Brown, head of botanical department of the Imperial College of Science and Technology, London; Wilfred William Roberts, professor of botany, University of California, 1948; Bacteria: William H. Taliaferro, department of bacteriology, University of Chicago, 1948.

NOTE: ±: Mathematical symbol for plus and minus when number is indeterminate.

[a] In scientific formulae, where small fractions occur, these are indicated by expressing the initial digits multiplied by a negative power of 10; as $.82 \times 10^{-24}$.

Note that here the exponent, $^{-24}$, indicates that the last significant figure appears in the twenty-fourth place following the decimal point.

Thus, the above percentage distribution if written in full would be: 82×10^{-24}% = 0.000000000000000000000082%, which expressed in words would be eighty-two septillionths of one per cent.

SOURCE: *Practical Mathematics,* National Education Alliance, 1948, Vol. I, p. 167.

THE ARITHMETIC OF PEOPLE

The relationship of the world's human population to its environment in terms of the world's natural resources can perhaps be most simply expressed as follows:

1. The world's annual production is the people's *dividend.*

2. The world's population is the *divisor.*

3. The number of times the number of people is contained in the quantitative annual production is the *quotient.*

Now this quotient can be increased in only two ways:

1. Enlarge the dividend by producing more, with the divisor remaining the same. Thus the quotient will be larger.

2. Lessen the divisor, with the dividend remaining the same. The quotient will also be larger.

Over the past century the world has managed to enlarge the dividend through increased mechanization, technology, invention, and discovery. Unfortunately, however, the divisor has not remained the same, but on the contrary has increased to a point which is now progressing at a rate faster than the dividend and the earth's ability to supply the materials from which the dividend must come.

TABLE VI-2. PRINCIPAL CHEMICAL ELEMENTS IN THE PEOPLE'S ENERGY-EXCHANGE CYCLE

	Human body	Vegetation	Top-soil	Water	Air
Oxygen	65.00000%	70.000000%	50.000000%	32.08375%	20.95000%
Carbon	18.0	18.0	.19	.03	.02757 [a]
Hydrogen	10.0	10.462	.95	61.72015	.00005 [b]
Nitrogen	3.0	.3	.02	.3	78.09
Calcium	1.5	.5	3.20	1.65	
Phosphorus	1.0	.07	.11	1.07	
Potassium	.35	.30	2.30	.025	
Sulphur	.25	.05	.11	.3	
Sodium	.15	.02	2.40	1.85	
Chlorine	.15	.04	.21	.0004	
Silicon	.15	.15	25.7	.3	
Magnesium	.07	.07	2.2	.6	
Manganese	.007	.007	.08	.014	
Iron	.004	.02	4.2	.004	
Fluorine	.003	.003	.02	.006	
Barium	.002	.003	.09	.005	
Boron	.001	.001	.001	.002	
Zinc	.0003	.0003	.0003	.0003	
Copper	.0001	.0001	.0001	.0001	
Iodine	.00004	.000001	.000001	.00004	
All other	.31356	.003599	8.21	.06	.92 [c]
Total	100.00000%	100.000000%	100.000000%	100.00000%	100.00000%

(Air column, Minute amounts in water vapor)

SOURCES: Human body: *Chemistry of Food and Nutrition,* Henry C. Sherman, 1927. Obtained from various estimates of different authorities, and is an approximation only; Vegetation: George E. Hutchinson, Yale University, *Encyclopaedia Britannica,* '48 ed., Vol. 3, p. 598A; Top-soil: J. D. Main Smith, University of London; Ernest E. DeTurk, professor of soil fertility, University of Illinois; Water: James Alexander Beattie, professor of physical chemistry, Massachusetts Institute of Technology; Air: Sydney Chapman, president, International Association of Meteorology, London.

[a] CO_2 (carbon dioxide) and some CO (carbon monoxide).
[b] Found in varying quantities in the atmosphere.
[c] See Table IV-7, chapter on Air.

The activities on which the life of a human being depends involve a continuous expenditure of energy and a constant exchange of material. As may be noted in Table VI-2, giving the approximate chemical composition of the human body, there are some twenty or more elements that are essential and must be maintained in the human diet. What goes on inside the body after man has secured these elements is largely beyond his direct control. What occurs before, in order that he secure them, is another matter.

Foremost among these essential elements are potassium, phosphorus, calcium, magnesium, and sulphur, the inorganic foodstuffs found in the earth's top-soil and, with the exception of phosphorus, to a lesser degree in water. Of the 100 known chemical elements in the world, only 10 have been man-made, and they are inedible.

TABLE VI-3.   CHANGES IN PER CAPITA FOOD CONSUMPTION IN THE
UNITED STATES, 1929–1949

(*In Pounds per Year*)

	1929	1949	Change	% Change
Meats	131.3	145.0	+ 13.7	+ 10.4%
Fats	44.5	42.7	— 1.8	— 4.0
Poultry	21.5	29.3	+ 7.8	+ 36.3
Eggs	41.7	5.8	— 35.9	— 86.1
Milk	812.0	760.0	— 52.0	— 6.4
Potatoes, white	155.0	108.0	— 47.0	— 30.3
Potatoes, sweet	23.8	14.1	— 9.7	— 40.8
Vegetables, fresh	223.0	251.0	+ 28.0	+ 12.6
Vegetables, processed	28.4	41.2	+ 12.8	+ 45.1
Dry beans	7.8	7.6	— .2	— 2.6
Fruits, fresh	144.3	128.9	— 15.4	— 10.7
Fruits, processed	12.3	40.5	+ 28.2	+229.3
Wheat flour	172.6	135.0	— 37.6	— 21.8
Corn meal	22.9	15.0	— 7.9	— 34.5
Other cereals	31.2	33.0	+ 1.8	+ 5.8
Sugar	97.0	95.5	— 1.5	— 1.5
Total	1,969.3	1,852.6	—116.7	— 5.9%
Calories per day	3,510.0 [a]	3,250.0 [a]	—260.0	— 7.4%
Calories per pound	650.6	640.3	— 10.3	— 1.6%

SOURCE: U. S. Department of Agriculture, Bureau of Human Nutrition and Home Economics.

NOTE: The Department has estimated calories according to the Atwater system, and in the latter year, allowance has been made for the enrichment or fortification of such foods as white flour, breads, and breakfast foods. The consumption of vitamins and mineral preparations other than those mentioned is not included in the above. For 1929, see Series C, 128–155, p. 53, *Historical Statistics of the United States,* 1949.

[a] Calories per day, Table 661, p. 607, Agricultural Statistics, 1950.

In Table V-3, giving pounds per capita in the United States, as an example, the nutritive values represent the food brought into the kitchen, and no allowance has been made by those composing the inventory for losses of nutrients that occur during handling, cooking, refrigeration, storage, and other kitchen practice involving waste, or amounts fed to household pets.

THE "NUMBERINGS" OF PEOPLE

When Adam Smith produced his famous *Inquiry into the Nature and Causes of the Wealth of Nations* there were no adequate measures of wealth and natural resources, and little more than vague guesses of population.

Although the efforts of mankind to count themselves extend back as far as recorded history, such efforts have never been popular. The "numberings" of people and national "stocktakings" were sternly objected to, the idea being that an inventory of people and their possessions was not only a dangerous undertaking but would be followed by "some great public misfortune." This was the argument advanced before the British House of Commons when the subject of a census was first taken up in 1753.

A SUBVERSIVE MATTER

At that time the spokesman for the majority in the House of Commons, indignantly objected to such a stocktaking. "I did not believe," he shouted, "that there was any set of men, or indeed any individual of the human species, so presumptuous and so abandoned as to make the proposal we have just heard. . . . I hold this project to be totally subversive to the last remains of English liberty."

The Bible tells of violent opposition to a census in Judea at the time of King David. Peoples everywhere have tried to escape the census takers, and their rulers, in turn, have tried to keep the results of the enumeration secret, or, as is said today, "for administrative uses only."

"The history of peoples always begins," says Spengler, "with an ordering of the common life with reference to an *Estate.*" The ideas of "power and booty" are seen here in classic union, where the conquering rulers always begin by counting their treasure. William the Conqueror lost little time in making his great survey of England as recorded in the *Domesday Book* in 1086, after the fashion of Charlemagne's Breviary some 300 years earlier. Both covered lands, extent, value, ownership—and people.

Operations of this character have been conducted from ancient times, first, to secure knowledge of the fighting strength of the country or people, and next, to secure knowledge of the property of the people for taxation purposes. Hence, it is only natural that such early enumerations were frowned upon by the rank and file. The principal emphasis was placed upon matters of war and taxes, with the actual numbers of the people subordinated to these interests. Therefore, accurate population figures covering many countries in early periods have been difficult to secure.

THE NUMBER OF PEOPLE

It is known that large aggregations of people lived in Asia, especially in Arabia, Persia, Africa, India, and China, at the time when the Americas of the Western Hemisphere were still covered with virgin forests and had but a scattered population of natives.

At the time of King Solomon, around 950 B.C., the total world population has been estimated at around 130 million human beings; and for the time of Augustus,

DETAIL VI–A

	Roman Empire (*Census*)	Non-Roman (*Estimate*)	Total
Africa	14,500,000	15,500,000	30,000,000
America		20,000,000	20,000,000
Asia	17,500,000	120,000,000	137,000,000
Europe	23,000,000	11,000,000	34,000,000
Oceania		5,000,000	5,000,000
Total	55,000,000	171,500,000	226,500,000

30 A.D. (when a census of the Roman Empire was taken), the world figure has been placed at between 210 and 250 million. These figures stand roughly as shown in Detail VI–A.

As it is the opinion of the various specialists that the world population in ancient times increased at a rate of barely $\frac{1}{10}$ of 1 per cent per year, these figures are shown here in order that a better conception of the accelerated growth in modern times may be obtained.

From the dawn of recorded history to the discovery of the Western Hemisphere, the population of the world was almost stationary. By following the best historical evidence, we can trace the slow growth of population through the earlier periods back nearly 5000 years to 3000 B.C. The present epoch from 1492 to 1955 when world population quintupled covers but 9 per cent of this total period, whereas during the 4492 years from 3000 B.C. to 1492 the average annual population increase was scarcely 2 one-hundredths of 1 per cent. For purposes of securing some insight over this vast expanse of time Detail VI–B may be helpful:

DETAIL VI–B

Era	Years	Years from Base Period	Cumulative Percentage from Base	Descriptive Periods	World Population	% of each Period to Present
A.D.	1955	4955	100.00%	⌠At present writing—	2,578,000,000	100.00
"	1952	4952	99.93	⎨period covered in	2,491,000,000	96.62
"	1882	4882	98.52	⌡this study, 1.48%.	1,434,000,000	55.62
"	1790	4790	96.67	Industrial Revolution	890,000,000	34.52
"	1500	4500	90.81	Commercial Revolution	528,000,000	20.48
"	1492	4492	90.65	Discovery of America	510,000,000	19.78
"	622	3622	73.09	Mohammedan Hegira	350,000,000	13.57
"	30	3030	61.15	Time of Christ	250,000,000	9.69
B.C.	350	2650	53.48	Time of Aristotle	175,000,000	6.78
"	950	2050	41.37	King Solomon	125,000,000	4.84
"	3000	0	.00	Recorded History Base	50,000,000	1.93

The peopling of the world has taken place over great stretches of time during which large migrations and shifts of peoples have been almost universal. These movements have, in the main, been traced to the need for food, and also to changes of climate. Ellsworth Huntington has written repeatedly on this problem and has accumulated evidence showing the fluctuations in the prosperity of ancient civilizations as correlative with climatic changes and the increasing scarcity of water.

The average person may be surprised to learn that, arithmetically speaking, human populations grow in accord with the same fashion or "law" of growth as bacterial populations. The growth curves of individual populations, including the human, are similar in design.

The growth curve of the human population in the United States increased in geometrical progression between 1660 and 1882 at the compound interest rate of 2.9 per cent per year. In fact it doubled every 24 years. Then it began tapering off, with a deviation that coincided with the end of the great migrations into the country and the end of the "free frontier land" era, with a consequent shifting of the population from the farm—where the wife and children were assets—to the urban centers, where the wife and children became liabilities.

Analyses of population facts have never been popular. Any suggestion relating to such concepts as moral restraints, responsibility for future generations, and the advisability of an intelligent limitation of offspring, meet not only with popular reactions of shock but frequently with anger.

Although the Malthusian law of population has long been recognized by the world's distinguished thinkers as one of the great achievements of thought, there probably is no blacker name in the history of economics than that of Malthus. It is largely because of his writings that economics has been called "the dismal science." Benjamin Franklin, Thomas Huxley, John Stuart Mill, David Ricardo, Herbert Spencer, and Charles Darwin all agreed with Malthus. Yet despite the logic and validity of these men's arguments, and the mass of evidence pointing to a world population crisis, there are equally distinguished men in other fields who still speak solemnly of "the now discredited Malthusian law of population"—as if this put an end to the matter.

Malthus published his *Essay on the Principle of Population as It Affects the Future Improvement of Society* in 1798, and it was much enlarged and improved in later editions. The writer suspects that many of those who are so critical and glib about his thesis have never taken the trouble to read the document.

Between 1882 and 1952 the population of Europe increased by 75 per cent, or a net increase of 247 million. During this period there was a net emigration from Europe of 35 million people. See Population Table VI–4.

POPULATION TABLE VI–4.   CHANGES IN THE WORLD'S POPULATION BY
MAJOR GEOGRAPHICAL DIVISIONS, 1882–1952

	1882	1952	Change	% Change
Africa	205,823,000	206,559,000	+ 736,000	+ .4%
America, North	71,495,000	227,208,000	+ 155,713,000	+217.8
America, South	28,920,000	115,098,000	+ 86,178,000	+298.0
Asia	795,591,000	1,354,288,000	+ 558,697,000	+ 70.2
Europe	327,743,000	574,900,000	+ 247,157,000	+ 75.4
Oceania	4,232,000	13,227,000	+ 8,995,000	+212.5
World total	1,433,804,000	2,491,280,000	+1,057,476,000	+ 73.8%

SOURCES: 1882: Pierre Emile Levasseur, French economist, author of *La Population,* 1889; Luigi Bodio, Italian political economist and statistical authority, 1829–1907; The *Statesman's Yearbook,* London; *Encyclopaedia Britannica,* 11th ed., Vol. XXII, p. 92, Table I. 1952: The Statistical Office of the United Nations, New York.

During the previous 70-year period, from 1812 to 1882, Europe's population increased by but 33 per cent, or a net increase of but 82 million persons while the rest of the world's population increased by some 382 million people, or 4 times that of Europe.

This unprecedented population increase and emigration, during the 1882–1952 period, brought an unbalance in world population and resources. It was during this same period that the European powers extended their political influence over approximately 57 per cent of all humanity. Today this dominance stands reduced to a bare 7 per cent of the world outside Europe.

This change is significant, and may be one that forebodes considerable ultimate influence on future population trends in Western Europe as well as elsewhere.

DETAIL VI–C

Popula- tion Trends	Europe		Rest of World		Total	
Last period:						
1952	564,915,000	172.4%	1,926,365,000	174.2%	2,491,280,000	173.8%
1882	327,743,000	100.0	1,106,061,000	100.0	1,433,804,000	100.0
70	237,172,000	72.4%	820,304,000	74.2%	1,057,476,000	73.8%
Prior period:						
1882	327,743,000	133.2%	1,106,061,000	152.9%	1,433,804,000	147.9%
1812	246,025,000	100.0	723,575,000	100.0	969,600,000	100.0
70	81,718,000	33.2%	382,486,000	52.9%	464,204,000	47.9%

During this full 140-year period of Western Europe's Industrial Revolution, and the settlement and colonial exploitation of the rest of the world, the non-European population increased some four times more than did that of Europe itself.

In other words the classical *carpe diem,* counting the surplus regardless of the people, is now bringing forth bitter fruits.

CURIOUS BEDFELLOWS—CURIOUS ARGUMENTS

Carey, List, and Marx all attacked Malthus. List, because he advocated the creation of an industrial monopoly through national protective tariffs, wherein, according to Dr. J. Shield Nicholson, of the University of Edinburgh, "he displayed a curious and perverse misrepresentation of Malthus through relying on the popular unin-formed dogma instead of going to the original source."

Carey (later called the List of the agrarian world), by a curious method of reason-ing put forward the agricultural economy as against the industrial and attacked Mal-thus on the ground that human fecundity is in the inverse ratio of organization, and that "thanks to the increasing fruitfulness of capital the means of subsistance in-creases faster than population." And then, in defense of his "harmony of interests," he produced the argument that:

. . . a steady and equable advance of all classes can only be secured *by ultimately re-turning to the soil all the mineral constituents that are taken from it in the crops,* for in default of this it will in the end become hopelessly impoverished. It is singular [he continued] that modern political economy should have so entirely overlooked the fact that man is a mere borrower from the earth, and that when he does not pay his debts, she acts as do all other creditors, and expels him from his holding [italics mine].

Marx formulated his objections to Malthus on the basis of an inversion of the Malthusian argument. Marx claimed that the surplus workers, who make up what he termed "the industrial reserve army," are *the outcome not of overpopulation but of the increasing use of labor-saving machinery.* Thus, what appears to be overpopula-tion is really a defect of distribution, not an outcome of the error in judgment of excessive breeding. Marx always considered that the industrial reserve army could immediately be turned to good use somehow by a socialized community. Hence, what appears as surplus population is *not an absolute, but a relative surplus.* Here, Marx is in agreement with List, in that List considered each economic order as hav-ing its own peculiar faculty for absorbing population. Marx always avoided a direct answer to the question of whether a Communist organization of society could temporarily absorb a surplus population.

THE LOCATION OF CONTROLS IN THE POPULATION BALANCE SHEET

The number of any species of living things depends on the one hand upon the rate of reproduction and growth, and on the other upon the death rate from wearing out, disease, accident, enemies. These are the chief controls in the population balance sheet.

Up to recent times, control by food alone has been a rare event in nature, particularly insofar as mankind has been concerned. True, there have been droughts and famines in various areas throughout history which have caused vast migrations of peoples. Great as these have been, however, they have had but a minor effect upon the steady upward growth of the total world population as will be observed by Table VI–4. In most cases, before the increase in numbers has brought the species in sight of food shortage, the factor of control by disease has stepped in.

In past periods the first pinch of food-pressure, with men as with wild animals, has led to migrations. And there were always, somewhere, new lands to which to migrate. Today this last resort of escape has been reduced to its apparent minimum for the first time in man's history. Hence, barring accident, wars, and some as yet unexperienced epidemic, man now faces his last and final control—food and water.

In all the successive controversies over the ideal population balance, and/or the population optimum, more and more emphasis has been given to the law of diminishing returns in both agriculture and industry. Here, it may be well to keep in mind that regardless of how any limiting factor may be labeled, the all-important fact is that *there is a limit*.

WORLD POPULATION AND ITS DISTRIBUTION

The area and population of the world as a whole have been the subject of many estimates in scientific works for the last three centuries. Every decade has brought a diminution in the field of conjecture, until today it may fairly be said that our knowledge of the world's population is far more reliable than at any previous time. Prior to 1882 there were many independent estimates of more or less reasonable accuracy, but by 1882 a carefully revised summary was published by Boehm and H. Wagner which, when taken in conjunction with the laborious investigations of Pierre Levasseur, French economist, and Luigi Bodio, Italian political economist and statistical authority, supplies us with an excellent figure for that year. (See Encyclopaedia Britannica, 11th edition, Vol. XXII, p. 92.)

The best known contemporary estimates of the populations of the world have been those of the League of Nations prior to World War II, and the United Nations since 1945. Prior to these periods the International Statistical Institute and the International Institute of Agriculture had supplied estimates for the world as a whole and for the six continents.

GROWTH OF WORLD POPULATION

The present population of the world is approximately 2500 millions. Although estimates of world population before 1882 may not be very trustworthy, Sir George Knibbs considered Michelot's estimate of 1009 millions for 1845 to be as well founded a figure as could be made, and then calculated the average annual increase to be about $7/10$ of 1 per cent. In other words it was increasing, between the years 1845 and 1914, at a rate which would double the population in 100 years.

Putting the rate of increase at but 628-thousandths of 1 per cent per annum, which was the rate of increase of world population between 1901 and 1924, Professor Alexander M. Carr-Saunders, Director of the London School of Economics, found that, should that rate continue, the world population would number 4 billions in the year 2031, 8 billions in 2131, and 16 billions in 2231.

Professor Carr-Saunders had based his rate of increase on the evidence of 26 countries—before the more recent figures were available—which were increasing at a rate which would double their population in about 60 years. In this study, with *world* figures now available, we have based our rate on the population behavior of 98 sovereign countries and 105 non-self-governing areas—in fact the *entire world*—wherein we find the present rate of increase to be 1.99 per cent per annum, or some three times faster over the past decade than during the first quarter of this century. This indicates that the population may double in the next 50 years.

These calculations suggest certain reflections. As has been noted, the average rate of increase was far lower in the distant past. It is probable that there were fluctuations of numbers in earlier centuries of civilization. It is almost certain that, disre-

TABLE VI-5. SUMMARY OF CHANGES IN BIRTH AND DEATH RATES PER 1,000
POPULATION, 1882–1952

	1882	1952	70-year change
Birth rates:			
Eastern countries of Eastern Hemisphere	39.3	35.3	− 4.0
European countries of Eastern Hemisphere	35.7	20.5	−15.2
Countries of Western Hemisphere	46.5	37.5	− 9.0
World average	40.5	31.1	− 9.4
Death rates:			
Eastern countries of Eastern Hemisphere	29.9	13.2	−16.7
European countries of Eastern Hemisphere	21.9	11.1	−10.8
Countries of Western Hemisphere	24.5	12.0	−12.5
World average	25.4	12.1	−13.3

SUMMARY OF CHANGES IN BIRTH AND DEATH RATES PER 1,000 POPULATION,
1935–1952

	1935	1952	17-year change
Birth rates:			
Eastern countries of Eastern Hemisphere	34.9	35.3	+ .4
European countries of Eastern Hemisphere	19.9	20.5	+ .6
Countries of Western Hemisphere	31.8	37.5	+ 5.7
World average	28.8	31.1	+ 2.3
Death rates:			
Eastern countries of Eastern Hemisphere	20.1	13.2	− 6.9
European countries of Eastern Hemisphere	13.5	11.1	− 2.4
Countries of Western Hemisphere	16.5	12.0	− 4.5
World average	16.7	12.1	− 4.6

SOURCE: *Demographic Yearbook,* United Nations, 1952.

garding these fluctuations, the rate of growth in former times taken over several centuries was very small, and that the rate of growth during the last century has been abnormally large—particularly over the last decade.

A clue to causes in the rate of increase and the prospects for the future may be obtained from an estimation of changes in the birth and death rates that have occurred over the long-term period 1882–1952, and the shorter period 1935–52, as shown in Table VI–5.

THE WORLD'S AGING POPULATION

Studies of the death rate contain no problems of such general interest as do those of the birth rate. Nevertheless the death rate has come to be of major importance, for it has markedly decreased in all civilized countries during the past seventy years. See Table VI–5.

In this connection it is desirable to distinguish between the concepts of the life span, average length of life, the prolongation of life beyond the standard duration which denotes the extreme limit of life, the average age of all persons living, and the life expectancy. While the life span has probably changed but little throughout all history, both the average age of life and life expectancy have been greatly extended in modern times. (See Table VI–6.)

TABLE VI–6. CHANGES IN PERCENTAGE OF TOTAL POPULATION 65 YEARS OF AGE AND OVER, 1882–1952

	1882	1952
By 1952 rank:		
1 France	7.1%	11.8%
2. United Kingdom	4.8	11.0
3 Austria	4.7	10.3
4 Sweden	5.4	10.1
5 Belgium	6.8	9.6
6 Norway	6.1	9.5
7 Switzerland	5.0	9.5
8 Denmark	5.3	9.3
9 Germany	5.4	9.3
10 Portugal	5.0	8.7
11 Russia	5.0	8.7
12 Canada	4.0	8.5
13 United States	3.4	8.2
14 Italy	4.8	8.1
15 Australia	4.3	8.0
16 Netherlands	5.5	7.7
17 Mexico	3.4	7.5
18 Japan	2.6	6.0
19 Spain	4.1	5.8
20 Greece	3.4	5.6
21 Union of South Africa	2.1	4.4
22 Honduras	1.7	3.9
23 Philippines	1.3	3.1
24 Egypt	1.8	3.0
25 China	1.3	2.5
Average	4.2%	7.6%

SOURCES: *Encyclopedia of Social Reform*, Bliss ed., 1908; *Demographic Yearbook*, United Nations, 1952.

As an example, Detail VI–D illustrates the significant changes that have occurred in the United States, as evidenced by census data over the past seventy years:

DETAIL VI–D

	1882	1952	Change
Average age of all persons living	20.9	30.2	+ 9.3
Life expectancy at age of 1 year	36.8	68.8	+32.1
Crude birth rate per 1000 population	31.5	24.5	— 7.0
Crude death rate per 1000 population	19.8	9.7	—10.1

Insofar as the world totals are concerned, there are approximately 100 million more persons of age 65 and over living in the world today than there were seventy years ago.

THE AGRICULTURAL PERSPECTIVE

In judging the agricultural potential of the world, we must bear in mind that land has other uses than raising primary foodstuffs and supporting domestic animals. Land must also be used for producing trees and fibers—industrial raw materials. The world's population requirements of building timber, fuel wood, paper pulp, rubber, cotton, linen, jute, hemp, gums, and other raw materials are, as will be seen in the following chapters on production and consumption, large and ever-expanding.

Since, in terms of material, the growth of forests is rarely at the rate of over 3 per cent per annum, the current rate of depletion of forests would seem to imply that, in the not distant future, land in many countries will need to be withdrawn from agriculture for reforestation. In other words, the growth of population may exceed the prospective rate of growth of the established stands of timber. All of these, as well as the vastly enlarged industrial natural resource requirements, lie wholly outside the Malthusian doctrine.

THE SIGNIFICANCE OF RATES OF CHANGE

The imperceptibility of change because of its gradual character has been one of the most difficult of all phenomena for man to comprehend. Everything in the world, including growth, consumption, and production, always stands in relation to its contrary. All such things operate in accordance with the law of diminishing returns. All living phenomena involve a continuous transformation of one form of energy and matter into another. In other words, all living things, including mankind, are transformers of energy and matter; and this involves various rates of change. "Change" is merely another name for "function in time," and when we are speaking of a *rate of change* we are comparing a certain quantity or amount of one thing to a quantity or amount of another thing or things.

We are also referring to Newton's Third Law of Motion: "To every action there is an equal and opposite reaction" in a world in flux—an indispensable tool of scientific activity. "Wages have gone up 20 per cent," but "What about prices?" "A growing child has gained fifteen pounds, but still he is hungry for he has grown three inches." "The ocean has made an inroad of five miles on the coastline—a disaster until one learns that it has taken a thousand years for this change to take place." We compare increases in wages with rise in prices before concluding that times are improving, increase in weight with growth, change in distance with change in time to realize the speed of the sea's advance. A *comparison of two related changes* is called for in each case. That is what the calculus is about.

Percentage increases or decreases are rates of change. It is frequently lost sight of that all percentage changes have to be viewed in relation to the magnitude involved. When magnitudes are small, large percentages are required to realize a substantial relative increase, and the opposite is true when magnitudes are large. In other words, at the time of King Solomon, when the world population was about 50 millions, the present annual average rate of increase, 1.22 per cent, would have increased the population by 61,000 people in one year; but when this rate is applied to a population of 2500 millions the actual increase amounts to 30,500,000, or an amount 500 times greater than 5000 years ago, although the same rate applies. The same thing applies to diminishing land resources. As more and more land is brought into use the magnitude becomes greater, and the same percentage of deflation results in a relatively larger annual loss.

TABLE VI-7. THE SIGNIFICANCE OF MULTIPLYING MAN AND THE WORLD'S VANISHING LAND

(At Present Average Annual Rates)

	Multiplying man	Diminishing land acres [a]
Per year	33,488,000	73,000,000
Per month	2,789,109	6,080,000
Per week	642,229	1,400,000
Per day	91,747	200,000
Per hour	3,823	8,331
Per minute	64	138
Per second	1	2

[a] Land acreage losses	Per year	Per month	Per week	Per day	Per hour	Per minute	Per second
To Seas	9,535,900	794,200	182,875	26,125	1,088	18	.3
To Deserts	53,739,957	4,475,883	1,030,531	147,233	6,135	102	1.7
To Built-on	9,705,886	808,397	186,144	26,592	1,108	18	.3
Total	72,981,743	6,078,480	1,399,550	199,950	8,331	138	2.3

NOTE: If the reader has just purchased this book, and has taken an hour before turning this page, the world's population has increased by approximately 4,000 people, and the world's food-producing land has simultaneously decreased by 8,000 acres. This means a *net* addition of people over all deaths of some 64 per hour, or at a far greater speed than anyone would be allowed to drive a car through traffic in terms of miles per hour.

In addition to this phenomenon, man is now multiplying at a rate over twice as fast as he is reducing his non-replaceable natural resources. This means that every year the world is adding the equivalent of more than the present population of the combined states of New York, New Jersey, Pennsylvania, and Connecticut, while at the same time subtracting 1·14,034 square miles, or 72,981,743 acres of usable land, which is in excess of the combined land area of these same four states.

Every species of living things naturally multiplies in proportion to its means of subsistence, and no species can ever multiply beyond it without suffering disaster. Adam Smith told us that 175 years ago.

Table VI-7 shows the population rate moving steadily upward, with the land rate moving progressively downward. The full significance of these rates of change, moving in opposite directions, is brought into sharper focus through the medium of a successive reduction in the same element involved. Here is a phenomenon that cannot continue indefinitely without catastrophe to mankind.

THE POPULATION OPTIMUM

As has been stated before, the present world population is approximately 2500 millions, and the total land area, excluding the arctic regions, is roughly some 28 billion acres, less than a third of which is regarded as arable. Since it has been competently estimated that four acres are required to sustain one human being, other things being equal, this would fix the limit of population of the globe at something around 2 billions—a figure indicating that we have already reached the saturation point.

The term "optimum population" came into common use after World War II as a conception of the relation between population and the produce of industry. This conception, which lies at the basis of the position now taken by virtually all authorities, holds that any given time the population which can exist on a given extent of land, consistent with the attainment of the maximum return to industry possible at the time, is definite. In other words, according to these authorities, for any given area of land under any given set of circumstances there is an optimum population. Also, any departure from this optimum, whether in the direction of deficiency or of excess, will be accompanied by a return per head less than the possible return. Departure in the direction of deficiency is called "underpopulation," and departure in the direction of excess is called "overpopulation."

It is important to realize that no distinction is drawn between agriculture and manufacture in this relation. Unfortunately, attempts to ascertain whether under- or overpopulation exists meet with considerable difficulties. Unemployment, as Professor Carr-Saunders has pointed out, is not necessarily an indication of overpopulation, and the comparison of figures for the national income over a period of years is an uncertain guide.

A REVALUATION OF MALTHUS

Unfortunately, what has been called Malthus's theory of population—instead of being a great discovery as some have represented it, or a poisonous novelty, as others have considered it—is actually no more than a formal enunciation of obvious though neglected facts.

In order that the famous two progressions—arithmetic and geometric—be clearly understood, here they are as Malthus stated them, and then as restated in tabular form in Detail VI–E.

DETAIL VI–E

Ordinal Time Period	Subsistence Arithmetic Progression	Population Geometric Progression
1	1	1
2	2	2
3	3	4
4	4	8
5	5	16
6	6	32
7	7	64
8	8	128
9	9	256

Taking the whole earth, instead of this island, emigration would of course be excluded; and supposing the present population equal to a thousand millions, the human species would increase as the numbers 1, 2, 4, 8, 16, 32, 64, 128, 256; and subsistence as 1, 2, 3, 4, 5, 6, 7, 8, 9. In two centuries the population would be to the means of subsistence as 256 to 9; in three centuries as 4,096 to 13, and in two thousand years the difference would be almost incalculable.

While the above is clear in all respects with the exception of the relationship of the two progressions to the time periods involved, yet it became common in the nineteenth century to disparage Malthus's doctrine as out of date during that period of intense migrations and colonization of the world's undeveloped frontiers. However, since World Wars I and II the specter of overpopulation has returned and Malthus seems to be coming into his own.

It is now realized that the earlier contentions were wrong in discarding the view that population tends to increase in geometrical progression. Their error was due to a misunderstanding of the time period, and virtually no serious authorities any longer dispute the geometrical progression. No doubt Malthus's cycle of 25 years for the doubling period proved too short. But spin out the time period as anyone may please, the time not only has come but bids well to come again, when the population doubles.

A doubled population will be ready, unless otherwise checked, to double itself once more; it follows, then, by indisputable evidence, that the increase does tend to occur by a series of successive doublings, that is to say, in geometrical progression. It may be that those who still insist otherwise are the "foolish" ones—not Malthus.

THE LAW OF DIMINISHING RETURNS

The *law of increasing returns* has operated powerfully in industry, but it is one of the gravest errors to assume that such a law is equally operative for population. It is the *law of diminishing returns* that gives to the principle of the population its chief importance as an element in economic problems.

To paraphrase Ricardo, population regulates itself by the resources which are able to sustain it, and therefore increases or diminishes with the increase or diminution of these resources. Improvements in the world's sustaining land situation are of three kinds:

1. Discovery and development of new land.
2. Increasing the productive powers of old land.
3. The ability by improved tools to obtain its produce with less labor.

As Othmar Spann, Professor of Sociology and Economics in the University of Venice, pointed out over a generation ago, an objector might contend that the returns from land will also double themselves after a time. If they have increased in proportion with the series 1, 2, 3, 4, they have doubled themselves twice. But the increase in land returns is on a different footing from that of population. For while population retains throughout its increase an undiminished capacity for expansion, cultivated land has a steadily diminishing capacity for an increase in its returns.

Moreover, an increase in the yield of land is uncertain and irregular. The principle of the matter is embodied in the *law of diminishing returns*, whose chain of reasoning may be summarized as follows: In industry, the demand for a double yield is satisfied by setting to work with two workers, two machines, and two units of raw material, where previously only one unit of each was utilized. But in work upon the land the surface of the area under cultivation cannot be increased, and the necessary amounts of sunshine, warmth, air, moisture, and nutrients can be increased only within strict limits. Consequently, in agricultural production, a number of the factors of production are capable of intensification only to a moderate degree. The only factor that can here be intensified as much as we please is the amount of capital and labor. But if some of the factors are incapable of intensification, it is impossible that intensification of the other factors should bring about an increase in the yield proportional to the increased expenditure. Additional increments of expenditure will necessarily lead to no more than progressively diminishing increments of yield.

NATURAL VERSUS NEGATIVE ARITHMETIC PROGRESSION

Malthus wrote his famous Essay containing the two comparative progressions a full quarter of a century before science had discovered "negative" numbers. Hence, for his illustration of subsistence he employed straight-line "positive arithmetical progression" for his comparison with the geometric progression of population. In this supposition no limits whatever were placed on the produce of the earth. In other words Malthus himself stated that "it may increase forever, and be greater than any assignable quantity."

If the reader will examine Table VI–7, "The Significance of Multiplying Man and the World's Vanishing Land," he will note that insofar as the time relationships are concerned we have two independent sets of primary phenomena—moving mathematically in opposite directions—one increasing, the other diminishing at two different rates. In other words, we are actually confronted with a *negative arithmetic progression,* and not with a positive natural or ordinal progression.

THE PHENOMENA OF COMPLEX NUMBERS

The whole of the phenomena of today's world, and of today's knowledge, if it is to be understood, involves a knowledge of the new algebra of complex numbers, which becomes of the utmost importance in population studies. Here we are confronted with Sir William Hamilton's discovery of "Quaternions" which postulated the existence of negative and complex numbers nearly thirty years after Malthus's work.

It was this great work of Hamilton, the Irish scientist, that led nearly one hundred years later to the quantum theory and the theory of atomic structure. As it may be expressed in economic terms, the quotient of two magnitudes and directions in relation to direction in time and space as expressible quadrinomally involves: (1) number of people; (2) product resulting from the number of people; (3) limited land area; and (4) land quality.

Past estimates of the possible maximum world population have varied from 3 billions to as much as 7 billions. All of these estimates have been made, however, without benefit of an over-all world resource inventory as shown in the preceding chapters on Land, Air, and Water.

If, however, the present rate of increase had obtained in the past, as shown in Tables VI–7 and VI–8, the earth's population would have been full to overflowing long ago. In other words it is easy to calculate that if this present rate of increase continues there will be very little room for further expansion after a certain date. Also there is nothing inevitable about the present rate of increase except catastrophe.

Tables VI–9 to VI–13, covering the world's densely populated areas and world population movements are given for purposes of aiding the reader in gaining a qualitative measure of the present population inventory.

POPULATION TABLE VI-8.   WORLD POPULATION BY CONTINENTS, 1882–1952; ESTIMATED POPULATION, 1955–2022

(*In Thousands*)

Year	Africa	America, N. & Central	America, South	Asia [a]	Europe [b]	Oceania	World total	Increase	Per cent increase
1882	205,823	71,495	28,920	795,591	327,743	4,232	1,433,804		
1952	206,559	227,208	115,098	1,354,288	574,900	13,227	2,491,280	1,057,476	73.7% [c]
1955	217,789	238,935	120,835	1,393,006	594,243	13,851	2,578,659	87,379	3.5 [d]
1960	238,978	260,442	131,301	1,461,968	628,420	14,989	2,736,098	157,439	6.1
1965	262,882	284,163	142,773	1,535,826	664,796	16,235	2,906,675	170,577	6.2
1970	290,027	310,330	155,350	1,615,031	703,584	17,612	3,091,934	185,259	6.4
1975	320,940	339,257	169,158	1,700,275	744,989	19,141	3,293,760	201,826	6.5
1980	356,316	371,256	184,341	1,792,578	789,149	20,822	3,514,462	220,702	6.7
1985	396,726	406,737	201,042	1,890,064	835,566	22,678	3,752,813	238,351	6.8
1990	443,123	446,034	219,435	1,996,070	886,328	24,738	4,015,728	262,915	7.0
1995	497,237	489,718	239,722	2,110,566	940,044	27,024	4,304,311	288,583	7.2
2000	560,074	538,331	262,114	2,234,741	996,364	29,565	4,621,189	316,878	7.4
2005	633,488	592,464	286,864	2,368,998	1,057,580	32,446	4,971,840	350,651	7.6
2010	719,575	652,838	314,250	2,514,689	1,122,630	35,553	5,359,535	387,695	7.8
2015	820,809	720,275	344,604	2,672,861	1,192,504	39,078	5,790,131	430,596	8.0
2020	940,376	795,686	378,272	2,844,909	1,267,203	43,027	6,269,473	479,342	8.3
2022	997,079	829,466	393,232	2,919,777	1,299,205	44,799	6,483,558	214,085	3.4% [e]

[a] Included in Asia: 21.18% of total population of U.S.S.R., and 92.3% of total of Turkey.
[b] Included in Europe: 78.82% of total population of U.S.S.R., and 7.7% of total of Turkey.
[c] 70-year period.
[d] 3-year period only.
[e] 2-year period only.

The current net rate of increase for each political division (see Table VI–7) has been applied to its own population figure regardless of migration changes, which would automatically be inclusive for the over-all periodic world totals, which should be viewed as approximations only.

TABLE VI-9. PRINCIPAL INDICES OF THE WORLD'S DENSELY POPULATED HUMAN PATTERN, 1952

	Health [a]	Literacy [b]	Median school years [c]	Per cent rural [d]	Crude birth rates [e]	Crude death rates [f]	Net increases [g]	Life expectancy [h]
Belgium	87	92.1	8.0	37.3	16.1	12.7	3.4	67.5
England, Wales	92	98.0	8.6	19.3	15.5	12.5	3.0	70.0
Netherlands	98	99.0	8.6	45.4	22.3	7.5	14.8	70.5
Japan	69	90.2	7.8	62.5	25.6	10.0	15.6	60.2
Germany	91	99.6	8.7	28.9	15.7	10.5	5.2	61.4
Italy	81	72.0	6.3	55.4	18.1	10.3	7.8	54.9
China	70	75.0	3.8	93.2	50.0	11.6	38.4	43.4
Czechoslovakia	77	92.9	8.1	51.2	22.1	11.7	10.4	69.0
Switzerland	93	99.6	8.7	63.5	17.2	10.5	6.7	64.9
Hungary	70	84.9	7.4	65.5	19.1	11.2	7.9	56.6
Poland	69	80.0	7.0	64.2	30.5	11.6	18.9	65.0
Denmark	92	99.8	8.7	32.7	17.8	8.8	9.0	70.9
Austria	83	98.9	8.6	50.9	14.6	12.7	1.9	64.7
France	87	91.1	7.9	47.1	19.4	13.2	6.2	67.9
India	45	9.5	1.5	82.7	32.0	16.6	15.4	26.8
Portugal	85	32.9	2.9	68.9	24.2	12.3	11.9	57.7
Romania	70	55.0	4.8	76.6	19.6	18.1	1.5	38.0
Bulgaria	68	60.0	5.2	75.4	24.0	13.4	10.6	46.3
Yugoslavia	70	55.0	4.8	83.8	27.0	15.4	11.6	44.7
Greece	75	78.2	6.8	52.8	26.1	10.7	15.4	50.0

SOURCES: [a] *Mainsprings of Civilization,* Ellsworth Huntington, p. 254; [b] *United Nations Statistical Yearbook,* 1950; [c] *United Nations Statistical Yearbook,* United Nations, 1952, pp. 168–186; [d] *Demographic Yearbook,* United Nations, 1952, pp. 226–230; [f] *Demographic Yearbook,* United Nations, 1952, pp. 267–271; [g] Difference between birth and death rates; [h] *Demographic Yearbook,* United Nations, 1952, pp. 448–451.

119

TABLE VI-10. PRINCIPAL WORLD POPULATION MOVEMENTS, 1950–1951
ANNUAL PERIOD

	Immigrants	Emigrants	Gains	Losses
Germany	413,711	188,753	224,958	
United States	203,407	27,881	175,526	
Canada	194,391	3,635	190,756	
Israel	173,901	7,371	166,530	
Finland	157,265	19,644	137,621	
Argentina	136,777	25,348	111,429	
Australia	132,542	20,855	111,687	
Japan	97,844	5,925	91,919	
United Kingdom	76,295	169,521		93,226
Guatemala	60,979	59,755	1,224	
Burma	49,585	54,800		5,215
Netherlands	45,003	67,377		22,374
Italy	41,435	140,204		98,769
Jamaica	32,922	34,639		1,717
Belgium	31,795	44,041		12,246
Sweden	31,603	16,580	15,023	
Denmark	24,485	25,873		1,388
New Zealand	18,234	7,788	10,446	
Southern Rhodesia	16,245		16,245	
Union of S. Africa	15,248	15,381		133
Spain	9,626	59,137		49,511
Portugal	7,963	12,838		4,875
Switzerland	2,590	3,622		1,032
Other areas		962,878		962,878
Total	1,973,846	1,973,846	1,253,364	1,253,364

SOURCE: *Demographic Yearbook*, 1952, United Nations Statistical Office.

NOTE: Immigrants and emigrants, as used by the United Nations Office, refers to "permanent" in the sense of departing or arriving for a stay of one year or more, on the basis of declared intention.

TABLE VI-11. GOVERNMENTAL STATUS OF THE PEOPLES OF THE WORLD, 1952

	Africa	America, N. & Central	America, South	Asia	Europe	Oceania	Total
Sovereign states	6	12	10	33	35	2	98
Non-self-governing	36	12	4	15	6	14	87
Trust territories	7					4	11
Former mandated territories	1			1			2
Condominium	1					1	2
International administration	1				1		2
Military government				1			1
Total	52	24	14	50	42	21	203

NOTES: Africa: non-self-governing: Belgium 1, France 9, Portugal 5, Spain 4, Britain 17; trust territories: Britain 3, France 2, Belgium 1, Italy 1; former mandated territories: Union of South Africa 1; condominium: Anglo-Egyptian 1 (Sudan); international administration: France and Spain 1 (Tangier).

America, North & Central: non-self-governing: Denmark 1, France 3, Netherlands 1, Britain 3, United States 4.

America, South: non-self-governing: France 1, Netherlands 1, Britain 2.

Asia: non-self-governing: France 1, Netherlands 1, Portugal 3, Britain 10; former mandated territories: Britain 1; military government: United States 1.

Europe: non-self-governing: France 2, Britain 1, United States 1, U.S.S.R. 1, Denmark 1; international administration: 1 (Trieste).

Oceania: non-self-governing: Australia 2, France 2, New Zealand 3, Britain 4, United States 3; trust territories: Australia 2, New Zealand 1, United States 1; condominium: Anglo-French 1 (New Hebrides).

TABLE VI-12. PRINCIPAL LANGUAGES OF THE WORLD, 1882–1952

Numbers speaking:	1882	1952	Numbers speaking:	1882	1952
Chinese	388,000,000	625,000,000	Abyssinian	6,800,000	12,000,000
Hindi & Urdu	294,000,000	433,000,000	Serbian	6,300,000	11,000,000
English	107,000,000	320,000,000	Gujarati	6,100,000	10,700,000
Russian	144,000,000	212,000,000	Hungarian	4,600,000	8,000,000
French	43,000,000	120,000,000	Afghan	4,400,000	7,600,000
German	56,000,000	110,000,000	Czech	4,300,000	7,500,000
Spanish	35,000,000	103,000,000	Greek	3,950,000	6,900,000
Japanese	47,000,000	98,000,000	Swedish	3,600,000	6,300,000
African	81,000,000	94,000,000	Bulgarian	3,500,000	6,100,000
Dutch	42,000,000	60,000,000	Nepali	3,400,000	6,000,000
Bengali	35,000,000	51,000,000	Slovenian	3,000,000	5,200,000
Italian	26,000,000	50,000,000	Danish	2,300,000	4,000,000
Portuguese	11,000,000	49,000,000	Flemish	2,000,000	3,500,000
Javanese	29,000,000	42,000,000	Finnish	1,700,000	3,000,000
Polish	22,000,000	32,000,000	Slovakian	1,650,000	3,000,000
Arabic	20,000,000	29,000,000	Norwegian	1,600,000	2,800,000
Telegu	17,000,000	25,000,000	Lithuanian	1,400,000	2,400,000
Turkish	23,000,000	24,000,000	Lettish	1,000,000	1,900,000
Punjabi	15,000,000	24,000,000	Estonian	700,000	1,200,000
Marathi	17,000,000	20,000,000	Albanian	790,000	1,100,000
Rumanian	14,000,000	19,400,000	Total above	1,562,690,000	2,699,600,000
Tamil	13,000,000	19,000,000	World population	1,433,804,000	2,491,280,000
Burmese	12,000,000	15,000,000	Speaking multiple languages	128,886,000	208,320,000
Persian	8,600,000	15,000,000			

SOURCES: Dr. Charles Earl Funk and Dr. Frank H. Vizetelley, editors of the *New Standard Dictionary*, and the French Academy for the period 1952. Mulhall's *Dictionary of Statistics*, and the *Encyclopedia of Social Reform*, Bliss ed., for the 1882 period.

NOTE: There is evidence, from the best available sources, that along with the increase in explorations and land resettlement over six hundred languages and dialects have disappeared from use during this period. According to the French Academy and the International Institute of Languages, London, the number of distinct languages and dialects are distributed approximately as follows: Africa, 226; North and South America, 1,325; Asia and Oceania, 766; Europe, 479; world total, 2,796.

TABLE VI–13. ESTIMATED PROPERTY HOLDINGS OF THE WORLD'S PRINCIPAL RELIGIONS, 1952

	Amount	% of Total
Roman Catholic	$ 7,333,000,000	21.4%
Mohammedan	5,817,000,000	16.1
Confucian	5,492,000,000	15.2
Hindu	4,698,000,000	13.0
Protestant	3,541,000,000	9.8
Buddhist	2,746,000,000	7.6
Eastern Orthodox	2,348,000,000	6.5
Primitive	1,587,000,000	4.4
Taoist	903,000,000	2.5
Judaism	509,000,000	1.4
Shinto	470,000,000	1.3
All other	292,000,000	.8
World total	$36,136,000,000	100.0%

SOURCE: Computed from basic data in the *Britannica Book of the Year,* 1953, and the *British Blue Book of Missions.*

NOTE: Social private wealth, such as churches, clubs, etc., is extremely difficult, both to allocate and adequately estimate. Statistics of the world's religions are only very rough approximations. Few religions attempt to keep statistical records of their property assets. The great cathedrals, church edifices, shrines, parsonages, hospitals, schools, burial grounds, and other property devoted to religious activities all amount to a very large sum, although the grand total represents but one-half of one per cent of the world's total assets.

The subtilty of nature is far beyond that of sense or of understanding; so that the specious meditations, speculations, and theories of mankind are but a kind of insanity, only there is no one to stand by and observe it.

—FRANCIS BACON, *Novum Organum*, Bk. I, x, 1620

VII

Production

PRODUCTION IS TRADITIONALLY the first of four main divisions of economics, the others dealing respectively with consumption, exchange, and distribution. Production is the process of creating economic "values" or "utilities" needed to satisfy human wants. In this broad sense production includes any activity which makes goods and services more easily available in the fields of agriculture, forestry, fisheries, mining, manufacturing, construction, transportation, and marketing. Production may be expressed in number of physical units or in their accepted representative monetary valuation.

All living creatures are by nature consumers first and producers next, or both consumers and producers concurrently. In the inescapable exchange system of matter and energy, production and consumption constitute interdependent phenomena. The sum of human wants, expressed economically as effective demands, can only work themselves out through the complex structure of the world's production-consumption-exchange system or systems. It is then in this field, dependent upon the effective utilization of the world's material resources in relation to people, that the real formation of wealth takes place. It is the sum of all of these activities, which serve to satisfy human needs in this interdependent production-consumption-equation, that is called the world economy, and it is important that a balance be maintained between them.

Popular discussion of economic questions are almost invariably characterized by the fact that only a small and arbitrarily selected part of the economic mechanism is taken into account. The most common and the crudest mistakes of popular opinion and of business and political strategy may be traced to this defect. Since materials and energy are consumed in production itself, and the "using up" of the world's matter and energy constitute concurrent phenomena—on a planet that is finite— and since the means and resources for satisfying human wants are usually available

124

only in limited quantity, whereas the wants of people as a whole are more or less unlimited, the means are therefore usually *scarce* in relation to the wants.

THE PROBLEM OF SECURING A SURPLUS

It is only means and resources of this kind that relate to the economy, and only scarce means that are economic means. Hence the world economy is conducted with the understanding that the means are scarce, and it is in this sense that writers have referred to the "principle of scarcity." The specific task of the word economy, therefore, has been that of securing as well as it could an adjustment between the consumptive demands and the means of supplying them; while the measure in which it succeeds in doing so has been spoken of as a "sound economy." In this respect the economic task, theoretically, has been so to control the wants at the beginning of a certain period that the available means might last for the whole period. This has been called "economizing"—a label and a principle rarely practiced in modern times with fidelity.

All sound economies in the past have attempted to classify needs according to their importance, and have developed different ways and degrees of meeting these needs. For instance, in a self-contained frontier agricultural economy, the provision of the means of living became the chief task at the moment, and only after this was met did other wants—better houses, clothing, etc.—come into being and seem necessary to the raising of the standard of living.

The principal fact, however, in all matters relating to the productive activities of man, is that man creates no new matter. Thus the main point is not whether the labors of men create new substance, but whether what is produced by that labor provides more utilities than the utilities expended in producing it. From the outlook of economic theory it is the surplus yield over the cost of production—the net product—that matters.

Past civilizations achieved for small groups at the expense of the majority what the modern resource pattern, theoretically, claims to make possible for all. The development of today's pattern makes possible wider division in some areas of the world, and at the same time offers to extend such wider distribution to an ever-widening area. Unfortunately there appears to be a gap between what is promised and what is actually achieved.

PHYSICAL AND MONETARY NET PRODUCT COMPARED

The capacity to accumulate such a surplus over and above the minimum subsistence required to support the population is dependent, as Professor Erich W. Zimmermann has well stated in his *World Resources and Industries*, on three factors: (1) The amount of "free" energy available; (2) The efficient use made of the available energy; and (3) The rational control of population growth.

However, if food should be the spontaneous product of sunshine, rainfall, virgin soil fertility, and other untransformed aspects of nature, then the energy derived from food may also be said to be free energy. But, as has been pointed out, man is the chief agent in the transformation of nature's materials, since the production of new material goods cannot be a creation out of nothing, but can only be a reshaping of the materials found in nature—some of which when used up cannot be replaced.

If, then, to quote Professor Zimmermann:

. . . the food must first be produced by man with the aid of animals bred and raised by him and the tools made by him, animate energy is to a high degree an artificial man-made product. In that case the energy spent in producing the necessary food and feed and tools must be deducted from the total energy derived from the food before the net energy available for work can be ascertained. Since, under civilized conditions, most food and feed are not spontaneous products of untransformed nature, but the result of past energy expenditure, most animate energy is *not a net addition to the energy supply* available to man. It is normally assumed that the energy derived from food and feed exceeds that required to produce the food and feed—in other words that portion at least represents a net product. Whether that assumption is justified depends on the efficiency of the productive system, and this, in turn, depends largely on the quality of the natural agents utilized and the amount of surplus which can be accumulated. [Italics mine]

An examination of this energy exchange, as computed for the United States for the year 1949, is shown in Production Table VII–1; and in Table VII–2 com-

TABLE VII–1. THE ANNUAL MAN-LAND ENERGY EXCHANGE IN THE
UNITED STATES, 1949

Pounds Avoirdupois and International Calorie Equivalents

(*In Millions*)

	Pounds	Calories
I. Popular conception:		
Total food produced	672,969	430,700,241
Farm workers' human energy expended	16,069	10,284,098
Popular conception of total energy net product	656,900	420,416,143
II. Actual total energy exchange:		
Total energy realized from food-producing land	672,969	430,700,241
Energy nutrients consumed by livestock	463,119	
Energy consumed in gas and oil by machines	46,104	
Energy consumed by electric current used	13,868	
Energy consumed by farm workers	16,069	
Energy consumed by repairs to equipment	31,489	
Energy contained in fertilizers added	31,052	
Energy allowance for depreciation, buildings & equipment	69,110	
Energy embodied in existing buildings & equipment	260,162	
Annual energy losses through land erosion	573,800	
Total energy expended by man	1,504,773	963,054,593
Actual annual energy net product [a]	−831,804	−532,354,352
III. Population-land-energy-yield lag:		
Increased energy demand of added population	4,739	3,033,241
Increased energy supply by added production	4,711	3,014,902
Current energy production lag behind population	−28	−18,339

SOURCES: U. S. Department of Agriculture, Yearbook Statistical Committee, *Agricultural Statistics*, 1950; Bureau of Agricultural Economics, *The Farm Income Situation*, 1952; *U. S. Census of Agriculture*, Bureau of the Census, U. S. Department of Commerce, Vol. II, 1950.
[a] Actual annual energy is 1,504,773 − 672,969 = 831,804.
Adaptation of Professor Erich Zimmermann's assumption, *World Resources and Industries*, p. 62, Harper & Brothers, New York and London, 1933.

TABLE VII-2. THE PHYSICAL TONNAGE EXCHANGE BALANCE SHEET AND THE MONETARY INCOME-OUTGO BALANCE SHEET, U.S.A., 1949

	Tons	Dollars
Total foodstuffs produced	336,485,000	$ 24,583,000,000
Materials consumed in production:		
Erosion losses during period	286,900,000	$ 937,000,000
Consumed by livestock	231,560,000	4,443,000,000
Embodied in buildings & equipment	130,081,000	1,694,000,000
Depreciation & depletion	34,055,000	775,000,000
Consumed by farm machinery	23,052,000	1,980,000,000
Fertilizers purchased	16,449,000	784,000,000
Embodied in repairs to equipment	10,745,000	3,707,000,000
Farm products consumed by farm labor	8,035,000	2,940,000,000
Consumed by electric current	6,934,000	638,000,000
Farmer's home consumption	6,845,000	2,504,000,000
Total materials consumed	754,656,000	20,402,000,000
Net product	−418,171,000	+$ 4,181,000,000

SOURCES: Adapted from basic data as reported by the U. S. Department of Agriculture, Bureau of Agricultural Economics, 1950; U. S. Department of Commerce, Bureau of the Census, 1950.

NOTE: It may be observed from the above comparative accounts that while the ratio of materials consumed to foodstuffs realized was 2.2 to 1, with the ratio of dollar costs to dollars received being but 0.8 to 1, resulting in a monetary gain of approximately $10 for the net tonnage employed in the exchange.

TABLE VII-3. FARM LAND USE IN THE UNITED STATES, 1949

The total acres of land in the 5,382,134 farms in the United States
in 1949 have been accounted for as follows:

	Acres	Acres	Acres
Total land in farms			1,158,566,000
Cropland:			
Harvested	344,399,000		
Lying idle or fallow	64,108,000		
Used for pasture	69,332,000		
Total cropland		477,839,000	
Pasture:			
Not plowable	415,650,000		
Woodland pastured	134,715,000		
Total pastured		550,365,000	
Forest and cut-over land		85,098,000	
Farmsteads, lanes, and wasteland		45,264,000	
Total land in farms			1,158,566,000
Total food-producing land accounted for:			
Cropland harvested			344,399,000
Less cotton acreage harvested		27,439,000	
Less flax acreage harvested		5,048,000	
Less tobacco acreage harvested		1,623,000	
Total non-food acres			34,110,000
Plus acreage in orchards & vineyards		5,145,000	
Plus acreage in vegetable & truck crops		3,718,000	
Total			8,863,000
Plus cropland used for pasture		69,332,000	
Plus pasture not plowable		415,650,000	
Plus woodland pasture		134,715,000	
Total land used for pasture			619,697,000
Grand total			938,849,000
Less acreage devoted to export [a]			99,858,000
Total domestic			838,991,000

[a] See accompanying tabulation, Table VII-3a.

parisons between the actual physical and the representative monetary equivalent are
shown. Here will be noted the rather high element of deception inherent in the
generally accepted pecuniary interpretation of net product and the more fundamental material *deficit* that actually accrued. A glance at Table VII-3a will disclose
that nearly 30 per cent of all U.S. cropland harvested was also devoted to exports
during the same year. If this were to be placed on a per-acre basis and applied to the
entire world, even after allowances for the less mechanized equipment, the average
annual dissipation must necessarily be enormous.

NOTE TO TABLE VII-3a.   ACRES DEVOTED TO PRODUCING FOODSTUFFS FOR EXPORT,
U. S. A., 1949

	Total acres	Pounds produced (000)	Pounds exported (000)	Per cent exported	Acres devoted to export
Corn	85,602,000	189,156,240	7,314,415	3.9%	3,338,478
Wheat	75,910,000	68,787,780	30,267,420	44.0	33,400,400
Hay	71,051,000	198,610,000	41,059,110	20.7	14,707,557
Oats	39,236,000	42,333,568	804,096	1.9	745,484
Soybeans	10,482,000	2,879,460	2,707,637	94.0	9,853,080
Sorghums	10,225,000	7,631,500	1,723,950	22.6	2,310,850
Barley	9,872,000	11,428,992	1,322,736	11.6	1,145,152
Peanuts	2,302,000	1,875,825	470,176	25.1	577,802
Beans	1,885,000	2,155,100	186,494	8.6	162,110
Rice	1,857,000	4,011,300	914,110	22.8	423,396
Rye	1,554,000	1,047,032	304,136	29.0	450,660
Buckwheat	269,000	452,920	38,168	8.4	22,596
Hops	38,000	49,819	20,264	40.7	15,466
Livestock[a]	758,568,000	51,132,791	2,123,747	4.2	31,859,856
Vegetables	3,718,000	54,518,080	1,195,477	2.2	81,796
Fruits	5,145,000	38,854,000	1,131,289	2.9	149,205
Sugar	1,026,000	1,040,000	161,616	15.6	160,056
Cottonseed oil	27,719,000	13,226,000	275,769	2.1	582,099
Tree nuts	3,812,000	413,214	13,007	3.1	118,172
Total[b]	1,110,271,000	689,603,621	92,033,617	13.3%[c]	100,104,215

SOURCE: Statistical Abstract of the United States, 1953.

Pasture	619,697,000
Other acres included in field crops	138,871,000
Total	758,568,000

[a] Includes other acres devoted to producing feed for livestock; see accompanying Table VII-3.

[b] The difference between total acreage shown here and total shown in preceding table represents double cropping, and acreage devoted to cotton, tobacco, and flax.

[c] Because of the variation in pounds produced per acre the percentage exported will not precisely equal the total acres devoted to export as shown in column five above.

129

LIMITED VERSUS ABSOLUTE SCARCITY

The scarcity of a material good is sometimes absolute, since the existing supply of it cannot be augmented. In other words, when it is used up, it cannot be replaced. As a rule, in the past it has been possible to produce an ever-increasing supply of raw materials and produce new goods of the same and even of an improved sort, and then augment the supply or replace the waste.

Since a good which is identical with another existing or used-up good clearly cannot be produced, then this scarcity can only be overcome if various specimens of the same kind of article can be *substituted* for each other. An old painting may be copied, but if the demand is for the original, the painting is irreplaceable. Apart from these circumstances, the replaceability of a material good depends entirely on the technical possibilities of producing one like it. In this respect the world has witnessed a tremendous substitution over the first half of the present century. One has only to scan the list of materials produced in the 1882 period and compare it with the broader list of today to note the extent of these substitutions.

Most material goods are, as economists still say, in this sense reproducible. However, this is not possible, save only in a qualified sense, in the case of land and many other given materials in nature.

At the turn of the century, when Gustav Cassel was beginning his outline of *The Theory of Social Economy,* it was the general inclination of economists, who thought they were taking the whole world into account, to view land as more than abundant for the needs of the human race. That there was then a scarcity they viewed as largely due to technical or local difficulties in the utilization of the existing land. With faith in an ability to overcome the difficulties, they did not view the scarcity of agricultural land as absolute. The same kind of thinking was applied to coal, petroleum, and wood products at that time. *Relative* scarcity was admitted, *absolute* scarcity was not. Again, in other words, this meant that while we were then living in a world of *relative values,* aside from the original paintings of the old masters we had no such thing as *absolute values* to contend with.

THE END OF FAMINES FORECAST IN 1889

"The day of famines for the people of all countries has passed forever," wrote Professor Wells in his *Recent Economic Changes,* published in 1889. Since that confident reassurance to the peoples of the world there have been eight major famines recorded, with a death toll of some 93 million human beings and some 151 million head of livestock. (See Encyclopaedia Britannica, 1948 edition, Vol. 9, pages 62–63.) The most terrible famine in the whole of the recorded history of the human race occurred some 30 years later in Southeast Russia, in 1921 and 1922, when over 15 million people perished. In addition, famines have recurred in China and India through all time.

THE MEANING OF MAN'S VAST PROCESS OF PRODUCTION

The world's urban building land area is essentially the outcome of man's productive activity. The relative scarcity of urban land is an important independent limitation on the existing supply of land, and as such is a factor in the process of production and distribution.

While the Food and Agriculture Organization has accounted for but 8.2 per cent of the world's inhabitable land area as urban built-on land, nevertheless, allowing for differences in definition, the total of such land approximates one-seventh of the present land surface of the earth, or about 13.6 per cent. Also about 1125 million, or nearly one-half, of the world's people live in urban areas, with the drift from rural to urban centers being quite significant since the turn of the century, as the Table VII–4 reveals.

TABLE VII–4.   CHANGES IN URBAN AND BUILT-ON LAND ACREAGE OF THE WORLD, 1882–1952

	1882	1952	Change	% Change
Categories:				
Industrial	32,235,000	335,780,000	+ 303,545,000	+ 941.7%
Military lands	181,700,000	850,392,000	+ 668,692,000	+ 368.0
Streets & Highways	43,720,000	131,294,000	+ 87,574,000	+ 200.3
Institutional	213,139,000	525,677,000	+ 312,538,000	+ 146.6
Railroads	51,914,000	120,730,000	+ 68,816,000	+ 132.6
Reservoirs	23,390,000	325,813,000	+ 302,423,000	+1,293.0
Other urban	397,994,000	516,875,000	+ 118,881,000	+ 29.9
Parks	889,460,000	775,690,000	− 113,770,000	− 12.8
Airports	–	45,274,000	+ 45,274,000	–
Total urban	1,833,552,000	3,627,525,000	+1,793,973,000	+ 97.8%
Farmsteads	347,092,000	424,318,000	+ 77,226,000	+ 22.2
Total built-on	2,180,644,000	4,051,843,000	+1,871,199,000	+ 85.8%

SOURCES: The chief sources have been the various reports of the Food and Agriculture Organization of the United Nations, supplemented by the reports of the U. S. Office of Foreign Agricultural Relations, and the Bureau of Agricultural Economics whose work now extends back over a period of thirty years. Various reports of the U. S. Bureau of Foreign and Domestic Commerce, the *Statistical Abstract for the British Commonwealth,* the *Statesman's Yearbook,* the various standard Atlases, the *Encyclopaedia Europa,* the *Encyclopaedia Britannica,* Mulhall's *Dictionary of Statistics,* and the United Nations *Demographic Yearbook.*

NOTE: In this wide sweep of the world's over-all pattern of urban and built-on land utilization there has been the utmost variation and development of the urban and near-urban use of land. Historically the pattern has changed as physical, economic, and social conditions have changed with an ever-increasing population. With the advance of industrialism the demands for urban land area and its development, has increased at a far more rapid rate than has the development of the world's food-producing cropland. (See Table III–1, Land chapter, for comparisons.) Over 1½ billion more land acres are devoted to urban land than to cropland, with this increase progressing at a more rapid rate than the population.

INDUSTRIAL LAND: Contains manufacturing plants, open-cut mining areas, and working facilities surrounding underground mining, sand, gravel, stone, and other quarries.

OTHER URBAN: Contains residential, commercial, and warehouse structures.

INSTITUTIONAL: Contains educational, hospitalization, religious, charitable, and correctional institutions.

The Statistical Office of the Department of Economic Affairs of the United Nations has recently made a revealing summary of the rates of urbanization covering 100 countries and territories, ranging over a 50-year period. As this study has covered about two-thirds of the world's population, its findings may be regarded as representative of the whole. While international comparisons of the relative magnitudes are affected by variations in definition, nevertheless the existence of direction may be safely compared. These tables are published in full in the *Demographic Yearbook,* 1952, of the United Nations. They further reveal the highly urbanized countries of the world to be approaching a "saturation point."

Urbanization as a result of industrialization brings with it a demand for land that, it will be noted, has increased as fast as the population itself, and at a rate some 17 per cent faster than the development of agricultural cropland. (See Table III–1.)

Production further requires the use of machines, factory buildings, storehouses, transport equipment, and prepared or half-manufactured goods—in short, materials which are themselves the result of production, and, like land, are a definite part of the means of production. The relative scarcity of the existing supply of both such goods and land at any given time presents a new limitation on the possibilities of production.

In the production process itself there are a number of transport operations—in the pig-iron and steel industry, or in agriculture and forestry, for instance, the innumerable transport operations within the process cannot be separated from them. Also the ultimate transport operations which convey the finished goods to the consumers are considered as a part of the great process of production. Production as a whole is to be regarded as a special side of the world's human economy—the creation of goods for the satisfaction of human wants—and cannot be confined to the creation or transformation process only. All services that directly satisfy needs are conceived as productive activities, and are commonly described as integral parts of the total process of production along with the mechanical power and energy required in the process. All have a share in the great economic process of satisfying needs.

The extension of the industrial system calls for production on a continuously widening scale, and a continuously increasing variety of both materials and services. The projection of modern mechanized civilization into the hitherto undeveloped areas of the world was, by 1952, in full swing.

In order to appreciate fully the significance of the world's productive demands the fundamental changes in the world's industrial production power, as shown in Detail VII–A are enlightening:

DETAIL VII–A

Year	Land-Power Acres	Mechanical Horsepower	Industrial Manpower
1952	335,780,000	62,310,892,000	157,500,000
1882	32,235,000	517,180,000	59,900,000
+70	+303,545,000	+61,793,712,000	+97,600,000

It will be noted that the increase in manpower working in the world's mines and quarries, forests, factories, and transportation was some 163 per cent, the increase in land-power area some 940 per cent, and the increase in mechanical horsepower— the equivalent of an inanimate slave-working population—nearly 12,000 per cent.

This vast increase in the means of production introduces an entirely new factor in the mounting population problem that Malthus and other earlier economists had not fully appreciated. If this were to continue at the same rate for the next 70 years, the productive capacity demands would be approximately as follows:

Year: 2022
Acres: 3,497,823,000
Horsepower: 7,251,890,000,000
Manpower: 414,067,000

Taking into consideration the present direct and indirect land requirements for food production and industrial and urban land requirements, omitting forest requirements completely, and allowing for the present rate of geological land erosion and population increase, we find the requirements some 70 years from now to be as tabulated in Detail VII–B.

DETAIL VII–B

Year 2022	Acres	Acres
Total available land surface of the earth		27,000,000,000
Industrial land area required	3,497,823,000	
Other urban land area required	1,874,662,000	
Food-producing land required	25,934,232,000	
Requirements at present living standards		31,308,000,000
Apparent land shortage		−4,308,000,000

See Table VII–4.

THE RELATION OF RAW MATERIAL RESERVES TO PRODUCTION

The materials found in nature, from which new material goods is produced are called *raw materials*. And the economic activity involved in getting these raw materials from nature is included in what the economist calls *production*.

This brings us to the question of raw material *reserves*. The practical miner and metallurgist is only indirectly interested in geological data on absolute totals. He is in business to make a profit. To him coal and ore are only mineral deposits whose exploitation yields a profit. In the case of coal, its mining requires transportation, and transport requires energy. The energy lodged in coal came originally from the sun, hence it is viewed as the product of past solar radiation; in fact it was *made* ages before the advent of man. The practical man views it as having been made without any expenditure of human energy; therefore the coal has an inherent advantage over other sources of energy, in that the coal raised and transported with the aid of coal may be said to raise and move itself. In other words, this raising of coal by itself is looked upon as "free" energy. The coal reserves may be used up more quickly—but the coal available for energy production over and above transportation is still viewed conveniently as a "net product." The same is held to be true of petroleum and natural gas.

NEED OF CAUTION IN THE INTERPRETATION OF COAL RESERVES

The miner works only those deposits whose exploitation is profitable under existing circumstances, regardless of quantity. Nevertheless quantitative data on mineral reserves, to be of practical value to the business world, must be interpreted in the light of economic realities. Statistical data on mineral reserves should be used with the greatest of care lest they create a false impression of the extent and accuracy of our present knowledge of the world's mineral reserves. Unless duly warned, the layman to whom the various findings on the world's coal reserves are presented in orderly columns of figures is apt to form an exaggerated opinion of their dependability. See Table VII–5 on Reserves.

TABLE VII–5.　THE WORLD'S BASIC INDUSTRIAL
MINERAL RESERVES, 1952

	Total world reserves (*Net tons*)
Metallic minerals:	
Aluminum	1,543,235,400
Antimony	3,858,089
Barium	106,451,000
Chromite	110,231,100
Cobalt	98,680,000
Columbium	267,523,600
Copper	220,462,200
Iron	142,019,544,618
Lead	45,000,000
Magnesium	2,602,137,000
Manganese	556,500,000
Mercury	131,480
Molybdenum	9,076,700
Nickel	7,857,143
Strontium	35,484,000
Thorium	45,774,000
Tin	7,280,000
Titanium	200,480,000
Tungsten	4,938,357
Uranium	215,700,000
Vanadium	271,820
Zinc	80,000,000
Total metallic minerals	148,180,616,507
Non-metallic minerals:	
Calcium	3,784,900,000
Fluorspar	67,000,000
Graphite	5,200,000,000
Phosphate (rock)	28,660,086,000
Potash	5,511,555,000
Sodium	2,838,695,000
Sulphur	78,400,000
Total non-metallic minerals	46,140,636,000
Fuels:	
Uranium	215,700,000
Coal	569,934,000,000
Natural gas	76,500,000,000
Natural gasoline	817,272,960
Petroleum	85,000,000,000
Total fuels	732,466,972,960
Grand total	926,788,225,467

SOURCES: University of Maryland, Department of Geography, Dr. William Van Royen; U. S. Bureau of Mines, Dr. Elmer W. Pehrson; The President's Materials Policy Commission Report, 1952.

By far the most comprehensive compilation of data ever made pertaining to the coal resources of the world was presented to the Twelfth International Geological Congress at Toronto, Canada, in 1913. Since that date the U. S. Geological Survey, the U. S. Department of State, and Dr. Pehrson of the U. S. Bureau of Mines have made comprehensive estimates of high reliability. Detail VII–C gives these estimates in short tons.

DETAIL VII–C

Year	Tons of Reserves	Authorities Supplying Data
1913	8,154,404,046,000	Twelfth International Geological Congress
1949	6,230,173,587,000	The President's Materials Policy Commission, 1952
1949	5,693,436,315,000	Dr. Elmer Walter Pehrson, U. S. Bureau of Mines
1949	4,992,068,895,000	U. S. Department of State

On the question of supply, it is not so much the duration of the world's ultimate resources of coal that matters, but rather how long will the better and more cheaply mixed coals last. When considered from the practical point of view, in the light of the theoretical assumption underlying most reserve estimates, it has recently been found by several authorities that all previous data have been exaggerated to the extent of nearly 90 per cent. This proportion has been confirmed by Dr. Clifford C. Furnas, Chancellor of the University of Buffalo.

Both the International Geological Congress and Dr. Edward A. Martin, F.G.S., of Great Britain, are in agreement that well over one-half of the world's coal-measures are not only unworkable but will always remain unattainable owing to the great depth and thickness of the strata. Working these measures out from the above admissions, and allowing for mine fires, coal left in mines, mine waste, and mining consumption, we secure the approximation of the probable coal reserves of the world as shown in Detail VII–D .

DETAIL VII–D

		Tons
Total reserves, 1949		5,693,436,315,000
Less volume that can never be mined	83.3%	4,742,632,450,000
Total available reserves		950,803,865,000
Less mine consumption and waste	41.0%	389,829,585,000
Total effective world coal reserves		560,974,280,000

When it is realized that it has taken over 15,000 years of geological processes to produce 1 inch of coal in the depth of the coal-measures, which constitute about 12 inches of the top-seams, and that since 1882 the people of the world have mined and consumed over 15 inches, or some 102 billion tons in the short span of 70 years, it will be seen that coal supplies—like land—are perilously near the absolute scarcity limit.

THE VAST CONFLAGRATION OF THE EARTH'S MATERIALS—CALLED PRODUCTION

In considering coal we have in reality been measuring the consumption of the world's past forests—in fact, vegetation. It has taken the geological processes of nature some 55 million years to actually *make,* through the biochemical lignification and the heat-friction-pressure processes, the world's supply of coal.

Were all the world's present forests uprooted and overthrown, to be covered by sedimentary deposits such as those which cover our present coal-seams, the amount of coal which would be thereby formed for use in some future age would amount to an aggregate thickness of some two or three inches. The world's present estimated coal-seams, under the surface of the ground-level, if placed one above the other in immediate succession, the world over, would amount to only 29 feet of coal—or about 100 times the present total standing forests. From this it is possible to form an idea of the enormous growths of vegetation required in the past to form the world's present diminishing coal-beds.

Along with the enormous quantity of coal that is brought to the surface and consumed annually, goes some 22.6 pounds per ton of 12 other valuable minerals. (See Table VII–2.) Recent analytical surveys of the U. S. Geological Survey have disclosed that the coal extractive industries of the world have been throwing away many of the earth's rare elements. This unintentional waste occurs because coal, in addition to its heating qualities, is also a natural storehouse for boron, titanium, nickel, copper, cobalt, and seven other valuable minerals including germanium, which is widely used in electronics in the manufacture of crystal diodes and transistors. These valuable minerals are present in most coals at the rate of nearly 23 pounds per ton, which means that over the past 70 years there has been wasted in the world well over 1 billion tons of minerals, and they are still being wasted at the rate of about 25 million tons per year.

SUBSIDIZING WASTE

As Zimmermann has pointed out, it has long been a strange spectacle to see the coal producing nations of the world behave, in the name of "business is business," as though their coal reserves were not the most valuable gift of nature, but rather a curse to be gotten rid of or passed on to other nations. Some governments have even rewarded their coal producers by paying them a premium on every ton which they ship out of the country. The cartels and coal syndicates have rewarded their members with a premium for coal exports at the expense of the domestic consumer. A strange anomaly of the "modern" profit and loss economy.

Despite the fact that coal mining is an extractive industry subject to the supreme law of all extractive industries—the law of diminishing returns—internal competition has long made for wasteful mining practices. The philosophy of *laissez faire,* which advocates unbridled competition, and the arguments of *rationalization,* which put a premium on the full utilization of the existing capacity, both become important factors in the promotion of overproduction, while neither seem to care about protecting and serving the public at large, either present or future.

THE WORLD'S WOOD, A LARGE FACTOR IN INDUSTRY

Nor is this sort of waste omitted from the profligate destruction of the world's forests, also in the name of production. The world production of wood amounts, on the average, to nearly 1½ billion tons of wood per year. This is at the rate of nearly one-half a ton per capita, or a yearly cut of 7.5 cubic feet per acre of forest. Of this over one-half, or some 60 per cent, is firewood, with the remaining 40 per cent used as saw-timber.

This is but a part of the picture, for the total annual drain, due to wood's waste and millwaste, brings the figure up to nearly 5 times the amount actually realized. In fact, the woodwaste in relation to the available supply is almost exactly the same proportion as that of the losses in coal mining—40 per cent.

THE CONFLICT BETWEEN A VEGETABLE AND A MINERAL BASED CIVILIZATION

As man has "progressed" through the use of mechanical power and the ability to tap the earth's store of energy, his capacity for "mastering" natural obstacles has increased manifold with the result that over a large part of the world he has viewed the forest as "conquered." Unfortunately, it is not only conquered, it has been virtually exterminated beyond much more than a possible chance of natural recovery.

The struggle of an ever-mounting population for new food-producing lands to sustain its increasing numbers has made great inroads on the world's forest lands. So much so, in fact, that scarcely one-third of the original accessible productive forest land now stands intact. The disappearance of the world's forests has not done away with the use of wood; on the contrary, it has intensified it.

As populations grow, living standards rise, and human wants become more complex, wood consumption increases in spite of the extensive and growing use of substitute materials, and in spite of the tendency to utilize wood more economically. These rapid inroads on the forests, aside from depriving the thickly settled countries of timber needed for their industries, have produced other economic and social effects of more profound concern than is generally recognized.

The stripping and "timber-mining" of the world's forests, which have accompanied the growth of industrialism, have resulted in an increase of land erosion, and in floods, and in a general change in the continental system of stream and water flow to the seas, with consequent effect upon the world's hydrologic cycle and general climate. Many authorities have considered this factor responsible for the physical deterioration of a large part of the world's population.

With about $2\frac{1}{4}$ billion acres of productive forest area in the world, and some $7\frac{1}{2}$ billion acres of presently inaccessible forest land, it would seem that there is enough timber to last for centuries. This would be true if all kinds of wood were capable of satisfying human wants and meeting the present timber requirements. However, in compiling an inventory of the world's wood resources vast areas of virgin forests must be left out of the account, because in their present condition there is no net growth in them.

CONSUMPTION IN THE PROCESS OF PRODUCTION

Etymologically the term "production" implies the act of bringing forth, and from J. R. McCulloch's definition, in his *Principles of Political Economy* in 1825, on down to the present this has been the generally accepted idea of production. Since McCulloch's definition is one rather difficult to improve on it may be well to state it here:

By production, in the science of political economy, we are not to understand the production of matter, for that is the exclusive attribute of nature, but the production of utility, and consequenly of exchangeable value, by appropriating and modifying matter already in existence, so as to fit it to satisfy your wants. . . .

TABLE VII-6. CHANGES IN PRODUCTION OF THE WORLD'S PRINCIPAL INDUSTRIAL MATERIALS, 1882–1952

(In Net Tons)

	1882	1952	Change	% Change
Sand & gravel	1,480,000,000	6,382,000,000	+ 4,902,000,000	+ 331.2%
Stone	1,203,024,000	3,771,576,000	+ 2,568,552,000	+ 213.5
Cement	721,932,000	4,304,831,000	+ 3,582,899,000	+ 496.3
Coal & lignite	423,287,000	2,211,000,000	+ 1,787,713,000	+ 422.3
Wood	1,122,486,000	1,403,107,000	+ 280,621,000	+ 25.0
Clay	312,377,000	782,900,000	+ 470,523,000	+ 150.6
Petroleum	211,000	690,000,000	+ 689,789,000	+326,914.2
Iron	23,752,000	120,515,000	+ 96,763,000	+ 407.4
Salt	35,128,000	46,405,000	+ 11,277,000	+ 32.1
Gypsum	8,102,000	27,007,000	+ 18,905,000	+ 233.3
Phosphate	6,595,000	21,275,000	+ 14,680,000	+ 222.6
Pyrites	3,361,000	10,472,000	+ 7,111,000	+ 211.6
Bauxite	a	8,267,000	+ 8,267,000	–
Sulphur	1,687,000	6,250,000	+ 4,563,000	+ 270.5
Nitrogen	876,000	4,362,000	+ 3,486,000	+ 397.9
Potash	887,000	4,169,000	+ 3,282,000	+ 370.0
Feldspar	783,000	2,899,000	+ 2,116,000	+ 270.2
Copper	124,000	2,480,000	+ 2,356,000	+ 1,900.0
Zinc	110,000	2,039,000	+ 1,929,000	+ 1,753.6
Chrome	25,000	1,989,000	+ 1,964,000	+ 7,856.0
Talc	391,000	1,709,000	+ 1,318,000	+ 337.1
Lead	2,497,000	1,653,000	− 844,000	− 33.8
Manganese	6,000	1,565,000	+ 1,559,000	+ 25,983.3
Aluminum	a	1,433,000	+ 1,433,000	–
Magnesite	345,000	1,323,000	+ 978,000	+ 283.5
Asbestos	176,000	1,174,000	+ 998,000	+ 567.0
Fluorspar	309,000	1,055,000	+ 746,000	+ 241.4
Tin	31,500	181,000	+ 149,500	+ 474.6
Graphite	66,880	176,000	+ 109,120	+ 163.2
Nickel	425,000	131,000	− 294,000	− 69.2
Mica	981,000	111,000	− 870,000	− 88.7
Arsenic	15,000	56,000	+ 41,000	+ 273.3
Antimony	5,849	42,000	+ 36,151	+ 618.1
Tungsten	1,240	20,000	+ 18,760	+ 1,512.9
Silver	1,145	6,000	+ 4,855	+ 424.0
Mercury	952	5,000	+ 4,048	+ 425.2
Molybdenum	258	1,862	+ 1,604	+ 621.7
Gold	84	832	+ 748	+ 890.5
Diamonds	92	58	− 34	− 37.0
Platinum	a	10	+ 10	–
	5,350,000,000	19,814,185,762	+14,464,185,762	+ 270.0%

SOURCES: United Nations Statistical Yearbook, 1952; *Encyclopedia of Social Reform*, 1908; Mulhall's *Dictionary of Statistics*, 1883.
ᵃ No data.

TABLE VII–7. CHANGES IN THE WORLD'S AGRICULTURAL PRODUCTION OF PRINCIPAL FOODSTUFFS, 1882–1952

(In Net Tons)

	1882	1952	Change	% Change
Eggs	334,900,000	620,160,000	+285,260,000	+ 85.2%
Milk [a]	186,788,000	273,423,000	+ 86,635,000	+ 46.4
Wheat, millet	88,672,000	180,984,000	+ 92,312,000	+104.1
Potatoes	131,410,000	180,228,000	+ 48,818,000	+ 37.1
Rice	45,792,000	169,535,000	+123,743,000	+270.2
Corn	78,196,000	145,615,000	+ 67,419,000	+ 86.2
Oats	45,802,000	55,446,000	+ 9,644,000	+ 21.1
Barley	25,733,000	51,147,000	+ 25,414,000	+ 98.8
Meats, poultry, fish [b]	32,012,000	50,814,000	+ 18,802,000	+ 58.7
Cassava	36,500,000	40,629.000	+ 4,129,000	+ 11.3
Grapes [c]	25,200,000	34,943,000	+ 9,743,000	+ 38.7
Sugar	13,000,000	34,282,000	+ 21,282,000	+163.7
All other tree crops [d]	26,138,000	32,673,000	+ 6,535,000	+ 25.0
All other truck crops	20,900,000	26,138,000	+ 5,238,000	+ 25.1
Rye	39,608,000	21,164,000	− 18,444,000	− 46.6
Sorghum	16,640,000	20,800,000	+ 4,160,000	+ 25.0
Soybeans	6,267,000	15,213,000	+ 8,946,000	+142.7
Citrus fruits	9,713,000	14,077,000	+ 4,364,000	+ 44.9
Beans	9,736,000	12,125,000	+ 2,389,000	+ 24.5
Peanuts	9,000,000	11,224,000	+ 2,224,000	+ 24.7
Peas	9,012,000	11,224,000	+ 2,212,000	+ 24.5
Bananas	7,518,000	10,912,000	+ 3,394,000	+ 45.1
Cotton seed	4,800,000	10,725,000	+ 5,925,000	+123.4
Butter	1,832,000	2,675,000	+ 843,000	+ 46.0
Coffee	1,314,000	2,348,000	+ 1,034,000	+ 78.7
Margarine	–	2,040,000	+ 2,040,000	–
Sunflower seed	1,983,000	2,039,000	+ 56,000	+ 2.8
Sesame seed	773,000	1,863,000	+ 1,090,000	+141.0
Palm oil	604,000	1,455,000	+ 851,000	+140.9
Olives & olive oil	1,126,000	1,157,000	+ 31,000	+ 2.8
Cheese	734,000	1,072,000	+ 338,000	+ 46.0
Dates	900,000	925,000	+ 25,000	+ 2.8
Coconuts	403,000	695,000	+ 292,000	+ 72.5
Tea	580,000	591,000	+ 11,000	+ 1.9
Figs	504,000	518,000	+ 14,000	+ 2.8
Hops	101,000	57,000	− 44,000	− 43.6
Total	1,214,191,000	2,040,916,000	+826,725,000	+ 68.1%

SOURCES: 1882: Mulhall's *Dictionary of Statistics*, 1883; 1952: Food and Agriculture Organization of the United Nations.

[a] Whole milk; [b] Meats: beef, pork, mutton, and lamb; [c] Grapes used for wine, and all other grapes; [d] Fruit and nut crops.

William Stanley Jevons, nearly a half a century later in his *Theory of Political Economy,* 1871, stated: "Production is one of the very few happily chosen terms which the economist possesses."

Though this definition of "production" is apparently simple enough, the treatment of the subject has varied from time to time in proportion to the changes which economic science has itself undergone. During this time much discussion has centered around not what is *productive* or *unproductive,* but the relative importance of the functions of *production* and *distribution.*

TABLE VII–8. CHANGES IN THE WORLD'S AGRICULTURAL PRODUCTION OF INDUSTRIAL PRODUCTS, 1882–1952

(*In Net Tons*)

1952 Rank	1882	1952	Change	% Change
Industrial fibers:				
Wood [a]	100,250,000	40,290,000	− 59,960,000	− 59.8%
Cotton	3,998,000	8,929,000	+ 4,931,000	+ 123.3
Wool	1,322,000	1,812,000	+ 490,000	+ 37.1
Rayon (fiber)	–	1,747,000	+ 1,747,000	–
Jute	1,522,000	1,565,000	+ 43,000	+ 2.8
Hides & skins (leather)	1,126,000	882,000	− 244,000	− 21.7
Sisal	300,000	309,000	+ 9,000	+ 3.0
Hemp	278,000	286,000	+ 8,000	+ 2.9
Flax (linen)	150,000	220,000	+ 70,000	+ 46.7
Mohair	221,000	201,000	− 20,000	− 9.1
Henequen	123,000	132,000	+ 9,000	+ 7.3
Abaca	86,000	89,000	+ 3,000	+ 3.5
Kapoc	40,000	44,000	+ 4,000	+ 10.0
Silk	23,000	20,000	− 3,000	− 13.0
Total	109,439,000	56,526,000	− 52,913,000	− 48.3%
Other industrial products:				
Rapeseed	2,255,000	5,434,000	+ 3,179,000	+ 141.0%
Tobacco	1,100,000	3,307,000	+ 2,207,000	+ 200.6
Linseed	1,952,000	2,866,000	+ 914,000	+ 46.8
Rubber	41,000	2,072,000	+ 2,031,000	+4,953.7
Total	5,348,000	13,679,000	+ 8,331,000	+ 155.8%
Total above	114,787,000	70,205,000	− 44,582,000	− 38.8%
Total foodstuffs [b]	1,214,181,000	2,040,916,000	+826,735,000	+ 68.1%
Total agriculture	1,328,968,000	2,111,121,000	+782,153,000	+ 58.9%

[a] Largely logs, fence posts, and firewood produced on farms. [b] See Table VII–7.

Since the "appropriation and modifying of matter already in existence" requires transport operations within the process itself, later economists have advocated the inclusion of all such operations in the productive process on down to the ultimate transport which conveys the goods to the consumer—which some now call "commerce" or "trade"—as a part of the great process of production. (See Gustav Cassel, *Theory of the Social Economy,* p. 21.) Production in this modern broader sense is thus not confined exclusively to "the modifying of matter already in existence," but has come to include all services that contribute directly to the satisfying of human wants.

Although this definition of productivity has been disputed, nevertheless it has been accepted as satisfactory from the standpoint of monetary measures of production. As a result the physical quantitative measures actually involved in physical production have tended to become more and more obscured, particularly as they relate to the physical materials consumed. The total physical quantitatives involved in production are the data to watch, not their monetary exchange valuation. In the end, insofar as mankind's relationship to the earth's materials is concerned, all of his "production" is consumed. It is only "money" and man that appear to be inexhaustible.

TABLE VII–9. CHANGES IN THE WORLD'S MONEY SUPPLY, POPULATION, AND PRODUCTIVE LAND, 1882–1952

	1882	1952	Change	% Change
Money supply:				
Africa	48,755,000	2,209,230,000	+ 2,160,475,000	+ 4,431.3%
America, North	1,340,768,000	137,309,374,000	+135,968,606,000	+10,141.1%
America, South	60,944,000	14,337,092,000	+ 14,276,148,000	+23,425.0
Asia	1,121,370,000	24,185,700,000	+ 23,064,330,000	+ 2,056.8
Europe	3,431,147,000	70,133,518,000	+ 66,702,371,000	+ 1,944.0
Oceania	91,416,000	3,852,341,000	+ 3,760,925,000	+ 4,114.1
Total	6,094,400,000	252,027,255,000	+245,932,855,000	+ 4,035.4%
Population:				
Africa	205,823,000	206,559,000	+ 736,000	+ .4%
America, North	71,495,000	227,208,000	+ 155,713,000	+ 217.8
America, South	28,920,000	115,098,000	+ 86,178,000	+ 298.0
Asia	795,591,000	1,354,288,000	+ 558,697,000	+ 70.2
Europe	327,743,000	574,900,000	+ 247,157,000	+ 75.4
Oceania	4,232,000	13,227,000	+ 8,995,000	+ 212.5
Total	1,433,804,000	2,491,280,000	+ 1,057,476,000	+ 73.8%
Productive land:[a]				
Africa	1,937,785,000	2,237,192,000	+ 299,407,000	+ 15.5%
America, North	2,320,781,000	2,389,861,000	+ 69,080,000	+ 3.0
America, South	2,590,561,000	1,718,200,000	− 872,361,000	− 33.7
Asia	3,180,211,000	2,037,877,000	− 1,142,334,000	− 35.9
Europe	1,998,677,000	978,283.000	− 1,020,394,000	− 51.1
Oceania	1,488,439,000	999,579,000	− 488,860,000	− 32.8
Total	13,516,454,000	10,360,992,000	− 3,155,462,000	− 23.3%

SOURCES: International Monetary Fund, 1952; Food and Agriculture Organization of the United Nations, 1950; Mulhall's *Dictionary of Statistics*, 1883.
NOTE: For breakdown of productive land see accompanying tabulation, Table VII–11.

[a] Acres of productive forests, pasture land, crop land, and orchards.

During the 70-year period from 1882 to 1952, while the world's production of principal industrial materials rose some 270 per cent the world's money supply had increased some 4035 per cent, as will be noted in Tables VII–6, VII–7, VII–8 and VII–9. Meanwhile the world's per capita production of foodstuffs had declined nearly 12 per cent, the per capita productive land supply had declined nearly 60 per cent, total forest reserves had declined 70 per cent, and the supply of exhaustible basic industrial mineral reserves had declined fully 100 per cent. From all standpoints of ordinary prudence, regardless of the morals underlying human responsibility, this procedure can scarcely be viewed as commendable.

TABLE VII-10. SUMMARY OF CHANGES IN PRINCIPAL INDUSTRIAL AND AGRICULTURAL MATERIALS PRODUCED, 1882–1952

(*In Total Tons, Tons Per Capita, and Acreage*)

	1882		1952		Change		% Change
Total short tons:							
Industrial materials	5,350,000,000	80.1%	19,796,186,000	90.4%	+14,446,186,000	95.0%	+270.0%
Agricultural materials	1,328,968,000	19.9	2,111,121,000	9.6	+ 782,153,000	5.0	+ 58.9
Total	6,678,968,000	100.0%	21,907,307,000	100.0%	+15,228,339,000	100.0%	+228.0%
Per capita:							
Industrial materials	3.7		7.9		+	4.2	+113.3%
Agricultural foodstuffs	.9		.8		−	.1	− 11.1
Total	4.7		8.8		+	4.1	+ 87.2%
Land use in acres:							
Top-soil for industry	7,702,650,000	47.5%	2,358,739,000	10.1%	− 5,343,911,000		− 69.4%
Sub-soil for industry [a]	2,798,835,000	17.2	13,104,146,000	55.8	+10,305,311,000		+368.2
Total for industry	10,501,485,000	64.7%	15,462,885,000	65.9%	+ 4,961,400,000		+ 47.2%
Total for foodstuffs	5,782,871,000	35.3	8,002,253,000	34.1	+ 2,273,382,000		+ 39.3
Grand total	16,284,356,000	100.0%	23,465,138,000	100.0%	+ 7,234,782,000		+ 44.6%

SOURCES: See Industrial and Agricultural Production and Land Use Tables for sources.
NOTE: Land Use figures inescapably contain some duplications.

[a] Compiled from the "Coal Area of the World," Century Book of Facts, 1900, p. 633; brought up to date from original data supplied the author by the late O. E. Baker.

TABLE VII-11. PRINCIPAL CATEGORIES OF PRODUCTIVE LAND ACREAGE, 1882–1952

	Productive forests	Pasture land	Crop land	Orchards	Total productive land	Per cent of total
1952:						
Africa	339,924,000	1,430,735,000	462,085,000	4,448,000	2,237,192,000	21.6%
America, North	746,616,000	1,040,310,000	595,522,000	7,413,000	2,389,861,000	23.1
America, South	633,435,000	847,568,000	158,147,000	79,050,000	1,718,200,000	16.6
Asia	307,405,000	869,807,000	854,982,000	5,683,000	2,037,877,000	19.7
Europe	222,228,000	306,410,000	416,039,000	33,606,000	978,283,000	9.4
Oceania	38,926,000	909,345,000	50,814,000	494,000	999,579,000	9.6
World total	2,288,534,000 [a]	5,404,175,000	2,537,589,000	130,694,000	10,360,992,000	100.0%
1882:						
Africa	797,458,000	851,641,000	285,118,000	3,568,000	1,937,785,000	14.3%
America, North	1,524,115,000	312,093,000	478,592,000	5,981,000	2,320,781,000	17.2
America, South	2,092,690,000	324,831,000	109,240,000	63,800,000	2,590,561,000	19.2
Asia	2,096,015,000	769,034,000	311,594,000	3,568,000	3,180,211,000	23.5
Europe	774,126,000	365,408,000	831,651,000	27,492,000	1,998,677,000	14.8
Oceania	283,459,000	1,184,091,000	20,365,000	524,000	1,488,439,000	11.0
World total	7,567,863,000	3,807,098,000	2,036,560,000	104,933,000	13,516,454,000	100.0%

SOURCES: 1952: *Yearbook of Food and Agricultural Statistics*, Vol. IV, Part I, and *Forest Resources of the World*, Food and Agriculture Organization of the United Nations; 1882: Mulhall's *Dictionary of Statistics*; *Forest Resources of the World*, Raphael Zon and W. N. Sparhawk; *Encyclopaedia Britannica*, 1948 ed., Vol. 9, page 502.

NOTE: "Productive forests," as distinguished between "other forests" and the "accessible" and "inaccessible" classifications of the F.A.O. World Forest Inventory, represents the forests upon which reliance for wood supplies of the future must be placed.

[a] The difference between this figure and that given in Table III-1 in the Land chapter, is that the latter table includes some public-owned wooded parks that are "accessible," but not to be presently classed as economically productive.

TABLE VII–12. PER CAPITA RELATIVE CHANGES IN THE WORLD'S MONEY AND PRODUCTIVE LAND SUPPLY, 1882–1952

(In U. S. Dollar Equivalents and in Acres of Land)

	Money supply				Productive land supply			
	1882	1952	Change	% Change	1882	1952	Change	% Change
Per capita:								
Africa	$ .24	$ 10.70	+$ 10.46	+4,358.3%	9.41	10.83	+ 1.42	+15.1%
America, North	18.75	604.33	+ 585.58	+3,123.1	32.46	10.52	− 21.94	−67.6
America, South	2.11	124.56	+ 122.45	+5,803.3	89.58	10.93	− 78.65	−87.8
Asia	1.41	17.86	+ 16.45	+1,166.6	4.00	1.50	− 2.50	−62.5
Europe	10.47	121.99	+ 111.52	+1,065.1	6.10	1.70	− 4.40	−72.1
Oceania	21.60	291.25	+ 269.65	+1,248.4	351.71	75.57	−276.14	−78.5
World total	$ 4.25	$101.16	+$ 96.91	+2,280.2%	9.43	4.16	− 5.27	−55.9%

NOTE: For sources and basic data see Table VII–9.

Many economists have believed that because one of the traditional
sections of books on economic theory is devoted to the exposition of
"The Theory of Production" there ought also to be a section of equal
status entitled "The Theory of Consumption."
—LINDLEY M. FRASER, *Economic Thought and Language*

VIII

Consumption

T HAS BEEN argued that consumption governs not only demand but, indirectly,
upply as well. The consuming public of the world has frequently been described
s a great "economic electorate," casting, through the daily purchases, the money
otes which determine how the world's capital and labor shall be distributed and
sed, which industries shall thrive and which shall perish.

The debate concerning whether consumption controls production or vice versa
an be misleading, as any dispute concerning which blade of the scissors does the
utting can be devoid of meaning. A more sensible policy is to view production and
onsumption, as interdependent, and in the world economy of today it has become
upremely important that a balance be maintained between them.

The funds that people as consumers have to spend originate from productive
ctivity. The wages and salaries, rent, interest, dividends, and profits which make
p consumer monetary incomes are derived, directly or indirectly, from industry and
griculture, and represent industrial and agricultural costs. The consumer repays all
f these sums to industry either by spending or by saving.

Modern industrial society, or "business" in the practical sense, has been likened to
unified system of which the most important constituent parts are the consumer,
he producer, the saver, and the institutions which serve as controls over the money
upply and credit. In this respect mutual interdependence is an essential part of the
ystem.

Consumption in its broadest sense means not onl ythe use of, but the *using up* of,
hings. Hence consumption is of a twofold kind. For in the process of production,
he means of production are themselves consumed. Tools, steel mills, railroads,
ridges, cars, engines, roadbeds are all "eaten up," as well as are the productive
owers of the soil. It is with this larger sense of consumption that we are here
oncerned.

Man is not the only consuming agent operating on earth. The great geologica and meteorological forces of erosion and metamorphic action, although sometime. aided by man, are always at work both within and upon the surface of the earth. Mar has thus far benefited by his appropriation of the results of these larger natura forces.

Consumption also involves the destruction and diminution of materials, and is this sense is precisely the opposite of production, whether it be in the interest o: production or not. A substance is consumed whether it be appropriated by man o by some other form of life or agency. Fuel is consumed by fire, food is burned up in the body, land is worn out, blown, or washed into the seas. Air itself is consumed and transformed in the bodies of plants and animals, and the engines of man. A all these demands can only work themselves out through the complex functiona structure of the world's consumption-production-exchange system, it would seem to be advisable that true economic science no longer neglect these forces and agents.

While nothing may perish in a cosmic sense, it is probably true that there are physical limits to the devastating powers of both man and nature. And in thi sense there is a capital decumulation as well as accumulation which sooner or late must be faced.

THERE CAN BE NO PRODUCTION WITHOUT CONSUMPTION

The resources of the earth are continuously being consumed. Marvelous and bountiful as it has been, it can no longer produce the "bread and butter of industry" —coal, oil, and iron—or the chemical nutrients of the food-giving soil, at a rat anywhere near that at which modern man has demonstrated his ability to consum them.

"Consumption is the sole end and purpose of all production," is the way Adar Smith summed up the matter, and then in his central charge against mercantilism continued, "and the interest of the producer ought to be attended to, only so far a it may be necessary for promoting that of the consumer. . . . But in the mercantil system the interest of the consumer is almost constantly sacrificed to that of th producer; and it seems to consider production, and not consumption, as the ultimat end and object of all industry and commerce."

THE PRODUCTION AND CONSUMPTION OF THE WORLD'S HUMAN POPULATION

No analysis of the production-consumption equation should ignore the "produc tion and consumption" of individual human beings. As we have carefully kep records of the annual production and consumption of domestic animals, so it woul seem that a like procedure might be established to cover the human population.

Over a span of years the turnover in the human population is enormous. In th accompanying Table VIII-1 an attempt has been made to ascertain the relativ magnitudes of this turnover during the 70-year period between 1882 and 1952. I Tables VIII-2 and VIII-3 the same data are treated both in "profit and loss" an in "inventory" forms.

Perhaps the most striking thing disclosed by this inventory comparison is the magnitude of human reproduction in relation to the enormity of human losses sustained over the period—losses almost equal to the entire human inventory at the end of the period. If this were to be interpreted in terms of change in inventory alone, as shown in Table VIII-3, with the 55,252,000 representing 100 at the beginning of the period, the inventory at the end of the period would be found to be 4,408.9 or an average annual rate of production approximating 61.5 per cent—

TABLE VIII-1. THE PRODUCTION AND CONSUMPTION OF THE WORLD'S HUMAN POPULATION, 1882–1952

	Number	%	Number	%
Gross production [a]			4,650,325,000	100.00%
Killed by natural causes:				
Disease, illness, maladies [b]	1,623,583,000	75.20%		34.91%
Stillbirths	98,040,000	4.54		2.11
Drought & famine	93,500,000	4.33		2.01
Senility	74,986,000	3.47		1.61
Deliveries [c]	13,600,000	.63		.29
Floods	9,000,000	.42		.19
Storms	2,500,000	.12		.06
Earthquakes	1,600,000	.07		.04
Total	1,916,809,000	88.78%		41.22%
Killed by man:				
Industrial accidents	102.675,000	4.76%		2.21%
Wars	60,950,000	2.82		1.31
Domestic accidents	36,100,000	1.67		.78
Transport accidents	20,422,000	.95		.44
Suicides	13,875,000	.64		.30
Homicides	5,550,000	.26		.12
Executions	2,664,000	.12		.05
Total	242,236,000	11.22%		5.21%
Grand total human consumption		100.00%	2,159,045,000	46.43%
Net remaining, end of period			2,491,280,000	53.57%

[a] See Note to Table VIII–2. In official birth statistics, each member of a multiple birth is counted separately. Stillbirths are not always recorded. It is generally agreed that a greater proportion of stillbirths than live births escape registration.
[b] Contains those classifications of diseases and other malignant pathological causes as classified according to the abridged list of the Fifth Revision of the International List of Causes of Deaths. See *Manual of the Statistical Classification of Diseases, Injuries and Causes of Death*, Vols. I and II, World Health Organization, Geneva, 1948.
[c] Death of mothers due to complications of pregnancy.

rate far in excess of any other known productivity relating to man's economic endeavors. On the other hand, of the total human beings produced over the period 47 per cent were consumed. Nevertheless, in terms of supply and consumption, the ratio of human supply to consumption was 2.1 to 1.

In the light of those who proclaim that population is self-regulatory, due to wars, pestilence, famine, and other disasters, it appears that these "regulators" have thus far had little more than a moderate effect.

The idea of obtaining symmetry and equilibrium between the factors of supply and the factors of demand has played a considerable part in the development of economic theory. Such a concept has been valuable and important, but it cannot be taken for granted without further examination. In such vitally important quantity ratios as those existing between land, natural resources, labor, and population complete symmetrical balance no longer exists. Marx went so far as to argue that precisely because, in equilibrium, demand and supply are equal, they "cancel each other out." "Therefore," said Marx, "they cannot be determinants of value." Unfortunately, however, they are rarely, if ever, in equilibrium.

TABLE VIII-2. THE WORLD'S HUMAN POPULATION PROFIT AND LOSS
INVENTORY STATEMENT, 1882-1952

Inventory of people, midyear, 1882		1,433,804,000
People produced over 70-year period [a]	4,650,325,000	
People consumed over 70-year period [b]	2,159,045,000	
Inventory of people, midyear, 1952		2,491,280,000
Net gain		1,057,476,000

SOURCES: Compiled from the investigations of P. F. Levasseur and L. Bodio; brought up to date (1952) from data in the *Statesman's Yearbook; Encyclopaedia Britannica; Encyclopedia of Social Reform; Statistical Abstract for the British Commonwealth;* Statistical Yearbook of the League of Nations, and the *Demographic Yearbook* of the United Nations (See Population Table I, Chapter VI.)

NOTE: Total number of births under "People produced" and "People consumed" contains both live and stillbirths over the period. The total population for 1952 contains 55,252,000 people 70 years of age and over. Adjustment for this figure will be noted in the inventory statement, Table VIII-3. The relation between the birth and death rates has long been the subject of much analysis and controversy. Changes in these rates as they have been reported for the years 1882 and 1952 are given as follows:

	1882	1952	Change
Total live birth rate per 1,000 population	32.7	25.4	− 7.
Total stillbirths per 1,000 live births	22.4	26.5	+ 4.
Total death rate per 1,000 population	22.3	11.9	− 10.
Infant mortality rate per 1,000 live births			
− (Deaths of infants less than 1 year of age)	191.3	56.9	−134.

These rates vary somewhat from year to year over the 70 years covered, with the cumulative results being shown in the middle over-all entries between the two periodic dates.

[a] and [b]: For complete breakdown see Table VIII-1.

While a ratio, mathematically, is a relationship to an equation, this does not mean that the equation is always met on equal terms. A ratio between demand and supply—consumption and production—is intelligible only if by consumption we mean the quantity *consumed,* and if by supply we mean the quantity *actually supplied*; the issue should not be confused by introducing the term "value." As a ratio can only be the quotient of two sets of numbers resulting from the division of one quantity by another, how, then, can there be a ratio between a quantity and a mere human desire?

In the total supply of human beings produced over the period 1882-1952, as shown in the accompanying Table VIII-3, we find that the ratio of total supply to total humans consumed (4,595,073,000 to 2,159,045,000) is 2.1 to 1. And this is a most encouraging ratio. But if we take the ratio of the total supply of minerals produced and consumed over the same period in relation to the reserve supply we find that the ratio of total consumption to supply is something approximating 1 to 4—or almost double the human ratio in reverse. In other words, diametrically opposing ratios—not at all encouraging.

C = B:E

In Chapter VIII the significance of the *rate* of change has been pointed out. Here we are referring to the significance of *ratio,* particularly the ratio of the world population to the carrying capacity of the earth. In other words, we are dealing with the ratio of the production-consumption phenomena to the known available resources—the ratio of demand and supply, not in relation to "value" but in relation to life and survival—the ratio between human populations and the supply of natural resources.

TABLE VIII–3. THE WORLD'S HUMAN POPULATION INVENTORY STATEMENT, 1882–1952

Human stock 70 years and over, born 1882 or earlier		55,252,000
Net production (less 70 years of age and over)[a]	4,595,073,000	
Losses through death over period	2,159,045,000	
Net cumulative addition over period		2,436,028,000
Inventory at end of period		2,491,280,000

[a] The gross figure has been ascertained by taking the average annual number of deaths over the 70-year period at 30,833,500 × 70 = 2,159,045,000 total deaths, and then adding the residual figure in 1952 of 2,491,280,000 total still living, which gives the total gross production of 4,650,325,000 over the period.

As there is no known means of augmenting the world's human population from outer planetary space, then the growth of the present population from 1,433,804,000 in 1882 to 2,491,280,000 in 1952 would require this accumulative gross performance. In other words, by proceeding as follows we achieve the same result:

Average gross birth rate of	65,643,900 × 70 =	4,595,073,000
Average gross death rate of	30,843,500 × 70 =	2,159,045,000
Residue figure		2,436,028,000
Plus those 70 years and over still living		55,252,000
Total human inventory at end of period		2,491,280,000

NOTE: An inventory statement covering the world's population cannot be accurately drafted, for balance sheet purposes, in the way business inventories are supposed to be drawn. In fact, modern accounting practices still debate whether "supplies" should be classified as a current asset appearing in the inventory or treated as a "deferred charge."

Most inventory statements contain *Finished Goods, Goods in Process,* and *Raw Materials.* As the various governments report only live births and total deaths with any degree of accuracy, it would be impossible to include more than a statistical expectancy covering the current magnitude of pregnancies "in process" at any given date. Although we know the world's population progresses on an "accrual" basis, nevertheless the population figures are only available on a "cash" basis in so far as such likeness to business accounting methods is concerned.

Also any correct determination of inventories involves questions of not only quantity, but *quality* and *condition* as well, in so far as the finished goods are concerned. As the stock of "finished" people of the world are in various ages and stages of condition, good or bad, well or ill, at any given date, it is beyond the immediate scope of this study to engage in any such determination. Suffice it to say, that on the basis of past governmental studies, some 20 per cent of the people are in varying stages of illness at all times.

Political and military leaders have been vainly trying to solve the complex problems of this one geographic ecological world in favor of a series of fragmented constituents, each to be utilized primarily for its catallactical profit ratio. It appears that they have been seeking the solutions of an extraordinarily complex equation while at the same time almost completely neglecting the major factors.

William Vogt, in his *Road to Survival,* 1948, suggested that perhaps a *"bioequation,"* that takes into account man's physical universe, might help us to clear our thinking and even prove helpful as a means toward a better regulation of those forces that have so preoccupied world leadership.

His formula was C = B:E.

In this simple formula C stands for *carrying capacity*; B means the biotic *potential*, which is the ability of the land to supply plants for food, clothing and shelter; and E stands for the *environmental resistance*, or the limitations that any environment places on the biotic potential or productive ability.

The *carrying capacity* is the resultant of the ratio between the biotic potential and the environmental resistance.

Like all equations, including the famous $E = mc^2$, this is perhaps oversimplified —but it does express certain fundamental relationships which, as Vogt has stated, "every minute of every day touch (and affect) the life of every man, woman, and child on the face of the globe."

NATIONAL PROBLEMS IN CONSUMPTION

The level of consumption of the people of the world is important since it is the principal factor in the economic relationships between people, either directly within a nation or indirectly between nations. The nation whose production exceeds its consumption is considered as progressing in the economic sense, while that nation whose consumption exceeds its production is on the decline. Any surplus will be the greatest in a given nation with a given population when all consume to the point where their production is greater than their consumption.

In view of the tremendous wastes in both production and consumption, it would seem advisable that there be adopted a material and ethical view of these processes, for the real power of any level of consumption depends not on whether it is considered "high," but whether it is efficient and within rational economic means. As population increases, unless it coincides with a change in technology and an accumulation of real resources, there will be a diminishing productivity per capita, and a correspondingly diminishing consumption per capita. In other words, those nations and peoples with the more efficient consumption will eventually drive the less efficient squanderers from the markets of the world.

On the other hand, if the population is kept within moderate limits relative to the natural resources of a country, then the per-capita production will be high and a high level of consumption may still remain an efficient one.

FACTORS NEEDING FURTHER INVESTIGATION

In judging the agricultural and industrial potential of the globe, we must remember that the diminishing land surface, besides producing primary foodstuffs and supporting domestic animals and an expanding population, must also be used for producing trees and fibers and other industrial raw materials. The world's consumption requirements for building timber, fuel wood, paper pulp, rubber, cotton linen, jute, hemp, sisal, gums, naval stores and other land-originated raw materials are large and for the most part expanding. The fact that modern technology is capable of increasing productivity indefinitely must not be interpreted as implying that the primary source of raw material supplies is capable of a like indefinite increase.

Considering the agriculture of the world dynamically, it may be separated int:

three principal divisions. One division includes land devoted to the breeding and support of the domestic food and work animal population as given in the accompanying Tables VIII–4 and VIII–5, and the land acres devoted to this division as given in chapter III. The land used to raise and maintain these animals is generally adapted to the raising of primary foodstuffs. The second division of agriculture

TABLE VIII–4. PRIMARY DOMESTIC FOOD-ANIMAL PRODUCTION AND CONSUMPTION OF THE WORLD, 1952

	Number	Tons live weight	Tons of feed consumed [a]
Produced:			
Cattle & calves	1,161,432,000	306,037,332	1,765,376,640
Sheep & lambs	1,202,232,000	56,504,904	1,442,678,400
Hogs & pigs	441,732,000	53,670,438	362,220,240
Poultry	3,485,648,000	8,714,120	125,483,328
Total produced	6,291,044,000	424,926,794	3,695,758,608
Slaughtered:			
Cattle & calves	358,882,000	94,565,407	545,500,640
Sheep & lambs	454,387,000	21,356,189	545,264,400
Hogs & pigs	165,155,000	20,066,332	135,427,100
Poultry	1,027,792,000	2,569,480	37,000,512
Total slaughtered	2,006,216,000	138,557,408	1,263,192,652
Natural loss:			
Cattle & calves	38,450,000	10,131,575	58,444,000
Sheep & lambs	24,045,000	1,130,115	28,854,000
Hogs & pigs	14,577,000	1,771,106	11,953,140
Poultry	361,794,000	904,485	13,024,584
Total natural loss	438,866,000	13,937,281	112,275,724
On farms, end of year:			
Cattle & calves	764,100.000	201,340,350	1,161,432,000
Sheep & lambs	723,800,000	34,018,600	868,560,000
Hogs & pigs	262,000,000	31,833,000	214,840,000
Poultry [b]	2,096,062,000	5,240,155	75,458,232
Total on farms	3,845,962,000	272,432,105	2,320,290,232

SOURCES: Computed from basic data of the U. S. Department of Agriculture, Bureau of Agricultural Economics, and Office of Foreign Agricultural Relations. Prepared and estimated on the basis of official statistics of foreign governments, the results of office research, and other information.

[a] Contains grains and other concentrates, hay, and other roughage fed during calendar year; does not include forage.

[b] Contains:

Chickens	1,882,717,000
Ducks	110,529,000
Geese	70,122,000
Turkeys	32,694,000
Total	2,096,062,000

includes land devoted to the raising of industrial plant products. The third division is devoted to the direct raising of primary foodstuffs—with such land also employed in raising feed for domestic animals. In this division it has been estimated that at present more than 2 billion tons of cellulose material is wasted in grain crops alone.

These principal divisions of agriculture overlap to some extent in all countries, varying according to climate and area location. The conversion of nutrients into animal products, see Tables VIII–4 and VIII–5, due to the metabolic and caloric requirements of the various animals, is a wasteful process—not only in terms of nutrients but in the corresponding vast land acreage requirements in a period of mounting land shortage.

TABLE VIII–5. PRIMARY DOMESTIC WORK-ANIMAL PRODUCTION AND CONSUMPTION OF THE WORLD, 1952

	Number	Tons live weight	Tons of feed consumed [a]
Produced:			
Horses	70,403,000	63,362,700	107,012,560
Mules	19,157,000	13,409,900	24,904,100
Asses	20,461,000	6,138,300	21,484,050
Buffaloes	14,498,000	13,048,200	22,036,960
Camels	8,820,000	9,261,000	10,584,000
Goats	150,400,000	6,392,000	6,768,000
Total produced	283,739,000	111,612,100	192,789,670
Slaughtered:			
Horses	2,700,000	2,430,000	4,104,000
Goats	9,680,000	411,400	435,600
Buffaloes	556,000	500,400	845,120
Total slaughtered	12,936,000	3,341,800	5,384,720
Natural loss:			
Horses	203,000	182,700	308,560
Mules	57,000	39,900	74,100
Asses	61,000	18,300	64,050
Buffaloes	42,000	37,800	63,840
Camels	26,000	27,300	31,200
Goats	420,000	17,850	18,900
Total natural loss	809,000	323,850	560,650
On hand, end of year:			
Horses	67,500,000	60,750,000	102,600,000
Mules	19,100,000	13,370,000	24,830,000
Asses	20,400,000	6,120,000	21,420,000
Buffaloes	13,900,000	12,510,000	21,128,000
Camels	8,800,000	9,233,700	10,552,800
Goats	140,300,000	5,962,750	6,313,500
Total on hand	270,000,000	107,946,450	186,844,300

NOTE: For sources and methodology see footnotes to Table VIII–4.

[a] Does not include forage.

With continued increase in population, the food supply will inevitably tend to contain more of the primary and less of the secondary foodstuffs. With a world population mounting toward the 6 billion mark, one can envisage their future diet as largely vegetarian, with only such animal products as would be secured incidentally from work animals and such cattle, sheep, goats, and swine as could subsist on land unadapted to the growing of primary foodstuffs.

This to an extent disregards the aquatic animals. Here one encounters an optimism not fully justified by the presently known facts. The resources of the sea are measurable with less accuracy and greater difficulty than those of land. The sea area of the world is three times that of land, but the productivity is very much lower.

Aquatic animals depend on aquatic plants, and there is little plant life in water over 200 feet deep. This shallow area of the sea is estimated at 2 billion acres, or one-fourth that devoted to food products on land. Even if the plant growth in the shallow sea were comparable with that of the land, the return in edible animal products cannot be as large relatively. Thus appraised, the food-producing potential of the seas appears low. Unfortunately, there is a popular notion that practically unlimited numbers of fish exist in the deeper and more distant waters, their availability merely awaiting improvement in fishing methods. Here, it may be well to keep in mind that the importance of such a deep-sea food suppy, like that of the reindeer on land, is more hypothetical than is yet capable of being demonstrated.

HARVESTING THE SEAS FOR FOOD— PAST AND PRESENT EXAGGERATED APPRAISALS

All of the original civilizations of the past grew up round the seas, and fishing prepared the way for sea trade, without which the development of modern civilization is almost inconceivable. As in his other endeavors, the attitude of man toward fisheries was that of the spendthrift. Nature gave the increase; he had but to use it if he could. There was always an "abundance" of fish, so why worry? For the most part the operations of fishing and harvesting the food products of the sea were treated largely as comparable with those of hunting, rather than with agriculture, and with the least possible account of considerations affecting the supply. When one area was "fished-out" another was resorted to.

With the growth of the population of the world, and the increasing demand upon resources of food, it slowly began to be recognized that perhaps man had hitherto failed to take full advantage of the resources of the sea. Yet "over-fishing" and the possible "impoverishment" of the sea were subjects of study throughout Europe and England as far back as 1885, when the institution of fishery statistics for England, Scotland, and Ireland began. The first necessity was to secure a rational conception of what the stock of fish might be, and what were the factors governing its fluctuations which had puzzled and alarmed generations of fishermen.

The world per capita annual total fish catch stands 20 per cent below that of 70 years ago—16.0 pounds per capita in 1882 as against 12.7 pounds in 1952, as evidenced from the statistics of the English Board of Agriculture and Fisheries in Detail VIII–A.

DETAIL VIII–A

Years	Total Pounds	Per Capita
1952	31,649,000,000	12.7
1882	22,960,000,000	16.0

Yet there are those who feel confident that science will find a way to conquer the "enormous food resources" of the sea. What is overlooked is that all animal life in the sea is ultimately dependent entirely upon plankton for existence, and that all sea life, including plankton, is dependent upon the phosphates, nitrates, and other nutrients so essential to plant growth on land. And further, in the chemical cycle of the plant this feeding "chain" has been vastly modified and interrupted by the world's vital land losses plus the industrial pollution of the seas.

While there is no reason to discourage researches on the artificial propagation of fish of every kind, the prospect of considerably increasing, by artificial means, the stocks of those multitudinous fishes which are the foundation of the great commercial fisheries of today is remote. The practical line of inquiry is that which aims at the prevention of further wasteful exploitation rather than at problematic artificial means of increase.

CONSUMPTION REQUIREMENTS OF THE MECHANICAL-SLAVE-WORKING POPULATION

The rapid ascendency of the mineral-using industry and the vast increase in mechanical power dependent upon an ever-increasing energy expenditure has involved a serious shift in the appraisal of the world's land resources. Again, unfortunately, the law of the conservation of energy furnishes no guarantee of an undiminishing supply of available energy even though man may continue to increase an energy consuming mechanical-slave population at a rate far faster than his own rate of increase. In fact at a rate nearly 40 times faster as will be evidenced in the accompanying Table VIII–6.

The fact is that the production, "feeding," and maintenance of this mechanical-slave population requires an annual consumption of the world's natural resources on a prodigious scale. Such a completely mineral-based civilization, dependent entirely upon exhaustible resources, may well prove to be nothing more than a passing phenomenon in human history. It seems to be erected on far too narrow a basis of natural resources to hope to endure indefinitely.

The bulk of the world's effective consumption of mechanical energy has occurred in a relatively few countries which are, of course, the world's industrial leaders. Seventy years ago the predominant share of this consumption was in Europe. By 1952 it had shifted to North America. Such data as shown in Table VIII–6 are usually presented for the purpose of disclosing the working and producing power of countries. They show that nearly 58 per cent of the world's total mechanical energy is consumed in North America, the bulk of it in the United States. This means that in a single year, 1952, 1353 quadrillion foot-pounds of work was accomplished by power-driven machines using energy derived from coal, petroleum, natural gas, and water power. This is the equivalent of 36 billion inanimate slaves, or 158 slaves per capita.

No other continent approaches North America in the total amount of such work performed, a fact that goes far to explain the enormous productivity of this continent and its people. It also means that more than one-half of all the consumption in the world today occurs in this area—a side of the balance sheet that is rarely spoken of by a society determined to pursue its course of maniacal consumption of resources.

THE PEOPLE'S ACCOUNT WITH NATURE

The fact that today such a large percentage of the population lives in cities and towns results inevitably in a detachment from the land, with a corresponding apathy as to how the resources of the world are treated. To this century there has fallen the

TABLE VIII-6. CHANGES IN THE DISTRIBUTION OF WORLD POPULATION AND CONSUMPTION OF MECHANICAL ENERGY, 1882–1952

	Effective consumption of mechanical energy quadrillions of foot-pounds [a]	Inanimate-slave population [b]	%	Human population	Per capita energy slaves
1952:					
Africa	40	1,061,479,000	1.70%	206,559,000	5.1
America, North	1,353	36,082,750,000	57.90	227,208,000	158.8
America, South	38	1,012,364,000	1.62	115,098,000	8.8
Asia	124	3,302,291,000	5.29	1,354,288,000	2.4
Europe	750	20,011,793,000	32.11	574,900,000	34.8
Oceania	32	840,215,000	1.38	13,227,000	63.5
Total	2,337	62,310,892,000	100.00%	2,491,280,000	25.0
1882:					
Africa	.05	1,231,000	.05%	205,823,000	c
America, North	4.33	115,390,000	5.50	71,495,000	1.6
America, South	.06	1,720,000	.08	28,920,000	c
Asia	.27	7,181,000	.34	795,591,000	c
Europe	73.97	1,972,452,000	94.01	327,743,000	6.0
Oceania	d	26,000	.02	4,232,000	c
Total	78.68	2,098,000,000	100.00%	1,433,804,000	1.5

SOURCES: 1952: Computed from data in United Nations *Statistical Yearbook*, 1952; 1882: Computed from data in Mulhall's *Dictionary of Statistics*, 1883.

Source: "U. S. Industrialization," E. R. Buckminster, *Fortune*, Vol. 21, February, 1940.
[c] Less than 1-tenth fraction.
[d] Less than 1-hundredth fraction.

[a] Computed at 4 per cent efficiency.
[b] Arrived at by dividing the figures of column one by 37,500,000; this figure represents the foot-pounds of physical work that it is estimated a man may maintain over a year, less the energy required for self-locomotion.

TABLE VIII–7.   UNRECOGNIZED CONSUMPTION DATA

	Tons	Pounds	Pounds per capita
Year 1882:			
Air [a]	2,305,987,177,900	4,611,974,355,800,000	3,216,600.3
Water [b]	1,467,541,481,500	2,935,062,963,000,000	2,047,046.2
Land [c]	1,051,193,689,360	2,102,387,378,721,600	1,466,300.4
Total	4,824,722,348,760	9,649,424,697,521,600	6,729,946.9
Year 1952:			
Air [a]	12,816,990,418,700	25,633,980,837,400,000	10,289,482.0
Water [b]	8,697,894,450,000	17,395,788,900,000,000	6,982,607.1
Land [c]	5,479,448,000,000	10,958,896,000,000,000	4,398,901.8
Total	26,994,332,868,700	53,988,665,737,400,000	21,670,990.9

[a] See Table IV–1. Comparisons, Air chapter.

[b] See Table V–1. Gallons have been converted to pounds and tons on basis of 1 gallon of water = 8.33 pounds, U. S. Bureau of Standards.

[c] See Table III–1. Both the natural geological erosion and man-made erosion are included, covering deserts and built-on land. Acreage computed on basis of 1,000 tons per acre of top-soil.

TABLE VIII–8.   OBSERVABLE PRODUCTION DATA

	Tons	Pounds	Pounds per capita
Year 1882:			
Top-soil minerals [a]	3,860,302,199	7,720,604,398,800	5,384.7
Fuels [b]	592,017,671	1,184,035,343,200	825.8
Sub-soil minerals [c]	565,205,537	1,130,411,073,600	788.4
Fibers [d]	760,489,641	1,520,979,283,200	1,060.8
Food	1,235,508,907	2,471,017,813,600	1,723.4
Total	7,013,523,955	14,027,047,912,400	9,783.1
Year 1952:			
Top-soil minerals [a]	11,644,900,000	23,289,800,000,000	9,348.5
Fuels [b]	5,715,100,000	11,430,200,000,000	4,588.1
Sub-soil minerals [c]	2,436,318,063	4,872,636,126,000	1,955.9
Fibers [d]	2,241,297,664	4,482,595,328,000	1,799.3
Food	1,973,093,760	3,946,187,520,000	1,584.0
Total	24,010,709,487	48,021,418,974,000	19,275.8

[a] Contains sand, clay, gravel, and stone, and the major top-soil nutrients.

[b] Contains coal, petroleum, natural gas, wood; and uranium for 1952. See Table III–12.

[c] Contains all of the principal minerals excepting coal and petroleum as given in Table III–11.

[d] Contains wool, cotton, silk, flax, hemp, abaca, sisal, henequen, jute, rubber, and wood.

TABLE VIII–9. ESTIMATED CHANGES IN THE WORLD'S ANNUAL TONNAGE CONSUMPTION, 1882–1952

(*In Net Short Tons*)

	1882	1952
Depreciation & obsolescence	7,226,370,000	109,616,320,000
Depletion & erosion [a]	7,000,000,000	33,881,408,000
Consumed in production [a]	32,653,273,000	333,174,594,000
Waste in consumption [a]	12,043,952,000	54,808,160,000
Consumed by fire, storm, etc.	1,204,395,000	16,442,448,000
Food & work animals	89,948,000	153,688,000
Human beings consumed	1,820,000	4,982,000
Total	60,219,758,000	548,081,600,000
World population	1,433,804,000	2,491,280,000
Per capita:		
Depreciation & obsolescence	5.040	44.000
Depletion & erosion	4.882	13.600
Consumed in production	22.774	133.736
Waste in consumption	8.400	22.000
Consumed by fire, storm, etc.	.840	6.600
Food & work animals	.063	.062
Human beings consumed	.001	.002
Total	42.000	220.000

SOURCES: See Note to Production and Consumption Tables, Chapters VII and VIII.

NOTE: In computing depreciation, obsolescence, and depletion there is undoubtedly some unavoidable duplication. For example, for every ton of pig iron produced, over 70 tons of material has been handled. (See Table VIII–10.) Also, there are large river and harbor dredging and draining operations, as well as large dam and reservoir projects which involve the handling and moving of vast tonnages of materials which rarely find their way into the customary commercial statistics. The same is true of the world's agriculture, where over 5 tons of additional materials are consumed annually for every ton of product. (See Table VII–7.) As disclosed in Table VII–4, it will be further noted that the world is consuming land acreage for various "built-on" purposes at an average annual rate of 22 million acres per year. As measured in terms of top-soil tonnage per acre this amounts to approximately 22 billion tons in addition to erosion.

[a] Contains water.

TABLE VIII-10.   THE WORLD'S CONSUMPTION AND PRODUCTION OF MATERIALS IN IRON-MAKING, 1882-1952

(*In Net Tons*)

	1882	1952	Change	% Change
Consumption of materials:				
Iron ore	41,566,000	232,955,495	+ 191,389,495	+460.4%
Coke	24,298,296	116,417,490	+ 92,119,194	+379.1
Limestone	12,778,576	58,208,745	+ 45,430,169	+355.5
Air blast	93,820,400	476,034,250	+ 382,213,850	+407.4
Water	672,965,416	3,414,551,495	+ 2,741,586,079	+407.4
Total	845,428,688	4,298,167,475	+3,452,738,787	+408.4%
Production:				
Slag	58,924,753	66,283,250	+ 7,358,497	+ 12.5%
Dust	2,778,984	14,100,255	+ 11,321,271	+407.4
Gas	87,074,832	682,837,990	+ 595,763,158	+684.2
Steam	672,898,119	3,414,430,980	+ 2,741,532,861	+407.4
Total	821,676,688	4,177,652,475	+3,355,975,787	+408.4%
Net pig iron produced	23,752,000	120,515,000	+ 96,763,000	+407.4%

SOURCES: *The Blast Furnace and the Manufacturing of Pig Iron*, Robert Forsythe, 1922; *Iron and Steel*, H. P. Tieman, 1933; Reports of the American Iron and Steel Institute; *The Encyclopaedia Britannica*, 1948 ed., Vol. 12, p. 653; United Nations Statistical Yearbook, 1952.

NOTE: Large tonnages of slag are utilized as a raw material in the manufacture of Portland cement. Also large tonnages of slag are utilized for railway and road-bed ballast, and for their filling material. Some of the gas is utilized in the steel industry, but it contains too much dust to be widely used without further cleaning. The water return serves largely to pollute the streams, as the air ballast pollutes the atmosphere. About 50,000 cubic feet of air per minute is necessary for a furnace making 600 tons of pig iron per day.

responsibility of having encouraged wanton consumption of natural resources and at the same time having unharnessed upon the field of history not only the greatest multitudes but also the most devastating manner of exterminating them. In scarcely two generations, and over the span of a single lifetime, there has come into existence a gigantic mass of humanity—now moving like a torrent over the world. This vast and virtually unshepherded horde seeks subsistence and survival under the principle of a pleasure economy—seeking "to get the most for the least"—while engaging in the most prodigious consumption of their capital resources since the age of the dinosaur, who destroyed himself by devouring his capital.

In Tables VIII–7, VIII–8, and VIII–9 are shown the unacknowledged consumption data in terms of their basic elements and in their quantitative measures and changes in total and in per capita consumption, from 1882 to 1952. These phenomena underlie, but are not shown in, a monetary balance sheet. Such a physical inventory would seem to be worthy of consideration in what might be termed the greatest of all balance sheets—man's account with nature.

In Tables VIII–10, VIII–11, VIII–12, the element of waste as it plays its part in the consumption-production equation is shown. This is not all waste, as part is salvaged for other economic uses; nevertheless it is consumption on a vast scale.

TABLE VIII–11.   ANNUAL WASTE OF MINERALS STORED IN THE WORLD'S COAL

	Grams per ton	%	Tons per year
Beryllium	100	1.0%	249,843
Boron	5,000	48.7	12,167,354
Titanium	2,000	19.5	4,871,939
Vanadium	90	.9	224,859
Chromium	200	1.9	474,702
Cobalt	200	1.9	474,702
Nickel	1,100	10.7	2,673,320
Molybdenum	30	.3	74,953
Copper	800	7.8	1,948,775
Gallium	40	.4	99,937
Germanium	600	5.9	1,474,073
Yttrium	100	1.0	249,843
Total	10,260	100.0%	24,984,300

SOURCE: Computed from data, U. S. Geological Survey, Circular 272.

MAN ALONE DOES NOT HAVE A CORNER ON CONSUMPTION

There are many forces, agencies, forms of life in continuous competition with man for the organic and inorganic substances of nature. The wind and the sea, the entire vast mechanism of the earth magma, are all engaged in that unceasing flux that transforms, changes, and consumes. Three billion tons of solid material are washed out of the fields and pastures of the United States every year. This is the equivalent of 3 million acres of top-soil land that is consumed annually by geological and meteorological erosion. That amounts to some 40 thousand pounds of land per person consumed each year. The same is true of water and of the air.

TABLE VIII-12. WOOD CONSUMPTION AND PRODUCTION IN THE UNITED STATES, 1882–1952

(In Net Tons)

	1882	% of total	1952	% of total	Change	% Change
Mill waste [a]	183,335,226	18.04%	136,813,452	14.19%	− 46,521,774	− 25.4%
Woods waste [b]	166,022,385	16.33	182,856,738	18.96	+ 16,834,353	+ 10.1
Total waste	349,357,611	34.37%	319,670,190	33.15%	− 29,687,421	− 8.5%
Insects, disease, wind	69,801,757	6.87%	22,163,250	2.30%	− 47,638,507	− 68.2%
Forest fires	83,946,600	8.25	97,875,000	10.15	+ 13,928,400	+ 16.6
Other losses	153,748,357	15.12%	120,038,250	12.45%	− 33,710,107	− 21.9%
Fuel wood	406,464,000	40.00%	172,608,000	17.90%	−233,856,000	− 57.5%
Lumber	76,995,000	7.58%	158,044,000	16.39%	+ 81,049,000	+105.3%
Manufactures	16,349,884	1.61	87,583,760	9.08	+ 71,233,876	+435.7
Pulpwood	2,787,149	.27	73,670,082	7.64	+ 70,882,933	+2,543.2
Posts	2,649,880	.26	4,785,000	.50	+ 2,135,120	+ 80.6
Railroad ties	2,211,218	.22	7,890,000	.82	+ 5,678,782	+256.8
Mine timbers	1,760,619	.17	2,676,140	.28	+ 915,521	+ 51.9
Wood distillation	1,151,863	.12	1,377,000	.14	+ 225,137	+ 19.5
Shingles and lath	1,142,910	.11	1,001,000	.11	− 141,910	− 12.4
Veneers [c]	534,154	.05	12,745,500	1.33	+ 12,211,346	+2,286.1
Cooperage	522,218	.05	105,488	.01	− 416,730	− 79.8
Poles	373,012	.04	568,470	.06	+ 195,458	+ 52.4
Other	358,093	.03	1,392,000	.14	+ 1,033,907	+288.7
Total production	106,836,000	10.51%	351,838,440	36.50%	+245,002,440	+229.3%
Grand total consumption	1,016,405,968	100.00%	964,154,880	100.00%	− 52,251,088	− 5.1%

SOURCES: U. S. Forest Service, *Forest Products of the United States*, 1906. Compiled from data of the Forest Service, U. S. Department of Agriculture, and the U. S. Department of Commerce, Bureau of the Census, 1952. See Reports Nos. 1 and 2, U. S. Forest Service, 1946, and *Encyclopaedia Britannica*, 11th ed., Vol. X, p. 658.

NOTE: The U. S. Forest Service estimates that in addition about 9,000,000 tons of lignin, cellulose, and other chemical residue are wasted annually.

[a] Includes bark, kerf, slabs, and edgings; [b] Includes tops, stumps, cull logs, [c] Includes plywood in 1952.

160

The laws of nature remain the same at all times and at all places, we are told. By discovering these principles of behavior man can and has made them work for him. By understanding them man has been able to speed up the processes of the slower natural evolutionary forces to an unprecedented extent. This he has done by creating what has amounted to a series of mutations—which he likes to call revolutions—each in itself aiding man, but also speeding up the consumption process.

Because of these basic facts man's civilization has been able to advance—by man's revolutions. Evolution is a long process. If man had been willing to be dependent upon evolution for better food, he would still be eating the insect-bitten, knotty, dwarfed food of his neolithic ancestors. The best grains, best fruits, best vegetables, are all the product of man-forced mutations—not evolution. These things have seemed so revolutionary that he has come to expect them to continue indefinitely. He no longer feels compelled to limit himself. The whole procedure has incited his appetite, which in principle can increase indefinitely. Thus, while man is actually living in a world economy of scarcity the feeling prevails that he is dwelling in an age wherein tomorrow will be still richer, ampler, more perfect, as if it too somehow enjoyed a spontaneous, mutational inexhaustible power of increase.

TABLE VIII–13.   SUMMARIZED WORLD TOTAL ANNUAL
CONSUMPTION, 1952

(*Total in Net Tons and Per Capita in Pounds*)

	Net tons	Pounds per capita
Air	12,816,990,418,700	10,289,482.0
Water	8,697,894,450,000	6,982,607.1
Land	5,479,448,000,000	4,398,901.8
Top-soil minerals	11,644,900,000	9,348.5
Fuels	5,715,100,000	4,588.1
Fed to livestock	3,888,548,278	3,121.7
Sub-soil minerals	2,436,318,063	1,955.9
Fibers	2,241,297,664	1,799.3
Human food	1,973,093,760	1,548.0
Top-soil nutrients	529,148,000	424.8

NOTE: For sources see preceding basic tables relating to above categories: VIII–7, VIII–8, III–12, VIII–4, VIII–5, VIII–8 and III–6.

In Table VIII–13 will be found a summarized statement covering the total consumption for the year 1952. If these data were to be projected over the coming 70 years to the year 2022 on the basis of the present rate of population increase, it would be found that the demands upon the planet earth by that time would be truly fantastic. The demands in land use terms alone would call for 47 billion acres of land on a globe that will have a total of but 27 billion acres. And if consumption and production rates were to continue to increase as over the past 70 years the results would appear fantastic in relation to any rational expectancy.

The idols of the market are the most troublesome of all, those, namely, which have entwined themselves around the understanding from the associations of words and names. For men imagine that their reason governs words, whilst, in fact, words react upon the understanding; and this has rendered philosophy, and the sciences sophistical and inactive. Words are generally formed in a popular sense, and define things by those broad lines which are most obvious to the vulgar mind; but when a more acute understanding, or more diligent observation is anxious to vary those lines to suit the true divisions of nature, words stand in the way and resist the change.
—FRANCIS BACON, *Magna Instauratio*, Bk. I, lix

IX

Money

EXCHANGE, THE third traditional division of economic theory, brings this work face to face with the phenomenon of money, the problems of supply and demand, and the theory of value. As the vast bulk of all internal and international transactions involve evaluation and payment in money we have labeled this chapter accordingly.

By the year 1882 the world economic system of exchange had displaced the older more or less barter-exchange valuation system of self-contained communities, and the general mediums of payment together with their corollary banking facilities, known as the monetary system, had become well established. It was, therefore, natural that the various values, in terms of price units, should lose their connection with the older standard goods and, regardless of money's relationship to the precious metals, gradually become purely abstract units for the estimating of values.

Theoretical discussions about money go as far back as human thought on any aspect of economics. Its influence on value as a power in exchange of goods and services and as a factor in the exchange system is indisputable. In the drafting of an exploratory world balance sheet, however, we need not concern ourselves with these and similar questions. What concerns us here is chiefly the money supply of the world, the established rates of exchange, and the larger fact that money and monetary values constitute the chief "economic compass" on which the business and political world depends for information about economic conditions.

Although physical resources are the foundation on which the structure of the world economy rests, nevertheless, in a market-price system money has come to be as necessary in the exchange of goods as language in the exchange of ideas. In fact the economic world could not exist without money. Money no longer merely *serves* for the understanding of economic intercourse; it *subjects* the exchange of goods to its own functional evolution. It values things no longer in relation to one another but with reference to itself. In this sense, money has become a power, and a power that is almost wholly abstract in its dimensions.

OF WHAT STUFF IS MONEY

Money is ordinarily used in political economy to mean any article generally acceptable as a medium of exchange. All modern economic life is founded on money. The whole industrial order is based on the production and consumption of goods not only in terms of money but at a money profit. In the world's warehouses, factories, shops, and stockyards are vast stores of wealth—apples and amethysts, beets and barrels, cars and cattle, and so on to the end of a list that, in its detail of grades, range and variety, sizes and styles, would outrun the pages of the largest dictionary. And in all these things the producing owners have one common, dominant interest, to exchange them as soon as possible for the largest possible amount of money. Most human interest tends to gravitate around money. So much so, in fact, that writers like Spengler have spoken of its "monstrous power," as "an unconditional dictatorship of money."

Such questions as "Does *good* money have an *intrinsic value* of its own?" or "Is its value the result of its accepted use as a medium of exchange?" have long been discussed. Also, "Are gold and silver commodities, like other goods, or are they chiefly common measures of the values of other commodities?" Again, "Is money capital, or is it merely the means with which productive capital goods are bought, and the measure of their value?"

"It may be doubted," stated Macaulay, "whether all the misery which had been inflicted on the nation in a quarter of a century, by bad kings, bad parliaments, and bad judges, was equal to the misery caused in a single year by bad money." Another well-known writer has referred to our present civilization as "materially a cash and credit system, dependent on men's confidence in the value of money."

VARIETIES OF MONEY

Money defined as a medium of exchange may or may not have intrinsic value. When a piece of metallic money, apart from its stamp, is of the commercial value stamped upon it, it is said to be "intrinsic money," having value in itself. When it has no value in itself, but simply represents a declared value which the government promises to pay out for it whenever demanded, it is called "representative money." The bulk of all money in use in the world by 1952 has been of this latter kind.

When, however, its value is not equal to its stamped value, though originally its intrinsic and commercial value were the same, it is called not representative money, but "depreciated money." Its value has been depreciated either voluntarily or otherwise.

Where money is issued by a government stamped as legal tender for a certain value, but with no guaranty by the government that it will be redeemed for intrinsic money, it is called irredeemable or fiat money. The government simply states it to be worth a specified amount.

SUBSTITUTE MONEY

International currency, money which can be exchanged directly for goods and services freely throughout the world, does not yet exist. Strictly speaking, money can only circulate freely within national boundaries and their dependencies. Payments from one country to another require the exchange of domestic for foreign money. In the past, and to a qualified degree at present, gold has approached the quality of an international money, where the import and export of gold are free, thereby permitting international payments to be accomplished through the medium of gold settlements. In countries where exchange restrictions exist the exportation of gold is sometimes prohibited. However, most international payments are cleared in one form or another and do not require any gold shipments.

In the absence of a readily acceptable common circulating international currency, the "bill of exchange" or "draft" has long served this purpose. The bill of exchange is primarily a substitute for money, in that it serves as a device to avoid the transmission of cash from place to place in the settlement of trade debts. Although drafts are a substitute for cash payment, and may constitute in value the commercial currency of a country, nevertheless they should not be confounded with money and do not enter into the world compilations of total money supply. Their importance is that they represent negotiable evidence of relative money indebtedness as a means of settling accounts in foreign trade.

Such drafts constitute orders for certain sums of money to be transferred on specified dates from one person or organization, owing the money, to the creditor to whom the money is owed. These remittances may be made in many ways; for example, by mail or cable direct, or through banking correspondents or such agencies as the Bank for International Settlements, the International Monetary Fund, the European Payments Union, and the International Bank for Reconstruction and Development.

Detail IX-A lists the changes in the total amount of these exchanges in world trade, in their U.S. dollar equivalents, between the two periods 1882 and 1952.

DETAIL IX-A

	Imports	Exports
1882	$ 2,432,000,000	$ 2,210,000,000
1952	79,825,000,000	74,137,000,000

The import and export amounts are never in complete balance due to the fact that international payments originate not only from the purchase and sale of goods but also from services rendered, such as shipping services and insurance charges. Today the imports are c.i.f. (cost, insurance, freight) which means that the selling price includes all insurance, freight charges, and export duties, in addition to the cost of the goods; and exports are f.o.b. (free on board) which means that the seller assumes all charges, including duties and risks on the goods until delivered on board the vessel or conveyance at the place designated. There are further differences due to the fact that although the reports contain the official clearances and entrances reported by the customs officials, nevertheless, as of any given date, there will always be some goods still en route, and also some goods in "free ports," which means excluded from the customs territory, awaiting storing, sorting, repacking, and reshipping before reporting.

In addition, the payments between any two countries will not tally unless they are artificially equalized through bilateral agreements. Even in the relation of one country to the rest of the world, imports and exports will not balance. There are goods and services consumed by tourists in foreign countries; there are capital exports (import of foreign securities) and capital imports (export of domestic securities); and there are interest and dividend remittances resulting therefrom. All of these *in* and *out* payments between one country and the rest of the world constitute a country's balance of payments, and therefore influence its foreign exchange market and the supply of foreign exchange on the markets of the world. In the long run, of course, the grand totals of all imports and exports for the world as a whole, with the exception of losses not fully covered by insurance, balance out.

All trade, whether domestic or international, is the result of the uneven distribution of resources throughout the planet, of the distribution of aptitudes and skills among people, and of the advantages in terms of productive efficiency. No longer can any single area produce all the varied materials which could be put to best use by its population; the need for an exchange of goods which may be relatively plentiful for one area and scarce or unavailable for another has always been the chief stimulator of world trade.

OMISSIONS IN THE OFFICIALLY REPORTED DATA

The official compilation of world trade for 1952, as published by the Statistical Office of the United Nations, the International Monetary Fund, and the Bank for International Settlements, omits the trade of the mainland of China, the U.S.S.R., Czechoslovakia, Eastern Germany, Hungary, Poland, Romania, Albania, Bulgaria, and North Korea. This means that the foreign trading of nearly one billion people, living on one-fourth the land area of the world, and in possession of approximately 17 billions of U.S. dollar equivalent of money supply, fails to be included in the reported world economic activity.

On the basis of data freely available through nonpolitical channels, and estimated by the same methods employed by the official agencies, the world foreign trade, adjusted to include all areas, stands approximately as listed in Detail IX–B.

DETAIL IX–B

Year 1952	Imports	Exports	Total Turnover
Reported	$79,731,000,000	$74,090,000,000	$153,821,000,000
Nonreported	5,900,000,000	6,224,000,000	12,124,000,000
Total world trade	$85,631,000,000	$80,314,000,000	$165,945,000,000

The pattern of foreign trade generally displays a considerable degree of stability, owing to the fact that a country's import requirements and the range of export goods it can supply naturally depend on its economic structure, which is not liable to sudden change.

On the basis of quantity in terms of short tons, the world's international trade for 1952 was approximately as appears in Detail IX–C.

DETAIL IX–C

	Imports	Exports	Gross Exchange
Reported	532,197,955	727,525,260	1,259,723,215
Nonreported	44,704,223	46,118,487	90,822,710
World total	576,902,178	773,643,747	1,350,545,925

A DYNAMIC THEORY OF MONEY

Since the beginning of statistical inquiry much attention has been given to the question: "What quantity of money does a country require for the proper working of its economic system?" If this approach to an understanding of the world's political economy be valid, and if economic progress is to be measured at all by the relative supply of money, then the most important aspect of this question, in modern times, is the relative division of the money supply between countries.

Regarded from this point of view, the quantity of money and credit that a country needs in a price exchange system is that which will keep its prices in due level with those of other countries with which it is trading. This is supposed to be a primary condition of world economic equilibrium.

Here the population, volume of transactions, development of credit, and the efficiency of money management are the important factors. As population, trade and credit are all undergoing change, such management is always faced with the problem of dynamic economics rather than a static world. It follows that the main work of money and credit, as instruments of exchange, must be done in the process of dynamic readjustment, and consequently the theory of money and credit tends to be a dynamic theory as against a quantity theory which rests upon notions of static equilibrium.

MEASURES OF WORLD CAPITAL CONSUMPTION IN MONETARY TERMS

World capital formation as expressed in monetary values and in accounting terms, consists of the production, transportation, and distribution of that portion of a nation's output of goods and services which is not consumed immediately, but is retained and added to the nation's inventory of wealth. If, in measuring this retained portion of current production, allowance is made for the current consumption of the already existing capital goods, the result will disclose the volume of *net* capital formation. When such allowances are not made, the volume measured is that of *gross* capital formation.

These balance sheet values constitute the essential data in estimates of wealth, capital, income, and profits. But rational use of such estimates cannot be made by economists, statisticians, investors, or statesmen without some consideration of the manner in which such assets have been so valued by businessmen and their accountants.

In a worldwide balance sheet accounting we are confronted by an ever-dynamic situation in which price levels and currency exchange rates fluctuate continuously. Depreciation, depletion, obsolescence with retirement and abandonment, destruction by fire, accident, and wars, repairs, renewals, and maintenance all become evident factors. Profit-making opportunities appear and disappear. Business and international good will grows and diminishes. Hence, if the records are to reflect the changing realities about such assets, a forced revaluation of them is inescapable.

Such revaluation can possess considerable significance, for it offers clues to the formation and consumption of the world's capital as it fluctuates and changes in accordance with the prevailing technology and institutional procedures. Any such estimates, covering all of these factors, present certain exceptions to the usual rules of accounting, with their number and amount suggesting the degree to which orthodox accounting technique must undergo certain disciplines to become an effective servant.

CIVILIZATION AND WORLD TRADE

The exchange of goods and services, as measured in money terms, within the borders of a country as well as between countries, lies at the very basis of modern civilization. While there may be many differing opinions as to the factors, cultural and otherwise, making up "civilization," nevertheless, there is one essential of civilization which all recognize. That is an orderly intercourse among people of the same nation and, as civilization advances, between the peoples of different nations—insofar as the exchange of goods and services is concerned.

Isolation, whether of the individual or the nation, is the contrast to civilization. Whatever hampers or impedes intercourse between men and nations promotes isolation, whatever facilitates such intercourse promotes civilization. Time and again in the study of economic questions men are brought face to face with the fact that they are affected by conditions outside the boundaries of their own country. Economic questions are essentially international questions, and whether or not one may believe in the principles of world order as outlined by Wendell L. Willkie in his *One World,* by William B. Ziff's *Two Worlds,* or by William C. Bullitt's *The Great Globe Itself,* the realistic fact is that the world has become one economic unit.

International exchanges have an unusual interest at the present time. Such basic matters as the volume of production, pattern of consumption, and the general level of prices are vitally affected by conditions in the world market. The economic life of every civilized country is a part of the economic life of the world. More than half of the materials contained in an American motorcar must be imported, many of them from far places. The reserves of easily accessible high grade industrial minerals are rapidly facing exhaustion in more than one country in the world. For the first time in his history *man is now face to face with the logic of economic event.*

A CONFUSED CIVILIZATION

The flood of published information about exports and imports, about business conditions in different countries, and about the fluctuations in exchange rates has come to the attention of a wider public than ever before. The recency of this wide popular interest has served to emphasize the misunderstanding with which international business transactions have long been surrounded.

Some underestimate the importance of international trade, and others overestimate it. Loans to countries, as a means of stabilizing and increasing international trade, have been approved in some quarters and disapproved in others for reasons of the most superficial character. These confusions obscure the fundamental principles which govern international transactions. An understanding of how these transactions

take place, how they are financed, is a first requisite for anyone who wishes to see
the real meaning of the many proposals involving international trade and to comprehend their practical significance.

Financial and general economic interests of the widest bearing are intimately
connected with these problems, and their intricacies are followed with keen attention
by banking and investment circles. The subject is more and more drawn both into
the internal political controversies of the various countries and into the sphere of
international discussion. It is, therefore, obviously of the highest importance that
some serious efforts be devoted to an analysis of the nature of international trade
and transactions—particularly as they affect the balance sheet of nations in their
relationship to the world balance sheet.

NEEDED—A SCIENTIFIC THEORY OF MONEY AND EXCHANGES

The multiplicity of explanations for the unprecedented depreciation in the value
of the gold dollar, the gold British pound, and the gold franc are excellent illus-
trations of the prevailing confusion of thought.

Laying a common foundation for a theory of international exchanges where trade
is carried on between countries with independent money systems and money standards is a difficult task. The characteristic feature that distinguishes international trade
from the internal trading and exchange poses an elemental question. For, from an
economic point of view, what characterizes two or more trading communities as
different nations, and their trade as an international exchange, is first of all the fact
that each of them possesses a monetary system of its own.

WHAT IS A NATION?

The resolution of such a question ultimately depends upon an understanding of
what constitutes a nation. Fundamentally a nation is the self-conception of a people
as a unit with more or less common interests, and a corresponding recognition of
responsibility of this unit for the general well-being of its members. In the economic
sphere the national interest may manifest itself in various policies framed to give
the economic life of the country what is considered to be its most favorable development. For this purpose a series of measures may be adopted and, particularly
in relation to other countries, more or less comprehensive programs may be entered
upon for an international trade policy, including protective tariffs, monetary measures, and other means of preferential treatment conceived as being in the national
interests.

The conditions of international trade are obviously much influenced by such
measures. Policies aiming at so-called stabilization, of the currency of a country,
always form a part of its economic policy, and this function is essentially a national
one. As the trade between countries must also ultimately be valued in their respective
currencies, the problem of keeping these currencies themselves and their rate of
exchange at a stable value, in a dynamic world, is in its turn intimately connected
with the movements of international trade.

At the first stage of a study of international trade we meet the question of how
payments are possible between countries with independent monetary standards. All
of which leads to an examination of the various rates of exchange between countries

and currencies and the way in which these rates are established. To answer this latter question would be, in fact, to clear up the fundamental principles of the existing theory of international trade.

THE MAJOR REQUISITES FOR AN EXPANDING WORLD TRADE

The Committee for Economic Development has formulated the following six requisites for an expanding world trade:

1. The emergence of world political security.
2. Internal high employment and stable prices.
3. A dependable currency and stable exchange rates.
4. Ability to work out the problem of trading between free-enterprise and state monopoly economics.
5. The economic rehabilitation of the war ravaged countries.
6. Reduction of artificial trade barriers.

Detail IX–D compares the relative importance of foreign trade to the national income of the world's leading nations in 1929 and 1952.

DETAIL IX–D

	1929 (per cent)	1952 (per cent)
Norway	48	60
Netherlands	48	60
Denmark	46	58
Belgium-Luxembourg	45	82
Austria	45	78
Finland	38	57
Italy	37	28
United Kingdom	25	45
France	24	28
Sweden	22	47
Australia	22	46
Canada	21	48
Germany	18	34
Japan	18	23
United States	5	9
China	2	2
U.S.S.R.	2	1

CHANGES IN THE DIVISION OF THE WORLD'S PRODUCT

What do all these figures signify as regards the division of the things produced among those who have shared in the world's efforts to bring them forth? It is hardly possible to secure a detailed answer to these questions for all industries in all nations. However, it is not necessary for the purpose of the main problem. There are sufficient data available covering some thirty-four of the world's leading nations and colonial areas to permit a good approximation.

What we wish to know, after all, is whether those who labor have fallen behind in the industrial procession over the past seventy years as a result of all those various forces, social and technological, that have occurred during these years, and whether those who own and manage the world's industrial enterprises have gained an unusual advantage from the occurrences of this period.

The proceeds of industry are divided between labor, government, and those who have contributed capital. In other words between wages, rent, interest, and profits, out of which government demands its share in taxes. The summary in Detail IX–E discloses the changes in the distribution of these proceeds between 1882 and 1952:

DETAIL IX–E

	1882	1952	Change	% Change
		(In Millions of U. S. Dollars)		
Wages [a]	$111,752	$538,980	+$427,228	+ 382.3
Rent	21,742	148,124	+ 126,382	+ 581.3
Interest	15,219	139,523	+ 124,304	+ 816.8
Profits [b]	68,703	129,013	+ 60,310	+ 87.8
Taxes	8,262	153,633	+ 145,371	+1,759.5

[a] Wages, rent, interest are before taxes.
[b] Profits are after taxes.

The change in the division of the product since 1882 discloses the shift of the larger share to labor, with the next largest going to government, while profits, formerly receiving the second largest share, have declined to receiving the smallest. In other words, while the share of profits was approximately 32 per cent in 1882, by 1952 it had shrunk to 13 per cent of the total product.

The modern industrial conflict between labor and capital is found wherever there exist large aggregations of plant, tools, and the materials with which labor must work if production is to take place. It seems clear that along with the advantages and privileges which the propertied or "capitalist" classes—as they are sometimes called—have enjoyed over this period, the bulk of the burden both in supporting government and in accumulating the necessary capital for industrial expansion, has fallen upon them. Throughout virtually the whole of this period the popular demand was for "more money," regardless of whether or not it was based upon false premises.

THE GOLD STANDARD WORLDWIDE

Before World Wars I and II deranged the gold parities of the world, all the principal trading nations had the gold standard both in law and in fact. In other words they had monetary units whose meaning was determined by a certain quantity of gold.

The fact that the monetary units of all these countries, together with others not listed, consisted in every case of a certain number of grams of gold, gave them a definite relationship to one another. This does not mean, however, that gold itself was in common use in ordinary trade, as in many countries silver, copper, and paper currency make up the bulk of the money in circulation except for external exchange. Goods priced in any of these currencies, however, are virtually quoted in terms of gold. How all of these monies have been maintained at a parity with gold can be seen by reference to the tables at the end of this chapter.

ATTEMPTS TO BREAK AWAY
FROM MONETARY ANARCHY

Monetary conferences were one of the features of the latter half of the nineteenth century. The disorganized state of the European currencies, which became more serious in consequence of the great expansion in trade and industry, came into notice through the gold discoveries and their effect on the relation between the precious metals—gold and silver.

France first attempted the creation of a currency union, which led to the formation of the Latin Union in 1863, including France, Belgium, Switzerland, Italy, and later Greece, with the British government being unable to obtain the assent of a Royal Commission to the assimilation of the English Sovereign to the French 25-franc piece. Each country in the union kept its own nomenclature for its currency, with France, Belgium, and Switzerland terming their monetary unit the franc, Italy the lira, Greece the drachma. World War I broke up the Latin Monetary Union, with each country fixing the gold price at a level considered most convenient to itself regardless of its former associates in the union.

Another important monetary union of the same type was the formation of the Scandinavian Union in 1873, comprising Sweden, Norway, and Denmark, with the common name of the national monetary units being the Krone, or Krona. This union also broke up during World War I and was never revived.

In 1929 the Bank for International Settlements (B.I.S.) was created in connection with the regulation of reparation payments by Germany. Although its primary function was to receive and disburse reparation payments, it was also authorized to act as a bank for other central banks.

The "Sterling Bloc" emerged after Great Britain went off the gold standard in 1931. The group forming the bloc comprised the British Commonwealth, with the exception of Canada, and also Portugal, the Scandinavian countries, and Latvia, Iran, and Iraq. The sterling bloc countries maintained their currencies in a fixed relationship with the pound sterling.

In 1944 the International Monetary Fund, to promote international monetary cooperation, was proposed at the Bretton Woods Conference, and has been in operation continuously since 1945 with some 54 member nations.

WORLD ECONOMICS AND THE SCALE OF OBSERVATION

Human observations are always relative to the system of reference chosen. By system of reference we simply mean the scale of observation.

There can be many illusions in respect to economic phenomena, due to the fact that we consider a particular phenomenon, as we observe it, in the frame of our current and more or less parochial life. Reality is not always identical with our perception of things. Reasoning and experience must intervene to correct the direct impression of the senses and to construct in our minds a picture which more adequately corresponds to what we call the objective external world.

Our average day-by-day common sense perceives the earth as flat, two plumb lines as parallel, and motion as a direct straight line—all of which are false. The earth is round. Two plumb lines are directed toward the center of the earth and consequently form an angle. A bullet or an airplane which seems to move in a straight line with respect to the earth *for a short time,* in reality follows a trajectory more closely resembling a kind of parabolic corkscrew with respect to a larger scale of reference. The illusion of progress as something which proceeds in a straight line is an example of that tendency to oversimplification which the human mind displays in virtually all of its activities.

As we have no other means of knowing and describing the world we live in but those given us by our senses and our reasoning faculties, we must never forget the "relativity" of the picture which we construct—a relativity with respect to the recording instrument, man. From the standpoint of man it is the scale of observation which portrays the phenomenon, and every time we change the scale of observation we encounter new phenomena.

OFFICIAL INTERNATIONAL BANKING AGENCIES

BANK FOR INTERNATIONAL SETTLEMENTS (B.I.S.): The oldest permanent independent nonpolitical international banking agency. A "central banks' bank," commercial in character, operating independent of political considerations. Receives no instructions from any government. Has no direct contact with the public. Originally created for the handling of reparations arising from the operations of the Young Plan after World War I. Confirmed by the Hague Conference of 1930. Began business May 17, 1930. Its primary purpose being that of promoting the cooperation of central banks of the world, and to provide additional facilities for international finance operations. Acts as trustee and agent in international settlements entrusted to it. Primarily European in character. In exchanges operates on "weight" unit basis in gold francs of 0.29032258.. grammes fine gold. The original capital subscribed was 500,000,000 Swiss gold francs, with 25% paid up. Total assets of March 31, 1955; 1,717,962,180 Swiss gold francs. Founded by central banks which are its shareholders, customers, and directors. Acts as agent for the European Payments Union, and as depository of the High Authority of the European Coal and Steel Community. A useful complement of the I.M.F. and I.B.R.D.; is registered correspondent for the purpose of gold operations.
Headquarters: Basle, Switzerland.

INTERNATIONAL MONETARY FUND (I.M.F.): Established December 27, 1945, for the primary purpose of promoting international monetary cooperation and exchange stability, and to assist in the removal of exchange restrictions for the facilitation of the expansion of world trade. The Fund has a membership of 55 nations, and was brought into a working relationship with the United Nations by an agreement signed April 15, 1948. Total subscriptions in gold and national currencies approximate $8,700,000,000.
Headquarters: 1818 H Street, N.W., Washington 25, D.C.

INTERNATIONAL BANK FOR RECONSTRUCTION AND DEVELOPMENT (I.B.R.D.): Established December 27, 1945, for the purpose of assisting in the postwar reconstruction and development of its member countries by facilitating productive investment and promoting long-range growth of international trade. Total subscribed capital stock the equivalent of $9,100,000,000. As of December 31, 1952, the Bank had made 74 loans to 27 of its 55 member countries, totaling $1,524,287,000.
Headquarters: 1818 H Street, N.W., Washington 25, D.C.

EUROPEAN PAYMENTS UNION (E.P.U.): Established in 1950 as a multilateral credit pool set up by the Organization for European Economic Co-operation (O.E.E.C.), with the Bank of International Settlements (B.I.S.) authorized as its agent. Foremost purpose that of facilitating the balance of intra-European trade payments, the promotion of European economic integration and the raising of European productivity. The initial working fund of the pool was $3,950,000,000, with the B.I.S. being entrusted with its operations and management. The member countries are Austria, Belgium, Denmark, France, West Germany, Greece, Iceland, Italy, Luxembourg, Netherlands, Norway, Portugal, Sweden, Switzerland, Turkey, and the United Kingdom.
Headquarters of Council: Paris, France.

TABLE IX-1. GOLD PARITY AND EXCHANGE RATIOS, 1882–1952

(U. S. Dollar = 100)

	Gold parity basis		Exchange basis		Variation of exchange rate over gold parity		1952
	1882	1952	1882	1952	1882	1952	
United States	100.00	100.00	100.00	100.00	.00	.00	Identical
United Kingdom	486.65	280.00	486.65	280.00	.00	.00	Identical
Canada	100.00	169.31	90.24	102.98	− 9.76	− 66.33	a
France	80.69	.83	19.30	.02	−61.39	− .81	
Germany	23.82	23.81	23.80	21.70	.02	2.11	a
Belgium	13.90	2.00	13.91	2.00	+ .01	.00	
Italy	5.26	5.26	5.23	.16	.03	5.10	Identical
Netherlands	40.20	26.32	40.16	26.32	− .04	.00	a
Japan	49.85	.28	46.10	.28	− 3.75	.00	Identical
Brazil	11.96	5.40	11.81	5.40	− .15	.00	Identical
Australia	486.65	224.00	486.65	224.00	.00	.00	Identical
Sweden	26.79	19.33	26.79	19.33	.00	.00	Identical
India	36.49	21.00	36.20	21.00	− .29	.00	Identical
Union of S. Africa	486.65	280.00	486.65	280.00	.00	.00	Identical
Switzerland	19.29	22.78	19.28	23.34	− .01	+ .56	Identical
Russia	51.46	25.00	51.50	25.00	− .04	.00	Identical
Denmark	26.68	14.47	26.68	14.47	.00	.00	Identical
Norway	26.79	14.00	26.68	14.00	− .11	.00	Identical
Argentina	96.47	181.50	95.13	25.00	− 1.34	−156.50	a
Venezuela	19.29	29.85	19.29	29.85	.00	.00	Identical
Mexico	49.84	11.56	48.18	11.56	− 1.66	.00	Identical
Finland	2.51	.43	2.51	.43	.00	.00	Identical
New Zealand	486.65	280.00	486.65	277.32	.00	− 2.68	
Austria	14.07	3.84	14.06	3.84	− .01	.00	Identical
Egypt	494.31	287.15	499.02	287.15	+ 4.71	.00	Identical

SOURCE: International Monetary Fund.

a Par value not yet established.

173

TABLE IX-2. THE WORLD'S HOLDINGS OF GOLD RESERVES, 1952

(U. S. Dollar Values)

International Monetary Fund	1,692,000,000
Bank for International Settlements	196,000,000
International Bank for Reconstruction and Development	177,000,000
European Payments Union	159,000,000
Total international agencies	2,224,000,000
Egypt	174,000,000
Union of S. Africa	170,000,000
Ethiopia	4,460,000
Total Africa	348,460,000
United States [a]	23,252,000,000
Canada	896,000,000
Cuba	214,000,000
Mexico	144,000,000
Panama	29,400,000
El Salvador	29,390,000
Guatemala	27,200,000
Dominican Republic	12,100,000
Nicaragua	2,760,000
Costa Rica	2,060,000
Honduras	110,000
Total N. America	24,609,020,000
Venezuela	373,000,000
Brazil	317,000,000
Argentina	288,000,000
Uruguay	207,000,000
Colombia	48,000,000
Peru	46,100,000
Chile	41,600,000
Bolivia	23,000,000
Ecuador	22,600,000
Paraguay	190,000
Total S. America	1,366,490,000

India	247,000,000
Indonesia	235,000,000
Turkey	143,000,000
Iran	138,000,000
Indo-China	121,072,000
Japan	121,000,000
Thailand	113,000,000
Burma	39,928,000
Iraq	38,000,000
Pakistan	38,000,000
Lebanon	30,630,000
Ceylon	18,000,000
Philippines	9,000,000
Israel	3,800,000
Other areas	15,000,000
Total Asia	1,310,430,000
United Kingdom [a]	1,500,000,000
Switzerland	1,411,000,000
Belgium-Luxembourg [a]	788,000,000
France [a]	593,000,000
Netherlands [a]	568,000,000
Italy	346,000,000
Portugal [a]	307,000,000
Sweden	184,000,000
Germany	140,000,000
Czechoslovakia	91,220,000
Poland	64,650,000
Hungary	59,740,000
Spain [a]	51,000,000
Norway	50,000,000
Denmark	31,300,000
Finland	26,400,000
Ireland	18,000,000
Yugoslavia	12,000,000
Austria	10,000,000
Greece	9,900,000
Bulgaria	8,293,000
Romania	5,077,000
Iceland	1,000,000
Total Europe	6,275,600,000
Australia	113,000,000
New Zealand	33,000,000
Total Oceania	146,000,000
Grand total	36,280,000,000

SOURCES: Reports of the International Monetary Fund, and the Bank for International Settlements.

COMMENT: There are no official data for China and the U.S.S.R. Soviet currency ceased to be redeemed in gold after March, 1926. The basis for Chinese currency is largely silver. On the basis of "gold disappearance" after official estimates for gold going into increases in reserves and for industrial uses since 1946, there was $1,960,000,000 in gold, either unreported or in private hoardings.

[a] Includes dependencies.

TABLE IX-3. THE WORLD'S CURRENCY SUPPLY, 1952

(U. S. Dollar Values)

International Monetary Fund	5,682,000,000	India	2,478,000,000
Bank for International Set-		Indonesia	354,488,000
tlements	246,000,000	Turkey	457,139,000
International Bank for Re-		Iran	214,520,000
construction and Develop-		Indo-China	556,603,000
ment	1,379,000,000	Japan	1,535,000,000
European Payments Union	67,000,000	Thailand	288,320,000
		Burma	86,518,000
Total international agencies	7,374,000,000	Iraq	84,000,000
		Pakistan	650,140,000
Egypt	592,977,000	Lebanon	93,542,000
Union of S. Africa	238,627,000	Ceylon	74,970,000
Ethiopia	49,554,000	Philippines	312,000,000
		Israel	296,800,000
Total Africa	881,158,000	Other areas [b]	225,000,000
United States [a]	27,500,000,000	Total Asia	7,707,040,000
Canada	1,432,080,000		
Cuba	385,000,000	United Kingdom [a]	4,073,630,000
Mexico	421,824,000	Switzerland	1,278,712,000
Panama	1,500,000	Belgium-Luxembourg [a]	2,042,000,000
El Salvador	38,472,000	France [a]	6,074,640,000
Guatemala	45,400,000	Netherlands [a]	653,131,000
Dominican Republic	29,640,000	Italy	2,162,000,000
Nicaragua	18,140,000	Portugal [a]	311,205,000
Costa Rica	22,315,000	Sweden	893,046,000
Honduras	14,460,000	Germany	2,433,382,000
		Czechoslovakia	2,476,880,000
Total N. America	29,908,831,000	Poland	1,668,197,000
		Hungary	238,958,000
Venezuela	267,456,000	Spain [a]	1,540,000,000
Brazil	1,704,197,000	Norway	390,740,000
Argentina	3,643,400,000	Denmark	273,471,000
Uruguay	18,557,000	Finland	203,580,000
Colombia	307,487,000	Ireland	196,377,000
Peru	78,724,000	Yugoslavia	999,200,000
Chile	370,553,000	Austria	338,063,000
Bolivia	99,827,000	Greece	148,560,000
Ecuador	34,196,000	Bulgaria	2,605,000
Paraguay	59,731,000	Romania	12,132,000
		Iceland	13,938,000
Total S. America	6,584,128,000		
		Total Europe	2,424,447,000
		Australia	754,880,000
		New Zealand	166,947,000
		Total Oceania	921,827,000
		Grand total	81,801,431,000

SOURCES: The Bank for International Settlements, and the International Monetary Fund; *The Statesman's Yearbook*, 1953.

[a] Includes dependencies.
[b] Estimates.

175

TABLE IX–4. THE WORLD'S PRIVATE DEMAND BANK DEPOSIT MONEY, 1952

(U. S. Dollar Values)

International Monetary Fund	765,800,000	India	1,255,800,000
Bank for International Settlements	110,000,000	Indonesia	202,115,140
		Turkey	498,567,640
International Bank for Reconstruction and Development	437,400,000	Iran	234,980,000
		Indo-China	55,376,000
European Payments Union	351,500,000	Japan	2,716,950,000
		Thailand	107,760,000
Total international agencies	1,664,700,000	Burma	45,974,480
		Iraq	42,000,000
		Pakistan	322,198,250
Egypt	460,885,520	Lebanon	137,345,800
Union of S. Africa	916,740,500	Ceylon	112,770,000
Ethiopia	23,120,000	Philippines	229,000,000
		Israel	450,800,000
Total Africa	1,400,746,020	Other areas [b]	6,458,913,000
United States [a]	101,500,000,000	Total Asia	12,870,550,310
Canada	3,740,920,000		
Cuba	1,159,000,000	United Kingdom [a]	11,041,342,000
Mexico	396,392,800	Switzerland	1,383,849,440
Panama	23,500,000	Belgium-Luxembourg [a]	1,530,000,000
El Salvador	28,728,000	France [a]	5,814,380,000
Guatemala	21,600,000	Netherlands [a]	1,005,133,470
Dominican Republic	35,360,000	Italy	3,254,040,000
Nicaragua	18,060,000	Portugal [a]	706,363,000
Costa Rica	24,522,670	Sweden	1,123,073,000
Honduras	245,540,000	Germany	2,497,669,000
		Czechoslovakia	600,000,000
Total N. America	107,193,623,470	Poland	1,122,803,000
		Hungary	549,475,450
Venezuela	302,380,500	Spain [a]	1,588,000,000
Brazil	3,925,651,000	Norway	798,420,000
Argentina	2,175,400,000	Denmark	736,734,000
Uruguay	23,599,630	Finland	101,790,000
Colombia	363,794,380	Ireland	247,508,200
Peru	128,573,480	Yugoslavia	1,194,200,000
Chile	697,244,500	Austria	377,677,600
Bolivia	62,724,620	Greece	169,860,000
Ecuador	34,997,080	Bulgaria	357,877,100
Paraguay	38,598,400	Romania	200,989,000
		Iceland	11,543,000
Total S. America	7,752,963,590		
		Total Europe	36,412,727,260
		Australia	2,412,480,000
		New Zealand	518,033,400
		Total Oceania	2,930,513,400
		Grand total	170,225,824,050

SOURCES: International Monetary Fund; The Bank for International Settlements; *The Statesman's Yearbook*, 1953.

[a] Includes dependencies.
[b] Estimates.

TABLE IX-5. THE WORLD'S TOTAL REPORTED CURRENCY AND DEPOSIT MONEY, 1952

(*In U. S. Dollar Values*)

International Monetary Fund	6,447,800,000	India	3,733,800,000
Bank for International Set-		Indonesia	556,603,140
tlements	356,000,000	Turkey	955,706,640
International Bank for Re-		Iran	449,500,000
construction and Develop-		Indo-China	611,979,000
ment	1,816,400,000	Japan	4,251,950,000
European Payments Union	418,500,000	Thailand	396,080,000
		Burma	132,492,480
Total international agencies	9,038,700,000	Iraq	126,000,000
		Pakistan	972,338,250
Egypt	1,053,862,520	Lebanon	230,887,800
Union of S. Africa	1,155,367,500	Ceylon	187,740,000
Ethiopia	72,674,000	Philippines	541,000,000
		Israel	747,600,000
Total Africa	2,281,904,020	Other areas	6,683,913,000
United States [a]	129,000,000,000	Total Asia	20,577,590,310
Canada	5,173,000,000		
Cuba	1,544,000,000	United Kingdom [a]	15,114,972,000
Mexico	818,216,800	Switzerland	2,662,561,440
Panama	25,000,000	Belgium-Luxembourg [a]	3,572,000,000
El Salvador	67,200,000	France [a]	11,889,020,000
Guatemala	67,000,000	Netherlands [a]	1,658,264,470
Dominican Republic	65,000,000	Italy	5,416,040,000
Nicaragua	36,200,000	Portugal [a]	1,017,568,000
Costa Rica	46,837,670	Sweden	2,016,119,000
Honduras	260,000,000	Germany	4,931,051,000
		Czechoslovakia	3,076,880,000
Total N. America	137,102,454,470	Poland	2,791,000,000
		Hungary	788,433,450
Venezuela	569,836,500	Spain [a]	3,128,000,000
Brazil	5,629,848,000	Norway	1,189,160,000
Argentina	5,818,800,000	Denmark	1,010,205,000
Uruguay	42,156,630	Finland	305,370,000
Colombia	671,281,380	Ireland	443,885,200
Peru	207,297,480	Yugoslavia	2,193,400,000
Chile	1,067,797,500	Austria	715,740,600
Bolivia	162,551,620	Greece	318,420,000
Ecuador	69,193,080	Bulgaria	360,482,100
Paraguay	98,329,400	Romania	213,121,000
		Iceland	25,481,000
Total S. America	14,337,091,590		
		Total Europe	64,837,174,260
		Australia	3,167,360,000
		New Zealand	684,980,400
		Total Oceania	3,852,340,400
		Grand total	252,027,255,050

SOURCES: The Bank for International Settlements, and the International Monetary Fund; *The Statesman's Yearbook*, 1953.

[a] Includes dependencies.

TABLE IX–6. PERCENTAGE DISTRIBUTION OF MONEY TABLES IX–2, IX–3 IX–4, and IX–5, 1952

Table	IX–2	IX–3	IX–4	IX–5
International Monetary Fund	4.7%	6.9%	.45%	2.6%
Bank for International Settlements	.5	.3	.10	.1
International Bank for Reconstruction and Development	.5	1.7	.25	.7
European Payments Union	.4	.1	.20	.2
Total international agencies	6.1%	9.0%	1.0%	3.6%
Egypt	.5%	.7%	.27%	.4%
Union of S. Africa	.49	.3	.52	.5
Ethiopia	.01	.1	.01	.03
Total Africa	1.0%	1.1%	.8%	.9%
United States [a]	64.1%	33.61%	59.63%	51.2%
Canada	2.5	1.75	2.20	2.1
Cuba	.6	.50	.70	.6
Mexico	.4	.52	.23	.3
Panama	.08	.002	.01	.01
El Salvador	.08	.05	.02	.03
Guatemala	.07	.06	.01	.03
Dominican Republic	.03	.04	.02	.03
Nicaragua	.008	.02	.01	.01
Costa Rica	.006	.03	.01	.02
Honduras	.0003	.02	.14	.10
Total North America	67.8%	36.6%	63.0%	54.4%
Venezuela	1.1%	.32%	.17%	.2%
Brazil	.9	2.08	2.30	2.2
Argentina	.8	4.45	1.27	2.3
Uruguay	.6	.02	.01	.02
Colombia	.1	.37	.20	.30
Peru	.1	.09	.07	.08
Chile	.1	.44	.40	.42
Bolivia	.06	.12	.04	.06
Ecuador	.06	.04	.02	.03
Paraguay	.0005	.07	.02	.04
Total South America	3.8%	8.0%	4.5%	5.7%
India	.70%	3.03%	.74%	1.5%
Indonesia	.64	.43	.12	.2
Turkey	.40	.56	.29	.4
Iran	.40	.26	.14	.2
Indo-China	.33	.68	.03	.2
Japan	.33	1.88	1.60	1.7
Thailand	.30	.28	.06	.16
Burma	.10	.11	.03	.05
Iraq	.10	.10	.03	.05
Pakistan	.10	.79	.19	.40
Lebanon	.08	.11	.08	.09
Ceylon	.05	.10	.07	.07
Philippines	.02	.38	.14	.21
Israel	.01	.36	.27	.30
Other areas	.04	.28	3.79	2.65
Total Asia	3.6%	9.4%	7.6%	8.2%

TABLE IX-6 (concluded)

Table	IX-2	IX-3	IX-4	IX-5
United Kingdom [a]	4.1%	4.99%	6.50%	6.0%
Switzerland	3.9	1.56	.81	1.1
Belgium-Luxembourg [a]	2.2	2.50	.90	1.4
France [a]	1.6	7.43	3.41	4.7
Netherlands [a]	1.6	.80	.59	.7
Italy	.95	2.64	1.91	2.1
Portugal [a]	.85	.38	.41	.4
Sweden	.51	1.09	.66	.8
Germany	.38	2.98	1.47	2.0
Czechoslovakia	.25	3.03	.35	1.2
Poland	.18	2.04	.66	1.1
Hungary	.16	.29	.32	.3
Spain [a]	.14	1.88	.93	1.2
Norway	.14	.48	.47	.5
Denmark	.09	.33	.43	.4
Finland	.07	.25	.06	.1
Ireland	.05	.24	.14	.2
Yugoslavia	.03	1.22	.70	.9
Austria	.03	.41	.22	.3
Greece	.03	.18	.10	.1
Bulgaria	.02	.003	.21	.1
Romania	.01	.02	.12	.08
Iceland	.003	.02	.01	.01
Total Europe	17.3%	34.8%	21.4%	25.7%
Australia	.3%	.9%	1.4%	1.2%
New Zealand	.1	.2	.3	.3
Total Oceania	.4%	1.1%	1.7%	1.5%
Grand total	100.0%	100.0%	100.0%	100.0%

NOTE: Column IX-2, gold; Column IX-3, currency; Column IX-4, bank deposits; Column IX-5, total money supply.

[a] Includes dependencies.

TABLE IX-7. PERCENTAGE DIVISION OF TABLE IX-2, GOLD; TABLE IX-3
CURRENCY; TABLE IX-4, DEPOSIT MONEY, 1952

Table	IX-2	IX-3	IX-4	Total
International Monetary Fund	20.8%	69.8%	9.4%	100%
Bank for International Settlements	35.5	44.6	19.9	100
International Bank for Reconstruction and Development	8.9	69.2	21.9	100
European Payments Union	27.5	11.6	60.9	100
Total international agencies	19.7%	65.5%	14.8%	100%
Egypt	14.2%	48.3%	37.5%	100%
Union of S. Africa	12.8	18.0	69.2	100
Ethiopia	5.8	64.2	30.0	100
Total Africa	13.2%	33.5%	53.3%	100%
United States [a]	15.3%	18.1%	66.6%	100%
Canada	14.8	23.6	61.6	100
Cuba	12.2	21.9	65.9	100
Mexico	15.0	43.8	41.2	100
Panama	54.0	2.8	43.2	100
El Salvador	30.4	39.8	29.8	100
Guatemala	28.9	48.2	22.9	100
Dominican Republic	15.7	38.4	45.9	100
Nicaragua	7.1	46.6	46.3	100
Costa Rica	4.2	45.6	50.2	100
Honduras	.04	5.6	94.4	100
Total N. America	15.2%	18.5%	66.3%	100%
Venezuela	39.6%	28.4%	32.0%	100%
Brazil	5.3	28.7	66.0	100
Argentina	4.7	59.7	35.6	100
Uruguay	83.1	7.4	9.5	100
Colombia	6.7	42.7	50.6	100
Peru	18.2	31.1	50.7	100
Chile	3.7	33.4	62.9	100
Bolivia	12.4	53.8	33.8	100
Ecuador	24.6	37.3	38.1	100
Paraguay	.2	60.6	39.2	100
Total S. America	8.7%	41.9%	49.4%	100%
India	6.2%	62.2%	31.6%	100%
Indonesia	29.7	44.8	25.5	100
Turkey	13.0	41.6	45.4	100
Iran	23.5	36.5	40.0	100
Indo-China	16.5	75.9	7.6	100
Japan	2.8	35.1	62.1	100
Thailand	22.2	56.6	21.2	100
Burma	23.2	50.2	26.6	100
Iraq	23.2	51.2	25.6	100
Pakistan	3.8	64.3	31.9	100
Lebanon	11.7	35.8	52.5	100
Ceylon	8.7	36.4	54.9	100
Philippines	1.6	56.7	41.7	100
Israel	.5	39.5	60.0	100
Other areas	.2	3.4	96.4	100
Total Asia	6.0%	35.2%	58.8%	100%

TABLE IX-7 (concluded)

Table	IX-2	IX-3	IX-4	Total
United Kingdom [a]	9.0%	24.5%	66.5%	100%
Switzerland	34.6	31.4	34.0	100
Belgium-Luxembourg [a]	18.1	46.8	35.1	100
France [a]	4.7	48.7	46.6	100
Netherlands [a]	25.5	29.3	45.2	100
Italy	6.0	37.5	56.5	100
Portugal [a]	23.2	23.5	53.3	100
Sweden	8.4	40.6	51.0	100
Germany	2.8	48.0	49.2	100
Czechoslovakia	2.9	78.2	18.9	100
Poland	2.3	58.4	39.3	100
Hungary	7.0	28.2	64.8	100
Spain [a]	1.6	48.4	50.0	100
Norway	4.0	31.5	64.5	100
Denmark	3.0	26.3	70.7	100
Finland	8.0	61.3	30.7	100
Ireland	3.9	42.5	53.6	100
Yugoslavia	.5	45.3	54.2	100
Austria	1.4	46.6	52.0	100
Greece	3.0	45.3	51.7	100
Bulgaria	2.3	.7	97.0	100
Romania	2.3	5.6	92.1	100
Iceland	3.8	52.6	43.6	100
Total Europe	8.8%	40.0%	51.2%	100%
Australia	3.4%	23.0%	73.6%	100%
New Zealand	4.6	23.2	72.2	100
Total Oceania	3.6%	23.1%	73.3%	100%
Grand total	12.6%	28.4%	59.0%	100%

SOURCE: See original Tables IX-2, IX-3, IX-4, and IX-5.

[a] Includes dependencies.

TABLE IX–8. THE WORLD'S CURRENCIES AND THEIR EXCHANGE EQUIVALENTS, 1952

(In U. S. Dollar Values)

	Currency unit	U.S. dollars		Currency unit	U.S. dollars
Africa:			**Asia: (continued)**		
Egypt	Pound	2.87156	Thailand	Baht	.08000
Union of S. Africa	Pound	2.79750	Burma	Kyat	.20964
Ethiopia	Dollar	.40000	Iraq	Dinar	2.80000
America, North:			Pakistan	Rupee	.30225
United States[a]	Dollar	1.00000	Lebanon	Pound	.45630
Canada	Dollar	1.04000	Ceylon	Rupee	.21000
Cuba	Peso	1.00000	Philippines	Peso	.50000
Mexico	Peso	.11560	Israel	Israeli Pound	2.80000
Panama	Balboa	1.00000	**Europe:**		
El Salvador	Colon	.40000	United Kingdom[a]	Pound	2.80940
Guatemala	Quetzal	1.00000	Switzerland	Franc	.23364
Dominican Republic	Peso	1.00000	Belgium-Luxembourg[a]	Franc	.02000
Nicaragua	Cordoba	.20000	France[a]	Franc	.00286
Costa Rica	Colon	.17809	Netherlands[a]	Guilder	.20597
Honduras	Limpira	.50000	Italy	Lire	.00161
America, South			Portugal[a]	Escudo	.03454
Venezuela	Bolevar	.29850	Sweden	Krona	.19330
Brazil	Cruzeiro	.05405	Germany	Deutsche Mark	.23810
Argentina	Peso	.20000	Czechoslovakia	Korunas	.02000
Uruguay	Peso	.05263	Poland	Zloty	.01000
Colombia	Peso	.51282	Hungary	Forint	.08519
Peru	Sol	.06474	Spain[a]	Peseta	.04000
Chile	Peso	.03225	Norway	Krone	.14000
Bolivia	Boliviano	.01666	Denmark	Krone	.14477
Ecuador	Sucre	.06666	Finland	Markka	.00435
Paraguay	Guarani	.16666	Ireland	Pound	2.80940
Asia:			Yugoslavia	Dinar	.02000
India	Rupee	.21000	Austria	Schilling	.03846
Indonesia	Rupiah	.08742	Greece	Drachma	.00006
Turkey	Lira	.35714	U.S.S.R.	Rouble	.25000
Iran	Rial	.03100	Bulgaria	Lev	.00349
China	Jen Min Piao	.20000	Romania	Leu	.06666
U.S.S.R.	Rouble	.25000	Iceland	Krona	.06140
Indo-China	Piastre	.04861	**Oceania:**		
Japan	Yen	.00277	Australia	Pound	2.24000
			New Zealand	Pound	2.77320

SOURCE: The International Monetary Fund, *International Financial Statistics*, Vol. VI, No. 8, 1953.

TABLE IX–9. THE WORLD'S MONEY SUPPLY, 1952

Country	Currency unit	U. S. cents per unit	Money supply	Total value in U. S. dollars	% of world total
Africa:					
Union of S. Africa	Pound	2.79750	413,000,000	1,155,367,500	.46%
Egypt	Pound	2.87156	367,000,000	1,053,862,520	.42
Total Africa				2,209,230,020	.88%
America, North:					
United States	Dollar	1.00000	129,000,000,000	129,000,000,000	51.18%
Canada	Dollar	1.04000	5,173,000,000	5,379,920,000	2.14
Cuba	Peso	1.00000	1,544,000,000	1,544,000,000	.61
Mexico	Peso	.11560	7,078,000,000	818,216,800	.32
Honduras	Limpira	.50000	52,000,000	260,000,000	.10
El Salvador	Colon	.40000	168,000,000	67,200,000	.03
Guatemala	Quetzal	1.00000	67,000,000	67,000,000	.03
Dominican Republic	Peso	1.00000	65,000,000	65,000,000	.03
Costa Rica	Colon	.17809	263,000,000	46,837,670	.02
Nicaragua	Cordoba	.20000	181,000,000	36,200,000	.01
Panama	Balboa	1.00000	25,000,000	25,000,000	.01
Total N. America				137,309,374,470	54.48%
America, South:					
Argentina	Peso	.20000	29,094,000,000	5,818,800,000	2.31%
Brazil	Cruzeiro	.05405	104,160,000,000	5,629,848,000	2.23
Chile	Peso	.03225	33,110,000,000	1,067,797,500	.42
Colombia	Peso	.51282	1,309,000,000	671,281,380	.27
Venezuela	Bolivar	.29850	1,909,000,000	569,836,500	.23
Peru	Sol	.06474	3,202,000,000	207,297,480	.08
Bolivia	Boliviano	.01666	9,757,000,000	162,551,620	.06
Paraguay	Guarani	.16666	590,000,000	98,329,400	.04
Ecuador	Sucre	.06666	1,038,000,000	69,193,080	.03
Uruguay	Peso	.05263	801,000,000	42,156,630	.02
Total S. America				14,337,091,590	5.69%

TABLE IX–9. THE WORLD'S MONEY SUPPLY, 1952 (Concluded)

Country	Currency unit	U. S. cents per unit	Money supply	Total value in U. S. dollars	% of world total
Asia:					
China	Jen Min Piao	.20000	46,557,000,000	9,311,400,000	3.69%
Japan	Yen	.00277	1,535,000,000,000	4,251,950,000	1.69
India	Rupee	.21000	17,780,000,000	3,733,800,000	1.48
U.S.S.R. [a]	Rouble	.25000	4,766,000,000	1,191,375,000	.47
Pakistan	Rupee	.30225	3,217,000,000	972,338,250	.39
Turkey	Lira	.35714	2,676,000,000	955,706,640	.38
Israel	Israeli Pound	2.80000	267,000,000	747,600,000	.30
Indonesia	Rupiah	.08742	6,367,000,000	556,603,140	.22
Philippines	Peso	.50000	1,082,000,000	541,000,000	.21
Iran	Rial	.03100	14,500,000,000	449,500,000	.18
Indo-China	Piastre	.04861	8,254,000,000	401,226,940	.16
Thailand	Baht	.08000	4,951,000,000	396,080,000	.16
Lebanon	Pound	.45630	506,000,000	230,887,800	.09
Ceylon	Rupee	.21000	894,000,000	187,740,000	.07
Burma	Kyat	.20964	632,000,000	132,492,480	.05
Iraq	Dinar	2.80000	45,000,000	126,000,000	.05
Total Asia				24,185,700,250	9.59%
Europe:					
United Kingdom	Pound	2.80940	5,380,000,000	15,114,572,000	6.00%
France	Franc	.00286	4,157,000,000,000	11,889,020,000	4.72
Italy	Lire	.00161	3,364,000,000,000	5,416,040,000	2.15
Germany	Deutsche Mark	.23810	20,710,000,000	4,931,051,000	1.96
U.S.S.R. [a]	Rouble	.25000	17,734,000,000	4,433,625,000	1.76
Czechoslovakia	Korunas	.02000	197,000,000,000	3,940,000,000	1.56
Belgium-Luxembourg	Franc	.02000	178,600,000,000	3,572,000,000	1.42

184

Spain	Peseta	.04000	78,200,000,000	3,128,000,000	1.24
Poland	Zloty	.01000	279,100,000,000	2,791,000,000	1.11
Switzerland	Franc	.23364	11,396,000,000	2,662,561,440	1.06
Yugoslavia	Dinar	.02000	109,670,000,000	2,193,400,000	.87
Sweden	Krona	.19330	10,430,000,000	2,016,119,000	.80
Netherlands	Guilder	.20597	8,051,000,000	1,658,264,470	.66
Norway	Krone	.14000	8,494,000,000	1,189,160,000	.47
Portugal	Escudo	.03454	29,200,000,000	1,017,568,000	.40
Denmark	Krone	.14477	6,978,000,000	1,010,205,060	.40
Hungary	Forint	.08519	9,255,000,000	788,433,450	.31
Austria	Schilling	.03846	18,610,000,000	715,740,600	.28
Ireland	Pound	2.80940	158,000,000	443,885,200	.18
Bulgaria	Lev	.00349	103,290,000,000	360,482,100	.14
Greece	Drachma	.00006	5,307,000,000,000	318,420,000	.13
Finland	Markka	.00435	70,200,000,000	305,370,000	.12
Romania	Leu	.00666	32,000,000,000	213,120,000	.08
Iceland	Krona	.06140	415,000,000	25,481,000	.01
Total Europe				70,133,518,320	27.83%
Oceania:					
Australia	Pound	2.24000	1,414,000,000	3,167,360,000	1.26%
New Zealand	Pound	2.77320	247,000,000	684,980,400	.27
Total Oceania				3,852,340,400	1.53%
World total				252,027,255,050	100.00%

SOURCES: The International Monetary Fund, *International Financial Statistics*, Vol. VI, No. 8, 1953; Mulhall's *Dictionary of Statistics*, 1883.

DEFINITION: Money supply contains currency in circulation, in hands of business, individuals, foreigners, and the government; *deposit money*: demand deposits of business, individuals, and foreigners with the Central Bank and other banks.

[a] U.S.S.R. total of $5,625,000,000 is divided 78.82% in Europe, 21.18% in Asia.

TABLE IX–10. PRINCIPAL CHANGES IN THE WORLD'S MONEY SUPPLY, 1882–1952

(*In U. S. Dollar Values*)

Paper money:

1952	77,874,463,000	
1882	1,354,858,000	
+70	+ 76,519,605,000	+5,647%

Gold reserves:

1952	36,280,000,000	
1882	700,000,000	
+70	+ 35,580,000,000	+5,082%

Bank deposits:

1952	170,225,824,000	
1882	3,936,982,000	
+70	+166,288,842,000	+4,224%

Total currency:

1952	81,801,431,000	
1882	2,157,418,000	
+70	+ 79,644,013,000	+3,692%

Metallic coins:

1952	3,926,468,000	
1882	802,560,000	
+70	+ 3,123,908,000	+ 389%

Total money supply:

1952	252,027,255,000	
1882	6,094,400,000	
+70	+245,932,855,000	+4,035%

SOURCES: Reports of The Bank for International Settlements and the International Monetary Fund.

NOTE: The above data, while compiled from the best available official sources, are not to be regarded as precise figures, but rather as an indication of the relative order of magnitude.

TABLE IX–11.   CHANGES IN THE WORLD'S CURRENCIES BY LEGAL GOLD CONTENT AND BY EXCHANGE RATES PER UNIT, 1882–1952

(In Relation to the U. S. Gold Dollar)

		Grams of Fine Gold per Currency Unit				Changes in Exchange Rates in U. S. Cents per Currency Unit			
	Unit	1882[a]	1952	Change	% Change	1882	1952	Change	% Change
United States	Dollar	1.50463	.88867	—.61596	—40.9%	100.00000	100.00000		
United Kingdom	Pound	7.32238	2.48828	—4.83410	—66.0	486.65000	280.00000	—206.65000	—42.5%
Canada	Dollar[b]	1.50463	1.50463	—	—	90.24720	102.98661	+ 12.73941	+14.1
France[b]	Franc	1.21423	.00746	—1.20677	—99.4	19.30000	.28571	— 19.01429	—98.5
Germany	Mark	.35842	.21158	—.14684	—41.0	23.80860	21.70117	— 2.10743	—8.8
Belgium	Franc	.20921	.01777	—.19144	—91.5	13.91240	2.00000	— 11.91240	—85.6
Italy	Lira	.07919	.04677	—.03242	—40.9	5.23340	.16000	— 5.07340	—96.9
Netherlands	Guilder	.60480	.23386	—.37094	—61.3	40.16220	26.31580	— 13.84640	—34.5
Japan	Yen	.75000	.00246	—.74754	—99.7	46.09970	.27778	— 45.82192	—99.4
Brazil	Cruzeiro	.18000	.04803	—.13197	—73.3	11.80780	5.40541	— 6.40239	—54.2
Australia	Pound	7.32238	1.99062	—5.33176	—72.8	486.65000	224.00000	—262.65000	—54.0
Sweden	Krona	.40323	.17178	—.23145	—57.4	26.78390	19.33040	— 7.45350	—27.8
India	Rupee	.54918	.18662	—.36256	—66.0	36.20200	21.00000	— 15.20200	—42.0
Union of S. Africa	Pound	7.32238	2.48828	—4.83410	—66.0	486.65000	280.00000	—206.65000	—42.5
Switzerland	Franc	.29032	.20242	—.08790	—30.3	19.27920	23.33722	+ 4.05802	+21.1
Russia	Rouble	.77423	.22216	—.55207	—71.3	51.50000	25.00000	— 26.50000	—51.5
Denmark	Krone	.40143	.12866	—.27277	—67.9	26.68020	14.47778	— 12.20242	—45.7
Norway	Krone	.40323	.12441	—.27882	—69.1	26.68270	14.00000	— 12.68270	—47.5
Argentina	Peso	1.45161	1.61290	+ .16129	+11.1	95.12740	25.00000	— 70.12740	—73.7
Venezuela	Bolivar	.29032	.26527	—.02505	—8.6	19.29730	29.85070	+ 10.55340	+54.7
Mexico	Peso	.75000	.10273	—.64727	—86.3	48.18300	11.56070	— 36.62230	—76.0
Finland	Markka	.03789	.00386	—.03403	—89.8	2.51600	.43285	— 2.08315	—82.8
New Zealand	Pound	7.32238	2.48828	—4.83410	—66.0	486.65000	277.32000	—209.33000	—43.0
Austria	Schilling	.21172	.03417	—.17755	—83.9	14.05750	3.84615	— 10.21135	—72.6
Egypt	Pound	7.43750	2.55187	—4.88563	—65.7%	499.02540	287.15600	—211.86940	—42.5%

SOURCES: 1882 period: *The New Encyclopedia of Social Reform*, Bliss ed.,1908; *Encyclopaedia Britannica*, 11th ed.; *Statistical Yearbook of The League of Nations*, Geneva, 1938; *The Statesman's Yearbook*, 1884; *Century Book of Facts*, 1904. 1952 period: International Monetary Fund.

a The year 1882 is nominal only, as the actual adopted standard has varied between countries: United Kingdom, from 1816; Germany, 1875; Egypt, 1885; Russia, 1885; Switzerland, 1883; Belgium, 1832; France, 1870; Japan, 1898; India, 1899; Austria, 1892; United States, 1900; Mexico, 1905.
b No par value established since 1948.

TABLE IX–12. MAJOR BALANCE OF PAYMENTS BY PRINCIPAL CATEGORIES, 1952

(In Thousands of U. S. Dollars)

	Net Balance of Transactions								Compensatory Financing			
	Goods & transportation [a]	Investment income [b]	Private capital [c]	Private donations [d]	Official donations [e]	Other services [f]	Errors, omissions [g]	Total	Total	Long-term [h]	Short-term [i]	Total
SECTION A: PRINCIPAL TRADING COUNTRIES:												
United States	+2,636,000	+2,248,000	−1,585,000	−430,000	−1,930,000	−1,839,000	+470,000	430,000	430,000	−147,600	+577,000	+430,000
United Kingdom	−30,903	+216,323	+261,274	−16,856	+255,655	+292,177	—	455,122	455,122	+25,285	−480,407	−455,122
Canada	+659,360	−277,680	+9,360	−36,400	+16,640	−171,600	—	147,680	147,680	+40,560	−188,240	−147,680
France	−783,100	+19,000	+49,100	+4,900	+299,800	+195,900	+6,600	259,000	259,000	+61,700	−320,700	−259,000
Germany, West	+413,500	+4,600	—	+8,500	+116,400	+139,300	+27,700	710,000	710,000	−191,100	−518,900	−710,000
Belgium-Luxembourg	+168,200	+16,600	+72,800	+4,000	+8,000	+18,400	+17,800	123,400	123,400	−39,000	−84,400	−123,400
Italy	−791,800	+12,900	+224,700	+132,400	+166,200	+166,200	+29,100	86,100	86,100	−15,800	+101,900	+86,100
Netherlands	+208,442	+46,755	+40,576	+6,797	+21,215	+129,967	+1,442	452,310	452,310	+35,633	+416,677	+452,310
Japan	−556,000	−4,900	+37,500	+27,000	+5,400	+754,200	+400	262,800	262,800	−116,700	−146,100	−262,800
Brazil	−505,854	−121,072	+653,140	+3,892	+1,730	+81,021	+49,293	106,262	106,262	+2,540	+103,722	+106,262
Australia	−1,080,352	−132,608	+163,072	+19,936	+7,840	+101,472	+144,704	994,560	994,560	+49,280	+945,280	+994,560
Sweden	+47,165	+13,531	+21,263	+6,766	+7,925	+22,230	—	60,888	60,888	+24,549	+36,339	+60,888
India	−166,110	−23,520	+3,990	+35,280	+24,990	+132,930	+148,680	149,100	149,100	+103,950	+45,150	+149,100
Union of S. Africa	−55,391	−130,644		+1,958	—	+6,155	+121,412	56,510	56,510	+40,844	+15,666	+56,510
Switzerland	−120,091	−79,438	−132,708	—	—	+183,875	+139,016	149,530	149,530	+20,560	+170,090	+149,530
Indonesia	−93,277	−79,727	+19,058	—	+7,256	+76,580	+42,224	303,610	303,610	+78,416	+225,194	+303,610
Denmark	+23,887	+10,423	+3,330	—	+6,370	+8,686	+37,060	68,910	68,910	−21,281	−47,629	−68,910

188

Statistical balance table (countries × account columns, in thousands). Signs (+ = credit, − = debit) as printed; blank cells indicate no entry.

Country	I	II	III	IV	V	VI	VII	Total	IX	X	Total
Norway	+ 22,680	− 8,120	− 30,940	− 1,120	+ 11,900	+ 26,320	+ 51,520	+ 19,600	+ 4,200	+ 15,400	+ 19,600
Argentina	− 425,400	+ 4,800	+ 68,600	−	−	+ 33,800	+ 17,400	+ 378,000	+ 4,600	+ 373,400	+ 378,000
Venezuela	− 558,400	+ 425,200	+ 117,900	+ 19,100	−	+ 89,300	+ 76,900	+ 65,800	− 3,600	+ 69,400	+ 65,800
Mexico	− 174,400	− 86,600	+ 73,000	+ 1,500	+ 1,600	+ 212,100	+ 54,900	+ 27,700	+ 21,500	+ 6,200	+ 27,700
Finland	− 33,843	− 12,267	− 17,705	+ 1,436	+ 35,757	+ 12,180	+ 23,359	+ 86,957	− 8,700	+ 95,657	+ 86,957
New Zealand	+ 38,270	+ 6,378	+ 9,152	+ 9,706	−	+ 36,052	+ 36,329	+ 25,513	+ 26,068	− 555	+ 25,513
Austria	− 165,600	− 1,100	− 17,000	−	+ 103,400	+ 60,000	+ 60,900	+ 62,200	+ 3,900	+ 58,300	+ 62,200
Cuba	+ 9,000	− 51,500	− 11,425	+ 1,500	−	+ 700	+ 40,500	+ 68,200	− 6,400	+ 74,600	+ 68,200
Pakistan	− 64,379	− 3,657	− 3,446	+ 7,556	+ 1,360	+ 174,338	+ 4,141	+ 264,136	+ 89,224	+ 174,912	+ 264,136
Egypt	− 107,971	− 34,746	− 43,071	−	−	+ 10,625	+ 1,722	+ 158,510	− 42,212	+ 200,722	+ 158,510
Turkey	− 175,677	− 4,786	+ 55,000	+ 52,321	−	+ 2,357	+ 12,107	+ 99,535	+ 1,500	+ 98,035	+ 99,535
China	− 156,000	− 5,000	+ 36,241	+ 212,000	−	+ 39,000	+ 82,000	+ 85,000	− 20,000	+ 105,000	+ 85,000
Ireland	− 196,939	+ 25,004	− 200	+ 1,124	−	+ 97,767	+ 21,352	+ 12,362	− 30,622	+ 42,984	+ 12,362
Colombia	+ 65,800	− 19,400	+ 980	−	−	+ 42,500	+ 12,300	+ 9,700	+ 47,300	− 37,600	+ 9,700
Yugoslavia	− 724,060	− 33,160	− 33,800	+ 1,500	+ 614,580	+ 27,000	+ 7,880	+ 53,800	+ 109,160	− 55,360	+ 53,800
Chile	+ 77,200	+ 67,100	+ 14,956	+ 122,740	−	+ 2,200	+ 16,000	+ 25,300	− 5,800	+ 31,100	+ 25,300
Portugal	+ 56,542	+ 1,796	+ 14,600	− 400	−	+ 29,221	+ 13,437	+ 15,958	− 6,804	+ 22,762	+ 15,958
Greece	− 138,100	− 2,000	+ 7,000	+ 10,327	+ 2,763	+ 4,400	+ 3,000	+ 18,800	+ 9,600	+ 9,200	+ 18,800
Israel	− 270,000	− 9,000	− 100	+ 18,000	+ 118,900	+ 21,000	−	+ 70,000	+ 71,000	+ 1,000	+ 70,000
Thailand	+ 100	− 1,700	+ 7,000	+ 138,000	+ 85,000	+ 10,000	+ 24,100	+ 29,600	+ 59,600	+ 30,000	+ 29,600
Burma	+ 69,160	+ 943	− 100	+ 100	+ 3,000	+ 10,042	+ 4,528	+ 29,600	−	+ 50,293	+ 50,293
Iraq	− 122,976	− 116,956	+ 41,580	+ 8,763	+ 7,401	+ 4,872	+ 9,044	+ 50,293	+ 1,708	+ 30,632	+ 32,340
Iran	− 32,209	− 1,922	−	+ 1,820	+ 476	+ 651	+ 11,687	+ 32,340	+ 589	+ 30,690	+ 30,101
Ethiopia	+ 2,920	− 640	+ 5,080	+ 1,040	+ 15,624	+ 2,840	+ 360	+ 30,101	+ 5,040	+ 1,880	+ 3,160
					+ 40			+ 3,160			
Total debits −	−6,942,368	−1,706,649	−2,149,698	−536,813	−1,990,237	−2,856,080	−606,808	−3,686,894	−735,112	−2,648,368	−2,821,453
Total credits +	+5,084,690	+2,654,847	+1,730,841	+673,437	+2,152,430	+2,412,878	+1,214,089	+2,821,453	+858,213	+3,390,708	+3,686,894
Net balance	−1,857,678	+948,198	−418,857	+136,624	+162,193	+443,202	+607,281	−865,441	+123,101	+742,340	+865,441

189

TABLE IX–12. MAJOR BALANCE OF PAYMENTS BY PRINCIPAL CATEGORIES, 1952 (Concluded)

(In Thousands of U. S. Dollars)

	Net Balance of Transactions								Compensatory Financing		
	Goods & transporta-tion [a]	Investment income [b]	Private capital [c]	Private donations [d]	Official dona-tions [e]	Other services [f]	Errors, omis-sions [g]	Total	Long-term [h]	Short-term [i]	Total
SECTION B: TRADING COUNTRIES:											
Anglo-Egyptian-Sudan	− 37,043	−	− 2,297	+ 287	−	− 2,872	− 2,297	− 44,222	− 10,625	+ 54,847	+ 44,222
Belgian Congo	+ 38,140	− 35,560	+ 15,260	+ 7,880	− 40	+ 30,680	+ 10,160	+ 10,600	+ 49,220	− 38,620	+ 10,600
Northern Rhodesia	+ 83,440	− 71,960	− 2,800	+ 840	+ 1,400	+ 5,600	+ 840	+ 4,480	− 2,800	+ 7,280	+ 4,480
Southern Rhodesia	− 105,280	− 11,480	−	+ 3,640	−	+ 2,800	+ 61,320	− 54,600	+ 41,160	+ 13,440	+ 54,600
Costa Rica	+ 6,800	− 14,700	− 500	−	+ 2,700	+ 1,600	+ 11,000	+ 6,900	−. 100	+ 6,800	+ 6,900
Dominican Republic	+ 17,600	− 14,400	+ 2,300	− 1,300	−	+ 7,700	− 2,900	− 600	−	+ 600	+ 600
El Salvador	+ 17,400	− 2,240	− 3,040	+ 160	− 80	+ 7,320	− 6,280	− 1,560	+ 3,520	− 1,960	+ 1,560
Guatemala	+ 12,500	+ 6,900	+ 16,000	−	− 100	+ 3,500	− 2,300	− 2,100	−	− 2,100	+ 2,100
Haiti	+ 2,820	− 3,840	+ 2,620	− 200	+ 780	+ 1,720	+ 3,120	+ 3,580	− 480	− 3,100	− 3,580
Honduras	+ 3,450	− 13,400	+ 13,250	+ 650	+ 150	+ 1,200	− 850	− 750	+ 1,900	+ 1,150	+ 750
Nicaragua	+ 5,900	− 5,400	+ 2,200	+ 400	+ 600	− 200	+ 5,400	+ 4,500	+ 1,800	− 6,300	+ 4,500
Puerto Rico	− 216,500	− 21,100	+ 21,800	+ 11,400	+ 15,500	+ 126,900	− 10,800	+ 51,200	+ 11,500	+ 39,700	+ 51,200
Bolivia	− 14,600	− 18,800	+ 2,100	−	+ 1,000	+ 9,600	+ 8,000	+ 10,300	+ 1,300	+ 11,600	+ 10,300
Ecuador	+ 33,000	− 17,500	+ 1,000	+ 100	+ 1,300	+ 3,200	− 2,000	+ 10,700	+ 1,700	+ 12,400	+ 10,700
Paraguay	+ 6,724	− 1,624	− 10,228	+ 356	+ 1,020	+ 1,547	− 3,201	− 2,204	+ 1,296	+ 3,500	+ 2,204
Peru	− 48,800	− 20,500	+ 35,600	+ 5,700	+ 3,000	+ 5,600	− 14,900	+ 4,500	+ 3,300	+ 1,200	+ 4,500
Surinam	+ 515	− 1,236	+ 906	−	+ 330	+ 494	−	− 1,009		− 1,009	− 1,009

	1[a]	2[b]	3	4	5	6	7	8	9	10	11
Uruguay	− 29,400	+ 4,900	+ 57,400	− 2,400	+ 300	+ 400	+ 10,400	+ 31,800	+ 2,100	− 33,900	− 31,800
Ceylon	− 55,650	+ 9,660	+ 5,250	− 21,840	−	+ 6,510	− 10,290	+ 78,120	− 15,750	+ 93,870	+ 78,120
Formosa	− 84,200	+ 300	+ 600	+ 1,700	+ 94,600	+ 11,500	+ 2,200	+ 3,100	− 1,200	+ 1,900	+ 3,100
Jordan	− 41,412	+ 112	+ 336	+ 6,888	+ 23,688	+ 4,340	− 2,828	+ 3,444	+ 4,956	+ 1,512	+ 3,444
Philippines	− 124,500	+ 18,500	+ 22,000	+ 15,000	+ 26,000	+ 90,000	−	+ 10,000	− 8,000	+ 2,000	+ 10,000
Syria	− 46,747	−	+ 10,999	+ 4,583	+ 5,041	+ 25,665	+ 11,916	+ 11,457	+ 16,957	− 5,500	+ 11,457
Iceland	− 8,915	+ 424	+ 147	− 55	+ 4,611	+ 1,848	+ 749	+ 2,039	+ 2,143	− 104	+ 2,039
Total debits −	819,771	268,836	27,837	34,841	140	95,949	23,468	263,389	57,608	118,985	90,376
Total credits +	221,565	25,700	200,796	50,538	182,100	256,847	160,283	90,376	124,199	225,407	263,389
Net balance	− 598,206	− 243,136	+ 172,959	+ 15,697	+ 181,960	+ 160,898	+ 136,815	− 173,013	+ 66,591	+ 106,422	+ 173,013

NOTE: The balance of payments data here presented have been supplied by the International Monetary Fund, and represent the most complete world coverage ever undertaken. All figures represent *net* transactions. Credits and debits: Plus sign (+) indicates a credit; minus sign (−) indicates a debit.

a Goods, transportation, and insurance: Contains all international merchandise transactions, both commercial and non-commercial. Exports and imports computed f.o.b. or f.a.s. Contains all transportation and insurance charges, and also non-monetary gold. Excludes military end-items and services donated. Represents by far the largest portion of total current international transactions.

b Investment income: Contains all interest, rents, dividends, and profits received by residents from investments abroad.

c Private capital: Includes private long-term and short-term foreign investments, security transactions, direct investment holdings, and bank deposits. Portfolio holdings include stocks and bonds, both government and corporate.

d Private donations: Includes personal and institutional remittances, migrant's transfers, and private gifts and legacies.

e Official donations: Includes grants such as those under the European Recovery Program, the UNRRA, reparations, Lend-Lease settlements, etc. Confiscation of enemy property is included under reparations.

f Other services: Includes government expenditure not classified elsewhere, and foreign travel.

g Unrecorded transactions: The total current transactions *minus* the total movement of capital and monetary gold. This category has been labeled by the I.M.F. as "Errors and Omissions," which largely reflects the unrecorded movements of private capital. In theory the total credit transactions equal the total debit transactions. The final balance that occurs in practice represents errors and omissions. Compensatory Financing:

h Long-term financing:

i Short-term financing: Covers transactions of official and banking institutions.

TABLE IX–13. THE WORLD'S TOTAL MONETARY NATIONAL INCOME BY ECONOMIC ORIGIN OF DOMESTIC PRODUCT, 1952

(*In Millions of U. S. Dollars*)

Countries in rank of foreign trade	Agriculture [a]	Industrial [b]	Utilities [c]	Trade [d]	Public [e]	Other [f]	Total national income
United States	20,414	110,819	23,330	49,576	34,995	52,495	291,629
United Kingdom	1,950	14,666	3,088	6,561	4,652	7,719	38,596
Canada	2,653	7,201	1,895	2,653	1,706	2,842	18,950
France	9,957	9,372	1,464	4,978	1,465	2,050	29,286
Germany	2,567	13,070	1,867	3,034	2,100	702	23,340
Belgium-Luxembourg	1,180	1,357	472	1,888	826	177	5,900
Italy	3,460	4,925	1,064	1,730	1,464	668	13,311
Netherlands	436	1,598	490	672	218	220	3,634
Japan	3,511	4,536	1,170	2,487	585	2,342	14,631
Brazil	5,482	6,127	322	645	3,547	–	16,123
Australia	1,746	2,698	634	1,349	714	795	7,936
Sweden	560	2,379	630	1,400	1,889	140	6,998
India	10,206	5,604	1,000	1,801	1,001	401	20,013
Union of S. Africa	525	1,330	280	455	350	562	3,502
Switzerland	991	2,124	188	660	614	143	4,720
U.S.S.R.	66,697	68,784	20,843	25,011	27,095	–	208,430
Indonesia	4,258	1,064	141	700	780	155	7,098
Denmark	691	1,099	314	503	251	283	3,141
Norway	356	926	404	308	95	286	2,375
Argentina	3,796	4,380	1,460	3,358	1,314	292	14,600
Venezuela	1,257	492	55	300	546	84	2,734
Mexico	874	1,049	219	1,335	218	677	4,372
Finland	687	1,057	185	344	238	132	2,643
New Zealand	491	436	18	272	236	366	1,819

	Agriculture[a]	Industrial[b]	Utilities[c]	Trade[d]	Public[e]	Other[f]	Total
Austria	411	1,259	231	206	206	256	2,569
Cuba	372	941	78	255	314	2	1,962
Pakistan	2,088	655	164	532	205	451	4,095
Egypt	435	300	30	240	315	180	1,500
Turkey	2,128	485	149	336	338	298	3,734
China	40,618	7,274	6,062	3,031	2,424	1,215	60,624
Spain	6,007	600	200	700	1,500	1,005	10,012
Ireland	363	159	34	285	102	192	1,135
Indo-China	342	96	6	90	66	–	600
Colombia	1,447	655	241	310	241	552	3,446
Yugoslavia	748	106	19	29	48	10	960
Chile	964	1,714	214	321	285	74	3,572
Portugal	446	553	153	307	76	2	1,537
Greece	171	108	27	50	41	53	450
Israel	219	700	415	525	216	112	2,187
Saudi-Arabia	115	864	28	778	1,095	–	2,880
Thailand	1,065	299	19	280	75	132	1,870
Burma	442	110	14	74	81	17	738
Iraq	39	90	3	45	123	–	300
Iran	469	194	71	82	204	–	1,020
Ethiopia	486	18	9	153	234	–	900
Total above	204,100	284,273	69,700	120,649	95,068	78,082	851,872
Rest of world	24,863	34,627	8,488	14,694	11,581	9,515	103,768
World total	228,963	318,900	78,188	135,343	106,649	87,597	955,640

SOURCES: *National Income Statistics,* Statistical Office of the United Nations; Volume 10, Conference on Research in Income and Wealth; See Table 157, pages 413–416, "Industrial Origin of Net Product," United Nations *Statistical Yearbook,* 1954.

^a Agriculture: Includes farming, fisheries, and forestry.
^b Industrial: Includes mining, manufacturing, and construction.
^c Utilities: Includes transportation, communications, and other utilities.

^d Trade: Includes wholesale and retail distribution.
^e Public: Includes government, administrative, defense, justice, and police.
^f Other: Includes banking, finance, insurance, and other services.

What is in fact characteristic of our development is that it has successively destroyed all the established social contexts; one after another they have been banished either by the slow usury of time or by violent revolution, and in such fashion that nothing has been developed to replace them.

—STANLEY CASSON, *Progress and Catastrophe*, 1937

This is a clear statement of the issue the civilized world is facing now, a rapid industrial, mechanical, physiochemical advance, so rapid that it has been destructive of all the historic, social and personal relationships. It is as though man himself is not expected to progress, but only his material surroundings. Cigar in corner of mouth, each talks incessantly of dollars. There is no active administrator of the present who does not fear that peace may see a return of social chaos. In these days of rapid and continuous change, the whole conception of social organization and social discipline must be radically revised.

—ELTON MAYO, *The Social Problems of an Industrial Civilization*, 1945

X

Balance

THREE OF THE principal divisions of economics—production, consumption, and exchange—have been approached in the preceding chapters. The fourth division—distribution—falls in this final chapter dealing with balance, for it is only through the utilization of the double-entry balance sheet that the final distribution can be ascertained.

Double-entry bookkeeping rests on the basic principle, logically carried out, of comprehending all phenomena purely as quantities. As such, in the words of Spengler, "double-entry bookkeeping discloses to us the cosmos of the economic world." Goethe once called double-entry bookkeeping "one of the finest discoveries of the human intellect," and Spengler without hesitancy ranked its author, Luca Pacioli, alongside his contemporaries Columbus and Copernicus in importance.

Unfortunately, however, the conception of "money" as identical with, and therefore representative of, the pure quantities of things has created one of the foremost delusions with which both modern civilization and economic theory has had to deal.

Especially is this true as it relates to the world economy which is based and ordered by the giant physical forces of energy and mass. When money-value is assigned to every material object, irrespective of its specified kind, a positive and negative effect value is recorded—which may not be always in accord with the actual positive and negative physical quantities it proposes to represent. Such procedures are frequently the more misleading because even the money-units themselves are not always the same kind or possessed of the same kind of money values.

Hence, entries in terms of numbers labeled dollars total both the number of real dollars in hand and the number of promises to pay real dollars—but do not distinguish between them, implying rather that both types of dollars are equal. This failure to observe the distinction between "identity" and "equality" or "quality" has all too often led to loose reasoning, for a quantity is not a mere "number," it is a number of some thing, or things, and not a quality.

There probably has never been a period in history when the balance between mankind and nature has been in greater disequilibrium than at present. Today's world balance sheet both physically and institutionally is so far out of balance that no artificial manipulation of money values can, in itself, hope to restore it.

From the standpoint of social unity and the wholesale destruction of individual social significance, the institution of the state itself as an effective moderator has deteriorated. Over this 70-year period the change from the smaller, more or less self-contained community type of social economy to the large, urban-center, interdependent, industrialized economy, has produced a diminished desire for collaboration—with an ever-growing social disunity.

During this period of scientific and material advance a sort of naïve exuberance over physiochemical and technical development—so rapid as to be destructive of all historic, social, economic, and personal relationships wherein people liked to work with and for each other for the benefit of the community—has led to little more than lip-service to the tradition of collaboration. *This has been a fundamental change.*

During this period large industrial organizations came into being, whose annual outlays were greater than their government's. These organizations began to think not in broad social terms but in terms of group self-interest. For the most part these large organizations were built and led by men of moderate education and knowledge. For the most part, they made little effort to see far, and in the light of the existing knowledge of the time they could not see far. Yet these were the men who were creating the forces that today have so shaped the World Balance Sheet, and the human capacity for collaboration both within and between nations, into chaos and toward anarchy.

THE QUEST FOR EQUILIBRIUM

The world economy is the organized activity through which 2500 million people function in the process of obtaining their daily living. Farmers raising food and fibers, miners extracting ore and coal, industrial workers fabricating raw materials into finished products, the vast network of the transportation system, wholesale and retail distributors making goods available to consumers, and a host of other workers performing the countless tasks required by modern living, all of these are combined in a huge complex interdependent producing network, in more or less organized form, which makes up the world economy. It is through this complex

organization that the world's resources, manpower, and materials are used to satisf'
the changing pattern of human wants. It is inevitable that such a complex systen
of human activity should fail to function properly. Resources are wasted or use
inefficiently as parts of the organization get out of adjustment with each other, o
as the organization fails to adjust to new conditions, as material resources are un
used, or as their effective use is impeded by man-made barriers, or as the mos
effective technology is not used, or its use prevented.

The fact that man's quest for balance is rarely achieved need not surprise us
Absolute equilibrium in nature does not exist. It is a goal toward which everythin;
is striving in an interminable series of actions and reactions to the complex of al
organic and inorganic matter. Even the so-called "equilibrium constant" in chem
istry is a man-made system of reference or scale of observation never achieve
absolutely in reality.

To the experienced ecologist the "balance of nature" does not exist, except as
convenient concept. For while animal numbers may always be tending toward som
ideal stability and harmonize working mechanism, nevertheless, something alway
happens before that happy state is reached. This liability to "upsets" of the balanc
of nature is a property of all animal communities, including man. The natura
environment of animals is so unstable itself that it would be surprising if some o
its irregularities were not reflected in the animal communities.

Equilibrium is a static condition. Any realistic description of society viewed ove
a given period of time cannot be based on a static theory. Dynamics are concerne
with change and the causes of changes in the data with which each successive stati
portrayal works. Double-entry bookkeeping cannot escape being a static portrayal
for whether it be a balance sheet dealing with the assets and liabilities at a partic
ular point of time, or a balanced accounting of income and outgo over a perio
of time—nevertheless it is a "snap-shot." Therefore, our first problem has bee
that of establishing a reconciliation between the static portrait and the dynami
process.

In this work we have tried to make use of the present advanced knowledge of th
various sciences in measuring the world phenomena, and in so doing have bee
seeking a unified system of measurement, regardless of whether the sciences them
selves have yet become unified. The work is thus a step toward reconciliation of th
existing unified scientific knowledge with the existing general economic theory.

Daily economic events have recently been of such a startling character as to diver
attention from theoretical complexities. Traditional treatments and traditional solu
tions are being seriously questioned, revised, and possibly improved. For the momen
controversy and doubt are on the increase. Every person will describe the worl
landscape for himself, and emphasize those features dearest to him and his prej
udices—all within the frame of reference that the scope of his knowledge permit
In the end, however, the activity of further research should do much to clear u
controversy and expand man's view of his problems.

CAN CONTINUED CREATIVE DESTRUCTION ACHIEVE BALANCE?

Economics today stands unique among contemporary sciences in that it appear
to be the only one in which eighteenth-century and earlier habits of thought sti'
serve in defining the prevailing tradition. The common definition of economics a

the science of wealth, with the implication of money values which the term "wealth" carries in today's world, is both an expression of this way of thinking and its corresponding identification of the world of commerce and "business" as the foremost field of inquiry in which such thinking prevails. The past several generations have followed the pattern of a system of ideas or set of "principles" which achieved general acceptance during the eighteenth century when the world still held vast unexplored frontiers open for exploitation and development. It is, therefore, only natural that many immature if not false premises relating to these "inexhaustible" undeveloped resources should find ready growth. Thus the process of "creative destruction" came into full bloom under the protection of all of the moral sanctions that could be summoned to its support during an imaginary golden age—motorcars running bumper to bumper under the banners of "Progress," "Profit," and "Profusion."

Can an observation of the world factual manifold serve to reveal any general pattern? What are the forces that shape this pattern? In what different aspects—of production, distribution, consumption—is the pattern manifest, and what are the relationships? What sort of balance prevails among them? What is the criterion of balance? These are the questions today's world balance sheet poses. With the sums of knowledge man today has deposited to his account it remains to be seen whether or not there is time for him to make a fresh start.

RECENT RESEARCH

Special attention has been given to the difficult task of attempting to present the striking results of some of the most outstanding recent investigations in such a manner as to make clear their importance without giving exaggerated impressions, and with due emphasis upon the fact that on many significant points any interpretation which can now be offered is necessarily tentative.

Recent research work is continuously revising current knowledge in this field. The F.A.O., with its 55 member nations, and the Inter-American Conference on Conservation of Renewable Resources have been prominent in the effort to enrich the store of available data. Forty-nine countries of the world were carrying on soil conservation work by 1948, patterned after the program of the United States. An understanding of the interrelationships of water, soils, climatic conditions, physiography, plant and animal (including human) life, as essential to successful reclamation and conservation projects, has been given additional emphasis throughout the world over the past few years.

The U. S. delegation to the Pan-American Institute of Geography and History proposed a land classification and land-use survey of the Western Hemisphere, emphasizing that such a survey would provide basic data for evaluating the need for conservation of natural resources. Unfortunately, little was done in the field of broad world policy, partly because of lack of authority and mainly because so little accurate data was available on *worldwide resources* at the time. This need for fundamental facts has been stressed at every geographic conference in recent years, and was stated concisely in a call for "*A World Inventory*" at the Lisbon Congress of the *International Geographic Union* in 1949.

In 1949 the deaths of O. E. Baker, Mark Jefferson, Bailey Willis, Wallace Atwood, and W. E. Ekblaw marked the passing of almost the whole of the first generation of American geographers. These pioneers in geographic work and teaching had received most of their scientific training in the allied fields of geology, geography, and economics. The generation now taking over the reins has been trained in the field of geography alone.

Both the area and the population of the world as a whole have been the subject of many estimates in scientific works for the past three centuries, and are still to some extent considered as largely matters of rough approximation. Every decade, however, has brought a diminution of the field of conjecture, as some form of civilized administration has been extended over the backward tracts, followed by a survey and a census, thus greatly reducing the area of speculation and narrowing the range of probable errors. Since 1882, the careful work of the International Earth Measurement and the respected works and investigations of H. Wagner, P. F. Levasseur, L. Bodio, plus the figures annually brought up to date by the British Statesman's Yearbook have been universally accepted as the best available reliable data.

There has also been increasingly reliable data on the subject of the world's soil's plant-nutrient supplying ability. Both the critical and the trace elements have been receiving increasing attention since 1934, due to an ever-widening recognition of the soil's deficiency for crop growth. The failure of earlier recognition may have come in part from failure to notice symptoms of such deficiency, from failure of accurate diagnosis, and from failure to notice, after adjustment for crop failure and new land supplanting retired areas, that the average yields of the world's principal crops have exhibited a marked horizontal trend ever since 1866.

Recognition of this decline in the land's basic nutrient supply, particularly in its relation to an ever-mounting population and its ultimate effect upon the human organism, has come slowly. In this respect far more emphasis has been placed on methods of increasing crop yields and the size and form of the product—together with the possibilities of augmenting human nutritional deficiencies via pills and vitamins—than on the more fundamental replenishment of the soil's basic nutrients from which the majority of all vitamins and other human nutritional augmentatives must ultimately be derived.

Although it has been known for years that soil fertility is important to human welfare because of its influence on the *quantity* of crops, nevertheless conflicting claims have appeared regarding the influence of soil fertility on the nutritional *quality* of crops and animal products. These arguments over the question of whether the fertility of the soil affects the nutritive value of the crops, the nutrition of the cow, the nutritive value of meat and milk, and the health of the ultimate human consumer have long been a matter of discussion; it was not until 1945 that a long-term study was initiated at the Michigan Agricultural Experiment Station.

Serious deficiencies, for example in phosphorus and calcium, have been known to bring about a decline in milk production and seriously affect the general health of the cow. Also, it will be recalled, ecologists have long since established that physical and chemical factors have a profound influence upon all animals and operate as a limiting factor both as to species and number. Ellsworth Huntington, in his *Mainsprings of Civilization*, has pointed out that if quantity in food alone were the chief factor, four English-speaking countries—the United States, Canada, Australia, and New Zealand—would be the best nourished parts of the world. Nevertheless, his index of diet and health discloses a remarkable correlation between the decline in soil nutrients per capita and a decline in health, vigor, and general alertness.

There is mounting evidence that the world's soils may only now be beginning to fail in supplying the small quantities of such elements needed for crops. By 1944 nutrients such as nitrogen, phosphorus, potassium, calcium, magnesium, and sulphur were viewed as especially critical elements. Hence the approaching physical crisis in world land use has become a crisis in the existing land's plant nutrient supply as well.

Nature automatically has placed the pressure of time on all life on earth. Plant life is dependent upon the atmosphere, water, soil, and sun-rays for existence. Animal life is dependent upon plant life, directly or indirectly, for its existence.

Within the specific periods of sunlight, darkness, and the seasons of the year the plant must accomplish so much of its task in building its life cycle. This "time-period" system is nature's way, and plant life has no choice but to conform. The plant uses the resources it needs, and does not destroy more than it needs. If the necessary resources are not available, it either grows into a defective plant, or dies. It has not the choice, as has animal life, of moving to another more suitable climate, with more sunshine, more water, and more needed elements in the soil. It must do with *what it has*, wherever it happens to be. At least that is the way it was in "pre-agriculture" times.

Animal life operates within hunger periods, which must be satisfied with proper nourishment if life is to be maintained. Our modern "civilization" has added to the original hunger pressures; our "industrial-commercial" system, with speeded up technology of production, high-fertility low-mortality population rates—together with our "time-money" combination—has added terrific pressures on human beings.

Man's proclivity to subordinate nature and the material world, while at the same time being dependent upon it, is surpassed only by his equal propensity to misapprehend the portents underlying technological industrialism. Man's most persistent possession, oddly enough, seems to be his tendency to work for his own ultimate dependence and enslavement.

The artificial lighting of the home is illustrative of these three stages: First, the transformation from the self-sufficient household industry of candlemaking of old; Second, the competitive industry supplying candles, lamps, whale-oil, and coal-oil; Third, the monopolistic collective industry as in electric and gas lighting, where central sources of supply are relied upon to satisfy all demands.

The same is true of water. The individual user of water in urban centers no longer depends for his supply upon his own well, nor does he buy from one of several competing sources. He resorts to a single *common source of supply* along with other users. This has been found to be more convenient, more economical, and indeed *the only practical solution*. The entire public utility system is based on this fact. This process of integration of supply has been a long process; one not yet fully realized in some parts of the world—in both the utilities and all other commodities.

Every public service must be in possession of the natural resources upon which that service or industry depends. And, above all, that service or industry *must make allowances in advance* for the increase in the required capacity to meet future demands.

Some people have called this "socialization."

That the world is moving toward the eventual socialization of its food supply is indicated by the present population-land ratio trend. This process may, of necessity, be of much shorter duration in its development.

Orthodox economic theory [stated John Holt Schooling in 1889] may be as symmetrical in construction as a spider's web, and may have the beauty of it. But economic theory has no stronger hold upon the actual material condition of international commerce than the filmy attachments of the spider's web have upon a stone wall. The orthodox economic theory of a country usually disdains the investigation of fact. Its publicized theories are merely brain-spun, and alone among all departments of human knowledge academic political economy remains to this day pre-Baconian in its methods.

TECHNICAL ASPECTS CONFRONTING A BALANCE SHEET OF WORLD ECONOMY

The principal technical problems have involved the following:

1. Problem of Accounting:

a. Along *Business Accounting* lines, wherein the conventional principles are set by the laws and the prevailing commercial customs, i.e., a standard system of accounts that are articulated and tied together by the formal rules of double-entry bookkeeping and based upon verifiable evidence. This is the *one-level* or mono-standardization approach.

b. Along *Social Accounting* lines, corresponding closely to business accounting, but proceeding on *two levels*, namely: first, the combination and completion of the evidenced accounts in accordance with the prevailing methods of business accounting, and second, the construction and recasting of the accounts to conform with the rules derived from the accepted economic theory.

c. Along *Physical Accounting* lines, which relates to both of the above procedures but must account for the physical assets and liabilities in the prevailing standards of the physical quantities involved relative to their current monetary values.

In other words, the above methods may be designed as:

a. National Business Accounting—measuring the efficiency of the Business System.

b. National Economic Accounting—measuring the functional efficiency of the over-all System.

c. International Resource Accounting—measuring the potentials and the limits of the physical economy of the world as related to the population.

On the above bases the method adopted in our approach has been to set up the major sector accounts in such manner as: First, to conform as nearly as possible with the logical extension of the present National Income Accounting System, in order that the corresponding Asset and Liability sector accounts may be achieved; and second, to permit the largest possible number of combinations the individual user may desire to recast or set up for purposes of his own uses.

2. Statistical Procedures:

On the first level of both business and social accounting it has been necessary to go beyond the combination of existing balance sheet and income account data in two directions:

First, a certain amount of standardization must be applied to the existing accounts unless the presentation result is to be a meaningless aggregate of noncomparable entries.

Second, gaps must be essentially filled in by the construction of accounts for many unit categories for which complete data are at present unobtainable, or which are not kept in a standard form suitable for our over-all purposes.

3. Controversial Areas:

The inference for wealth studies has hitherto been that of a need for monographic treatment of the wealth position of various classes of *economic units*, and their apparent interplay in operations.

For some areas, especially the corporate financial and non-financial categories, we have a more or less *prefabricated source book material* which makes it fairly easy to build up an approximate picture of considerable authenticity.

On the other hand, we have thus far had only fragmentary evidence as to the wealth position of *Households* (especially on the dispersion of such position) and on the position of *unincorporated business.*

As to the above two, the *Household or Personal Chattels* and the non-farm non-corporate *Business* categories have long been by far the *weakest areas* in all our wealth data, not only as to identity by *type-of-unit* but as to identity by form-of-asset.

Another area long in dispute has been that of the true distribution of private corporation securities among the people. Here is usually found a wide variety of estimates ranging in spread from 6 to 16 million individual shareholders, and from one-half million to over 8 million corporate bond holders.

Far from the least of all controversial matters has been that surrounding the possibility of the existing statistical data being sufficiently adequate to permit the drafting of a satisfactory national balance sheet showing what we need to know about how current operations of business, government, philanthropy, and households are influenced by the composition of their respective assets and liabilities.

AN EXPLORATORY WORLD BALANCE SHEET

In accounting for the world economy as a whole, certain procedures not customary with an individual enterprise have to be taken into consideration. Simply stated, these major principles are as follows:

1. Physical assets always constitute those items of property which can enter into no other balance sheet sector other than the one in which they figure.

2. Claims, however, have the quality of appearing on all balance sheets, i.e., they appear as an asset of the sector wherein they are held, and they concurrently appear as a liability in the sector against which the claims are made.

3. Finally, the sum of the claims assets and the liabilities, after allowance for all offsetting items, will be exactly equal, and therefore the sum of the physical assets will approximate the sum of the net worth after adjustment for net property holdings abroad.

Therefore, the best that can be achieved under existing reporting conditions is to identify as many of the known assets and liabilities as possible, country by country, as shown in Tables X–1, X–2 and X–3.

TABLE X–1. THE DISTRIBUTION OF THE WORLD'S ESTIMATED TOTAL PROPERTY ASSETS BY PRINCIPAL ECONOMIC SECTORS, 1952

(*In Millions of U. S. Dollars*)

	Total private business	Agriculture [a]	Industry [b]	Utilities [c]	Trade [d]	Financial [e]	Government [f]	Institutional [g]	Households [h]	Total
United States	885,714	170,480	153,649	82,247	57,800	421,538	503,054	97,794	594,182	2,080,744
United Kingdom	186,300	8,008	20,339	3,571	7,653	146,729	66,590	11,144	78,653	342,687
Canada	47,077	11,059	9,993	2,188	3,093	20,744	32,636	4,200	38,548	122,461
France	94,120	41,471	12,999	1,690	5,807	32,153	50,437	6,168	59,574	210,299
Germany, West	48,363	10,678	18,128	2,161	3,535	13,861	40,218	4,370	47,503	140,454
Belgium-Luxembourg	18,079	4,957	1,901	542	2,193	8,486	10,219	1,419	12,070	41,787
Italy	42,464	14,396	6,809	1,230	2,020	18,009	22,911	3,387	27,061	95,823
Netherlands	10,928	1,811	2,211	570	773	5,563	6,264	1,059	7,398	25,649
Japan	40,291	14,682	6,279	1,356	2,888	15,086	25,219	2,914	29,787	98,211
Brazil	54,089	22,785	8,489	371	757	21,687	27,856	4,124	32,902	118,971
Australia	26,514	7,245	3,758	732	1,578	13,201	13,681	2,327	16,159	58,681
Sweden	14,184	2,288	3,316	732	1,625	6,223	12,032	1,306	14,212	41,734
India	60,534	42,519	7,782	1,157	2,099	6,977	34,449	2,024	40,689	137,696
Union of S. Africa	9,815	2,193	1,857	325	537	4,903	6,098	927	7,203	24,043
Switzerland	15,689	4,099	2,963	217	773	7,637	8,077	1,457	9,540	34,763
U.S.S.R.	374,754	192,269	95,373	24,101	29,161	33,850	359,489	17,652	424,610	1,176,505
Indonesia	21,306	17,732	1,459	163	821	1,131	12,197	359	14,407	48,269
Denmark	9,363	2,860	1,503	362	584	4,054	5,439	757	6,425	21,984
Norway	8,072	1,525	1,282	470	363	4,432	c4,121	776	4,867	17,836
Argentina	39,462	15,826	6,058	1,690	3,913	11,975	25,219	2,460	29,787	96,928
Venezuela	7,919	5,243	663	63	347	1,603	4,780	303	5,646	18,648
Mexico	9,066	3,623	1,459	253	1,562	2,169	7,582	492	8,956	26,096
Finland	5,496	2,860	1,459	217	394	566	4,615	284	5,451	15,846
New Zealand	5,784	2,002	619	18	316	2,829	3,132	473	3,699	13,088
Austria	6,022	1,716	1,724	271	237	2,074	4,450	511	5,257	16,240
Cuba	9,842	1,525	1,327	90	300	6,600	3,297	1,078	3,894	18,111
Pakistan	12,202	8,676	929	190	615	1,792	7,088	378	8,372	28,040

	Agriculture [a]	Industrial [b]	Utilities [c]	Trade [d]	Financial [e]	Government [f]	Institutional [g]	Households [h]	
Egypt	5,075	398	36	284	2,546	2,637	397	3,115	11,224
Turkey	12,829	663	172	394	2,734	6,428	473	7,593	27,323
China	190,783	10,081	7,006	3,535	1,037	104,501	1,514	123,431	420,229
Spain	35,737	840	235	820	8,769	17,307	1,305	20,442	74,791
Ireland	3,433	221	36	331	1,320	1,978	208	2,336	7,955
Indo-China	1,965	133	9	110	283	989	57	1,168	4,179
Colombia	9,463	928	280	363	1,886	5,934	378	7,009	22,784
Yugoslavia	9,929	133	18	32	6,600	1,648	927	1,947	14,451
Chile	10,787	2,388	244	379	3,772	6,099	851	7,203	24,940
Portugal	6,973	752	181	363	3,866	2,637	624	3,115	13,349
Greece	1,833	133	27	63	943	824	151	973	3,781
Israel	5,566	973	479	615	2,546	3,791	473	4,478	14,308
Saudi-Arabia	2,974	1,194	27	899	377	4,945	208	5,841	13,968
Thailand	5,794	398	18	331	566	3,297	132	3,894	13,117
Burma	2,324	133	18	79	283	1,319	57	1,557	5,257
Iraq	657	133	3	47	283	494	57	584	1,792
Iran	2,819	265	81	95	471	1,813	95	2,142	6,869
Ethiopia	2,323	44	9	174	94	1,483	19	1,752	5,577
Total above	2,374,713	394,138	135,856	140,658	854,248	1,469,274	178,069	1,735,432	5,757,488
Rest of world ([i])	211,885	48,018	9,818	17,137	33,379	179,003	11,125	211,429	613,442
World total	2,586,598	442,156	145,674	157,795	887,627	1,648,277	189,194	1,946,861	6,370,930

SOURCES: United Nations Statistical Yearbook, 1954, Table 157, pages 413–416; Statesman's Yearbook, 1954; Volumes 10 and 12, Studies in Income and Wealth, Conference on Research in Income and Wealth, National Bureau of Economic Research, New York.

NOTE: Total assets include reproducible and non-reproducible physical assets together with the claims' holdings for each sector. All data are inclusive of corporate and non-corporate enterprise.

[a] Agriculture: Includes farming, fisheries, and forestry.

[b] Industrial: Includes construction, manufacturing, and mining.

[c] Utilities: Transportation, communications, and other utilities.

[d] Trade: Wholesale, retail, and services.

[e] Financial: Banking, insurance, brokerage, and other services.

[f] Government: Federal, state and local, administrative, legislative, justice and police.

[g] Institutional: Private and public educational plant, religious property, burial grounds, and all other tax-exempt philanthropic property.

[h] Households: All private real and personal property, tangible and intangible, held by individuals and families.

[i] Includes the countries and areas as given in detail in Table IX.

TABLE X-2. THE DISTRIBUTION OF THE WORLD'S ESTIMATED TOTAL LIABILITIES BY PRINCIPAL ECONOMIC SECTORS, 1952

(In Millions of U. S. Dollars)

	Total private business	Agriculture	Industry	Utilities	Trade	Financial	Government	Institutional	Households	Total
United States	463,903	8,758	31,959	19,518	22,889	380,779	654,985	33,500	97,285	1,249,673
United Kingdom	141,157	825	4,230	2,584	3,031	130,487	77,844	3,432	11,562	233,995
Canada	23,034	1,139	2,078	1,583	1,225	17,009	38,151	1,294	5,667	68,146
France	36,861	4,271	2,704	1,223	2,299	26,364	58,961	1,900	8,757	106,479
Germany, West	19,199	1,100	3,771	1,563	1,400	11,365	47,015	1,346	6,983	74,543
Belgium-Luxembourg	9,123	510	395	392	868	6,958	11,946	437	1,774	23,280
Italy	19,355	1,483	1,416	889	800	14,767	26,783	1,043	3,978	51,159
Netherlands	5,926	187	460	412	306	4,561	7,322	326	1,088	14,662
Japan	17,312	1,512	1,306	981	1,143	12,370	29,481	897	4,379	52,069
Brazil	22,463	2,347	1,766	268	300	17,782	32,564	1,270	4,837	61,134
Australia	13,507	746	782	530	625	10,824	15,993	717	2,375	32,592
Sweden	7,203	236	690	530	644	5,103	14,066	402	2,089	23,760
India	13,387	4,379	1,619	837	831	5,721	40,271	624	5,981	60,263
Union of S. Africa	5,079	226	386	235	212	4,020	7,129	286	1,059	13,553
Switzerland	7,763	422	616	157	306	6,262	9,442	449	1,402	19,056
U.S.S.R.	105,178	28,601	19,837	17,438	11,547	27,755	353,328	2,058	52,478	513,042
Indonesia	3,500	1,826	303	118	325	928	14,259	111	2,118	19,988
Denmark	4,425	294	313	262	231	3,325	6,359	233	944	11,961
Norway	4,542	157	267	340	144	3,634	4,817	239	715	10,313
Argentina	15,482	1,630	1,260	1,223	1,550	9,819	29,481	758	4,379	50,100
Venezuela	2,175	540	138	46	137	1,314	5,588	93	830	8,686
Mexico	3,256	373	303	183	619	1,778	8,863	152	1,317	13,588
Finland	1,375	295	303	157	156	464	5,395	87	801	7,658
New Zealand	2,792	206	129	13	125	2,319	3,661	146	544	7,143
Austria	2,527	177	359	196	94	1,701	5,202	157	773	8,659

Cuba	6,029	157	276	65	119	5,412	3,854	332	572	10,787
Pakistan	2,936	893	193	137	244	1,469	8,285	116	1,231	12,568
Egypt	2,495	187	83	26	112	2,087	3,083	122	458	6,158
Turkey	3,573	913	138	124	156	2,242	7,515	146	1,116	12,350
China	26,834	17,418	2,097	5,069	1,400	850	122,161	466	18,144	167,605
Spain	10,442	2,582	175	170	325	7,190	20,232	402	3,005	34,081
Ireland	1,442	157	46	26	131	1,082	2,312	64	343	4,161
Indo-China	457	147	28	6	44	232	1,156	17	172	1,802
Colombia	2,705	619	193	203	144	1,546	6,937	117	1,030	10,789
Yugoslavia	5,789	324	28	13	12	5,412	1,927	286	286	8,288
Chile	4,328	412	497	177	150	3,092	7,129	262	1,059	12,778
Portugal	3,788	187	156	131	144	3,170	3,083	192	458	7,521
Greece	914	69	27	20	25	773	963	47	143	2,067
Israel	2,978	98	202	347	244	2,087	4,432	146	658	8,214
Saudi-Arabia	982	49	248	20	356	309	5,780	64	858	7,684
Thailand	1,152	461	83	13	131	464	3,854	41	572	5,619
Burma	491	187	28	13	31	232	1,541	17	229	2,278
Iraq	301	20	28	2	19	232	578	17	86	982
Iran	734	196	55	59	37	387	2,119	29	315	3,197
Ethiopia	367	206	9	6	69	77	1,734	6	258	2,365
Total above	1,029,261	87,522	81,980	58,305	55,700	745,754	1,717,581	54,846	255,108	3,056,796
Rest of world [a]	61,909	10,663	9,988	7,103	6,786	27,369	209,254	3,426	31,080	305,669
World total	1,091,170	98,185	91,968	65,408	62,486	773,123	1,926,835	58,272	286,188	3,362,465

NOTE: Total liabilities include current accounts payable, bonds, notes, and mortgages payable maturing in less than one year and in more than one year. Also included are other liabilities such as deferred and suspense items, accrued expenses, dividends payable, funds held in trust. In the financial sector, deposits (time savings, demand), bank notes outstanding in circulation, borrowed securities, building and loan association certificates of deposit, and net value of outstanding insurance policies and annuities.

For description of sector contents see footnotes to preceding table in Table IX–8.

a Includes the countries and areas as given in detail in Table IX–8.

TABLE X-3. THE INDICATED DISTRIBUTION OF THE WORLD'S TOTAL EQUITIES OR NET WORTH, BY PRINCIPAL ECONOMIC SECTORS, 1952

(*In Millions of U. S. Dollars*)

	Total private business	Agriculture	Industry	Utilities	Trade	Financial	Government	Institutional	Households	Total
United States	421,811	161,722	121,690	62,729	34,911	40,759	−151,931	64,294	496,897	831,071
United Kingdom	45,143	7,183	16,109	987	4,622	16,242	−11,254	7,712	67,091	108,692
Canada	24,043	9,920	7,915	605	1,868	3,735	−5,515	2,906	32,881	54,315
France	57,259	37,200	10,295	467	3,508	5,789	−8,524	4,268	50,817	103,820
Germany	29,164	9,578	14,357	598	2,135	2,496	−6,797	3,024	40,520	65,911
Belgium-Luxembourg	8,956	4,447	1,506	150	1,325	1,528	−1,727	982	10,296	18,507
Italy	23,109	12,913	5,393	341	1,220	3,242	−3,872	2,344	23,083	44,664
Netherlands	5,002	1,624	1,751	158	467	1,002	−1,058	733	6,310	10,987
Japan	22,979	13,170	4,973	375	1,745	2,716	−4,262	2,017	25,408	46,142
Brazil	31,626	20,438	6,723	103	457	3,905	−4,708	2,854	28,065	57,837
Australia	13,007	6,499	2,976	202	953	2,377	−2,312	1,610	13,784	26,089
Sweden	6,981	2,052	2,626	202	981	1,120	−2,034	904	12,123	17,974
India	47,147	38,140	6,163	320	1,268	1,256	−5,822	1,400	34,708	77,433
Union of S. Africa	4,736	1,967	1,471	90	325	883	−1,051	641	6,144	10,490
Switzerland	7,926	3,677	2,347	60	467	1,375	−1,365	1,008	8,138	15,707
U.S.S.R.	269,576	163,668	75,536	6,663	17,614	6,095	+6,161	15,594	372,132	663,463
Indonesia	17,806	15,906	1,156	45	496	203	−2,062	248	12,289	28,281
Denmark	4,938	2,566	1,190	100	353	729	−920	524	5,481	10,023
Norway	3,530	1,368	1,015	130	219	798	−696	537	4,152	7,523
Argentina	23,980	14,196	4,798	467	2,363	2,156	−4,262	1,702	25,408	46,828
Venezuela	5,744	4,703	525	17	210	289	−808	210	4,816	9,962

Country	(1)	(2)	(3)	(4)	(5)	(6)	(7)	(8)	(9)	(10)
Mexico	5,810	3,250	1,156	70	943	391	— 1,281	340	7,639	12,508
Finland	4,121	2,565	1,156	60	238	102	— 780	197	4,650	8,188
New Zealand	2,992	1,796	490	5	191	510	— 529	327	3,155	5,945
Austria	3,495	1,539	1,365	75	143	373	— 752	354	4,484	7,581
Cuba	3,813	1,368	1,051	25	181	1,188	— 557	746	3,322	7,324
Pakistan	9,266	7,783	736	53	371	323	— 1,197	262	7,141	15,472
Egypt	2,580	1,624	315	10	172	459	— 446	275	2,657	5,066
Turkey	9,256	7,953	525	48	238	492	— 1,087	327	6,477	14,973
China	163,949	151,706	7,984	1,937	2,135	187	— 17,660	1,048	105,287	252,624
Spain	25,295	22,491	665	65	495	1,579	— 2,925	903	17,437	40,710
Ireland	1,991	1,368	175	10	200	238	— 334	144	1,993	3,794
Indo-China	1,508	1,283	105	3	66	51	— 167	40	996	2,377
Colombia	6,758	5,387	735	77	219	340	— 1,003	261	5,979	11,995
Yugoslavia	4,140	2,822	105	5	20	1,188	— 279	641	1,661	6,163
Chile	6,459	3,592	1,891	67	229	680	— 1,030	589	6,144	12,162
Portugal	3,185	1,624	596	50	219	696	— 446	432	2,657	5,828
Greece	919	598	106	7	38	170	— 139	104	830	1,714
Israel	2,588	855	771	132	371	459	— 641	327	3,820	6,094
Saudi-Arabia	1,992	428	946	7	543	68	— 835	91	4,983	6,284
Thailand	4,642	4,020	315	5	200	102	— 557	40	3,322	7,498
Burma	1,833	1,624	105	5	48	51	— 222	40	1,328	2,979
Iraq	356	171	105	1	28	51	— 84	66	498	810
Iran	2,085	1,711	210	22	58	84	— 306	13	1,827	3,672
Ethiopia	1,956	1,796	35	3	105	17	— 251		1,494	3,212
Total above	1,345,452	762,291	312,158	77,551	84,958	108,494	− 248,307	123,223	1,480,324	2,700,692
Rest of world	149,976	92,870	38,030	2,715	10,351	6,010	− 30,251	7,699	180,349	307,773
World total	1,495,428	855,161	350,188	80,266	95,309	114,504	− 278,558	130,922	1,660,673	3,008,465

NOTE: See notes to preceding tables and to Balance Sheet in Chapter X.

THE INDICATED WORLD COMPOSITE BALANCE SHEET

From the foregoing basic data it becomes possible to draw up an indicated structural composite balance sheet of the world economy. By "indicated" we mean that the facts we have been able to gather up to this writing, the functional world monetary economy being what it is, can supply something more than a mere inkling or glimmer, but rather a fair foreglimpse or representative clue as to the over-all approximate composition. In other words the collateral evidence points strongly in such a direction, at least so strongly as to warrant our attention to such phenomena.

As was pointed out some twenty years ago,[1] the scientific analysis of economic statistics and the careful preparation of accounting data antedate World War I and have given a new stimulus to the previously slow development of both statistics and accounting as scientific instrumentalities. In this respect two techniques have grown up side by side, yet without sufficient interchange.

Accountants have, meanwhile, come to realize that their art is in some respects purely a statistical operation, and that most of the recorded financial statements constitute data for statistical series of great importance. Economic statisticians, on their part, have become more aware of this rich data-source which has long remained undeveloped.

In the Composite World Balance Sheet, Table X–4 an exploratory attempt has been made to assemble and coordinate the various national statistics in formal accountancy form. Such a balance sheet must of necessity represent a highly summarized composite of all national economies, as it would be impossible to show all individual national balance sheets within the confines of this small volume.

In obtaining a picture of the production and consumption of the world's commodities, we have, for the purpose of condensation, limited ourselves to 100 of the principal industrial and agricultural basic materials. To list all of the many thousands of different commodities passing into the world's markets each year would have been as impractical as it would prove unnecessary for the purposes of fundamental study.

OBSTACLES CONFRONTING THE DRAFTING OF A COMPLETE WORLD BALANCE SHEET

In a highly nationalized world with both individual interests and nations operating on a competitive basis, where knowledge itself is viewed as a commodity, the objective research worker is not operating in a bed of roses. The degree of cordial and cooperative receptivity to such an undertaking cannot be said to be great. Living, as we do, in a world where all things are relative, much of one's knowledge, intelligence, and values depends upon where one stands in respect to his prejudices and preconceived notions. Also in an era wherein the currently successful businessman dominates the religious, philanthropic, educational, and research institutional pattern of large sectors of the world pattern, independent studies that do not lend themselves to an optimistic point of view, insofar as the immediate future is con-

[1] Bureau of Business Research, College of Commerce and Business Administration, University of Illinois, Bulletin No. 54, 1936.

cerned, are apt to be frowned upon. Whether these institutions will survive this trusteeship may be one of present-day civilization's moot questions.

An attempt has here been made to obtain as enlightened a picture of the world we live in as present-day advanced knowledge in the various fields permit. It is against such a background of reality that man's various assumptions, theories, and behavior are now taking place. It is to be hoped that some of these assumptions, theories and beliefs will develop in wisdom as our knowledge increases.

TABLE X–4. INDICATED COMPOSITE BALANCE SHEET OF THE WORLD ECONOMY, BY PRINCIPAL SECTORS, YEAR ENDING DECEMBER 31, 1952

(In Millions of U. S. Dollars)

	Money supply	Accounts receivables	Government obligations	Other investments	Intangible assets	Total claims' assets	Stocks of goods	Buildings & equipment	Land	Total physical assets	Total assets
Assets:											
Business	156,000	268,428	492,087	230,236	58,923	1,205,674	72,329	1,050,046	258,549	1,380,924	2,586,598
Government	12,097	60,280	436,576	56,482	21,406	586,787	556,505	346,037	158,948	1,061,490	1,648,277
Households	83,174	14,375	953,855	406,867	53,461	1,511,732	185,197	168,394	81,538	435,129	1,946,861
Institutions	756	1,377	44,317	11,822	–	58,272	53,782	60,110	17,030	130,922	189,194
Total assets	252,027	344,460	1,926,835	705,353	133,790	3,362,465	867,813	1,624,587	516,065	3,008,465	6,370,930

	Accounts payable	Long-term debts	Other liabilities	Total liabilities	Net Worth Section			Non-corporate proprietor's equities	Total equities	Total liabilities & net worth
					Capital stock common	Capital stock pref'd	Surplus			
Liabilities:										
Business	222,521	379,246	489,403	1,091,170	391,600	86,800	485,551	531,477	1,495,428	2,586,598
Government	72,681	1,025,455	828,699	1,926,835				–278,558	–278,558	1,648,277
Households	43,746	177,722	64,720	286,188				1,660,673	1,660,673	1,946,861
Institutions	5,512	38,285	14,475	58,272				130,922	130,922	189,194
Total liabilities	344,460	1,620,708	1,397,297	3,362,465	391,600	86,800	485,551	2,044,514	3,008,465	6,370,930

NOTE: Principal sectors: *Business* includes agriculture, industry, utilities, trade and finance. *Government* includes all divisions of public legislative, administrative, defense, police and all other public activities of government. *Households* refers to private citizens and families. *Institutions* includes all private philanthropic activities: schools, colleges, hospitals, churches, foundations, welfare agencies, social clubs, etc.

Assets: Money supply contains all currency in circulation outside the treasury, and demand deposits, corresponding with I.M.F. "money supply" definitions. *Accounts receivable* contains all current receivables and notes and mortgages maturing in less than one year. *Government obligations* contains all Federal, state and local bonds, notes, certificates, and treasury bills outstanding. *Other investments* contains the holdings of all corporation capital stock (preferred and common shares), including foreign investments; also includes all bond, debenture, and other private mortgages held. *Intangible assets* includes patents, formulas, copyrights, trademarks, leaseholds, and "good will." These are largely offset as they are written off and provided for under "Surplus reserves" on the liabilities side of the balance sheet. *Stocks of goods* contains all raw materials, semi-finished goods, finished goods, supplies on hand, and in the government sector contains the gold and silver coin and bullion, while in the household sector all stocks of goods on hand include chattel goods, household furnishings, and motor vehicles. *Buildings and equipment* includes all equipment of a fixed character. In the *Government* sector all military and naval grounds, buildings and equipment as well as all government-operated enterprises that are considered essentially commercial in character, such as financial and credit corporations, state alcoholic monopolies, housing authorities, water supply systems, municipal transit systems, electric light and power systems, gas supply systems, port facilities, airports, irrigation and drainage systems, the post office and other miscellaneous enterprises are included. All physical assets are given net of depreciation and depletion, in fact, on a book-value basis. *Institutions* contains all church and religious property, endowed institutions such as private schools, colleges, universities, social agencies, hospitals, clinics, libraries, museums, foundations, etc.

Liabilities: *Accounts payable* contains all current payables including tax liabilities, and notes and mortgages maturing in less than one year. *Long-term debts* contains all mortgages and long-term obligations, and in the case of government, all continuous treasury financing. *Other liabilities* includes deferred and suspense items, accrued expenses, dividends payable, funds held in trust, borrowed securities, overdrafts, the net value of outstanding policies and annuities of life insurance companies, time, savings, and demand deposits and bank notes in circulation of all banks including certificates of deposit of loan associations. In the case of the government sector trust funds, at all levels of government, the present value of claims of beneficiaries has been arbitrarily assumed to equal the entire net assets of the funds although the probable liability is considerably larger. In the *Net worth section*, capital stock is carried at book value, and surplus includes surplus reserves, paid in capital surplus, earned surplus, and undistributed profits.

Appendix A. Acknowledgments

ACKNOWLEDGMENT is here gratefully given for the invaluable assistance and constructive suggestions contributed so willingly by the many individuals and organizations, both governmental and private, without whose experienced help and creative guidance this study could never have been brought to completion.

As is frequently the case in a work of this type, the number of persons who have assisted directly or indirectly is so large that it is not always feasible to name them all. Nevertheless, because of the technical nature of much new material not customarily found in world inventories, we shall try to make such acknowledgment as complete as possible.

Due to the wide diversity and frequent lack of agreement on figures relating to geographic areas found in many of the popular almanacs, yearbooks, and atlases, particular care had to be taken in securing the latest authoritative definitive factual data available. Therefore, on the technical side, there appeared certain prerequisites as indispensable in our obtaining authentic data in the fields of geodesy, geography, geology, geophysics, and geopolitics. All of these fields are international by nature, and in their respective classifications and content are, within themselves, highly complex sciences demanding the consultation and advisory assistance of many specialists and organizations.

The assembly and preparation of materials such as those contained in our geographical summaries demands long hours of patient research and careful attention to detail. It also demands the unlimited use of publications, of specialized facilities, and the full cooperation of librarians and specialists to whom our requests for information must go. These published sources, comprising hundreds of publications, including atlases and gazetteers, will be found listed under the Bibliography in the appendix to this volume.

For the basic geographical data herein given we are heavily indebted to the valuable material afforded by the International Geodetic Association of Sevres, France; the International Geodetic and Geophysical Union of Cambridge, England; the Royal Geographic Society of London; the U. S. Coast and Geodetic Survey; the U. S. Navy Hydrographic Office; the National Geographic Society of Washington; the American Geographical Society of New York; the United Nations Geographical Office; the Office of the Geographer, U. S. State Department, Washington, and to the Denoyer-Geppert Company of Chicago; and to the following specialists affiliated with these above named organizations; Messrs. Robert W. Knox, A. G. Anderson, William G. Watt, George Crossette, Dr. Clarence B. Odell, John Bartholomew, F.R.G.S., Dr. S. W. Boggs who is special geographic advisor to the U. S. State Department, Christopher Tietze of the State Department's Division of Functional Intelligence, and to Miss Nordis Felland, librarian of the American Geographical Society.

Regarding the established scientific advances covering the fields of Energy, Physics, Calorimetry, and their recognized International Standard Physical Units, a technical symbolic "short-hand" is universally employed, such as "$E = mc^2$," "$z = xy$," "$M = 6 \times 10^{24}$," "$c^2 = 9 \times 10^{20}$," etc. Well understood by the scientists, and of the utmost significance as an integral part of today's resources, nevertheless they can scarcely be entered into a world balance sheet until they have been re-interpreted and otherwise converted into their mathematical counterpart full meaning.

Here we are heavily indebted to Dr. Albert Einstein of Princeton University, Dr. Henry Margenau of Yale University; Dr. Hurd Curtis Willet of the Geophysical Union, Washington; Dr. Karl Ketchner Darrow of the International Union of Physics; Dr. J. Robert Oppenheimer of Princeton; and to the works of Hobart C. Dickinson of the Washington Academy of Science, Dr. Irving Langmuir of the General Electric

Research Laboratory, Professor Gale Young of Olivet College, Professor P. M. S. Blackett of Manchester University, Dr. Eugene Wigner of Princeton, Dr. Derwent Whittlesey of Harvard, Dr. Charles Schuchert of Yale, Prof. Hugh L. Callender, Walter Davis Lambert of the U. S. Coast and Geodetic Survey, and the late Ellsworth Huntington of Yale. Also, Dr. Edward Kassner of Columbia and Dr. Edna E. Kramer of the American Mathematical Society; the International Bureau of Weights and Standards, Sevres, France, and the U .S. Bureau of Standards, Washington, D. C.

In addition there have been many other significant advances in modern science in the fields of Agrobiology, Agrology, Agronomics, Bacteriology, Biology, Chemistry, Ecology, Meteorology, Mineralogy, Oceanography, Petrology, Photosynthesis and Hydroponics, Radiation and Radioactivity, and Zoology.

In these fields we are especially indebted to the late Dr. Oliver E. Baker of the Department of Agriculture, who was ever-unfailing in seeing that we were supplied with an abundance of factual matter. Also to Dr. O. S. Aamodt, agronomist, and founder of the Soil Conservation Society of America; to Dr. Edward H. Graham, Chief of the Biology Division of the U. S. Soil Conservation Service, and to Sir Robert Muir, Sir John Charles Grant, Sir Joseph A. Arkwright, Dr. A. C. Thaysen, and S. G. Paine in the field of Bacteriology. In Mineralogy much is due to Dr. Ernest Edgar Thum, Dr. William A. Phair, Dr. Joseph E. Pogue, Dr. E. de Golyer and Leonard M. Fanning. In Meteorology we owe much to Douglas Archibald, M.A., of the Royal Meteorological Society, Dr. Abbe Cleveland, and Dr. John Aitken. In Biology, Dr. Charles Singer, Sir John Arthur Thompson, Samuel Brody, Dr. V. B. Wigglesworth, Dr. John T. Nichols, Dr. J. Cecil Drummond, Dr. George E. Hutchinson, Professor Harry S. Smith and Eric J. Hill. In Petrology; Dr. Cecil Edgar Tilley, Sir Sidney Colvin and Dr. Henry G. Watt. In Chemistry; Dr. J. D. M. Smith. In Ecology; Dr. Homer LeRoy Shantz. In Radiation and Radioactivity; Sir Ernest Rutherford, Edward N. da Costa Andrade, Glen T. Seaborg, James Chadwick, and James D. Stranathan. Acknowledgment is also made to the clarifying work of Dr. Arthur H. Compton in the field of radiation, particularly to his establishment of the existence of the photon as one of the fundamental units of matter. In Photosynthesis and Hydroponics; Professor Hans Gaffron, University of Chicago, and Leon T. Eliel. In Oceanography; Dr. Sidney J. Hickson, F.R.S., Mr. E. J. Allen, and Dr. W. A. Herdman. In Zoology; Dr. L. H. Hyman and Dr. B. Linsay of Cambridge, England.

In the all-important field of the world's physical resources we are deeply indebted to Dr. Elmer W. Pehrson, Chief of the Statistical Division of the U. S. Bureau of Mines, and co-editor of the University of Maryland's study of World Mineral Resources, who so kindly permitted this author to review his advance manuscript and make use of his findings. Also to the University of Maryland, Department of Geography, College of Business and Public Administration, Dr. William Van Royen, Department Head, and Dr. Oliver Bowles, research professor at the university.

Next has been the indispensable world survey of agriculture by the Food and Agriculture Organization of the United Nations, Rome, Italy; the Reports of the Economic Development Section of the Division of Economic Stability and Development of the United Nations Department of Economic Affairs; the Forest Resources of the World by the Division of Forestry and Forest Products of the F.A.O. (Unasylva) and the Timber Resources of the United States by the Forest Service of the U. S. Department of Agriculture, with special mention for the direct helpfulness of Mr. H. R. Josephson, Chief of the Division of Forest Economics. The Fisheries of the World by the International Council for the Exploration of the Sea, the British Marine Biological Board, the U. S. Bureau of Fisheries, and special gratitude for the work of Mr. Henry Gascoyen Maurice. In addition, the work of the U. S. Bureau of Mines must again be mentioned in connection with their study of the Mineral Position of the United States in 1949, and the very valuable Report of the President's Materials Policy Commission of 1952.

Adding further to all of the above have been the further valued works in this field of Harry Oliver Buckman, Junius D. Edwards of the Bureau of Standards, Nathan Clifford Grover, Edwin C. Eckel, Arthur Notman, Arthur B. Parsons, Leurs Radcliffe, Thomas Thornton Read, Gar A. Roush, Beram D. Saklatwalla, Alonzo E. Taylor, Edwin Ward Tillotson, Arthur E. Wells, John Robbins Mohler of the U. S. Bureau of Animal Industry, and Raphael Zon.

In the political and monetary fields we have been extremely fortunate in having an abundance of data placed at our disposal. Foremost among the agencies consulted, and whose research files were made available throughout, have been the well-indexed records of the Memorial Library of the Woodrow Wilson Foundation, which houses the complete files of the League of Nations, and upon whose remarkable original international studies much of our political sub-divisional work has been dependent. In this connection the guiding and experienced assistance of Miss Harriet Van Wyck, librarian, Mrs. Eleanor Steiner-Prag, reference librarian, and Miss Marina Knapp, assistant librarian, have proved especially helpful. In further direct relation to our access to essential basic material outside the regular official channels, particular mention must be given for our appreciation for the counsel of Dr. Andre Bernard of the Legislative Reference Service of the Library of Congress in Washington, and of the rich store of material that great library made readily available to us. We have been equally indebted for the rewarding guidance of Mr. Gerald D. MacDonald of the New York Public Library and the American Library Association's member of the Document's Division of the United Nations. The splendid cooperation of the New York State Library in Albany proved of great help throughout. All of the above have contributed unstintingly to the efficiency of the research so essential to this work.

We owe a profound debt to the unexcelled and indispensable helpfulness of the Office of Statistics of the United Nations, and of the United Nations World Statistical Congress and their continuing International Seminars on Statistical Organization. A great debt is further due the United Nations Department of Economic Affairs for their many valuable World Economic Studies and Reports. We are grateful for the invaluable work of the Statistical Divisions of The Bank for International Settlements, particularly to Mr. T. R. Lauger, head of its Statistical and Documentation Service, and to valuable reports of the International Monetary Fund for both their currently maintained International Financial Statistics and their reports on the Direction of International Trade, and further to the reports of the International Bank for Reconstruction and Development, particularly their reports covering the devastated areas. Also are we grateful for permission of use of findings of the Industrial Survey of Japan by Overseas Consultants, Inc., New York, as well as for the various Reparations and Restitution Reports of the Military Governments of Germany, Austria, Italy, and Japan.

We are greatly indebted to the remarkable work of the International Reference Service of the Office of International Trade, Bureau of Foreign and Domestic Commerce, U. S. Department of Commerce; a work of incalculable value and one which the author deeply regrets has recently been discontinued for lack of Congressional appropriation.

Outstanding among the private non-governmental agencies without whose practical original work this study would have been grievously handicapped, has been the cooperative helpfulness of the economic research departments of the National City Bank of New York, the International Telephone and Telegraph Company confidential files, the New York Stock Exchange Department of Research and Statistics, the London Stock Exchange, the U. S. Bureau of Statistics, the Department of Financial and Business Research of the Chase National Bank of New York, the International Division of the Chemical Bank and Trust Company of New York, Thomas Skinner & Company, London, the Bank of Norway, the Skandinavishka Banken and the Swenska Handelsbanken of Stockholm, the Netherlands Trading Society (Nederlandsche Handel-Maatschappij) of Amsterdam, the Banco di Roma, Rome, Italy, the Institute of International

Finance of New York University, the research department of Merril, Lynch, Pierce, Fenner & Beane of New York, and the original international studies of Redmond & Company, New York, and the libraries of the Lehman Corporation and the McGraw-Hill Publishing Company of New York. Further, no work of this magnitude could omit paying grateful tribute to the currently maintained statistical and historical annual of The Statesman's Year-Book under the superb editorship of Dr. S. H. Steinberg, Fellow of the Royal Historical Society, London.

Our appreciation is extended to the many Consulates, Embassies, and Official Information Services of the various governments of the world, especially to Mr. David Davis of the British Information Service, to Mr. Ivan Jacobsen of the Royal Norwegian Information Service, to Mr. Anthony Antonakakis, director of the Greek Information Office, to Mr. Emilio de Motta, vice-consul of the Spanish Consul General's Office, to Mr. Jaume Miravitlles, Director of Information, Spanish Government in Exile, to Mr. M. M. Lourens of the Netherlands Information Bureau, to Mr. K. Christensen, financial consul, Danish Embassy, to Mr. Gil Stone, director Information Bureau of the Portuguese Government, to Mr. Basil Bass, the American Russian Institute, to Mr. Nikolai V. Novikov of the U. S. S. R. Embassy, to Mr. Milan Pitlik, acting Consul General, and Mr. Frank Vrba, cultural attaché of the Czechoslovak Consulate, to Mr. Pavel Fedosimov, vice-consul, U. S. S. R., to Mr. M. Nolett, Ministry of Finance Department of the French Embassy, to Mr. Ahmet Cemil Conk, commercial counselor of the Turkish Embassy, to Mr. Helgi P. Briem, Consul General of Iceland, to Mr. Andre Wolff, Commissioner, Government of the Grand Duchy of Luxembourg, to Mr. Frank A. Southard, Jr., Director, Office of International Finance, U. S. Treasury Department, to Mr. Drew Dudley, Director Public Relations, International Bank for Reconstruction and Development, to Mr. Guido Carli, Executive Director, International Monetary Fund, and with particular gratitude to the tireless efforts of Mrs. Erna Walmsley of the Press Liaison Office of the United Nations Public Information Service.

In further addition there have been the immensely valuable works of Prof. Erich W. Zimmerman's *World Resources and Industries,* Prof. J. Russell Smith's *Industrial and Commercial Geography,* the National Resources Board *Reports of 1934* and their *Report on Technological Trends and National Policy,* all of which have proven of great usefulness.

Further, these acknowledgments could not possibly be complete without referring to the vastly important field of developing policies aiming at raising standards of living throughout the world, and the creation of awareness everywhere of the economic problems of each country. Here the extensive cooperation among economists and statisticians has been very active in recent years, notably the exhaustive undertakings of the Conference on Studies in Income and Wealth under the auspices of the American Statistical Association and the National Bureau of Economic Research. Also the work of the Combined Production and Resources Board of the United Kingdom, the United States, and Canada (the CPRB) and the Inter American Statistical Institute (the IASI) have proven of immense aid.

Most of all the author owes a deep sense of gratitude to all those who, throughout his long vigil and quest through a literal quagmire of languages and figures, have expressed their sincere interest in the task and a hope for its final completion. Their helpful suggestions and stimulating considerations have proven an abiding inspiration and encouragement to our effort.

Foremost among these have been Mr. James B. Orrick, Chief of Non-governmental Organizations of the United Nations; Mr. Clyde Nichols, Special Advisor to the Secretary General of that organization; Mr. Stanley Lebergott, Division of Statistical Standards, U. S. Bureau of the Budget; Mr. Harlow D. Osborne, National Income Division, U. S. Department of Commerce; Mr. B. W. Bratt, Chief of Statistical Division, U. S. Treasury Department; Mr. Frank A. Southard, Jr., Director, Office of International Finance, U. S. Treasury Department; Miss Lillian Epstein, Secretary to the National Conference on Studies in Income and Wealth; Dr. E. A. Kincaid, Professor of Finance, University of Virginia; Dr. Ernest D. Phelps, Professor of Economics, Worcester Polytechnic Institute; Miss Dorothy A. Judson, Librarian, New York Stock Exchange Department of Research and Statistics; Mr. William F. Meyer, Executive Secretary Industrial Relations Program, National Council of the Y.M.C.A.; Mr. C. C. Day, Clerk, U. S. Senate Committee on Foreign Relations; Mr. Norman C. Firth, Editor, Dun's Review; Mr. Mark A. Rose, Senior Editor of the *Reader's Digest;* Miss Emma R. Broisman, Librarian, International Labor Organization; and to Mr. Joseph Sigrist, our chief liaison officer throughout; to the loyal support of Dr. Charles Newton Wonacott, Philanthropic Counselor of the Hanover Bank of New York, whose unflagging confidence has proven an ever-encouraging force over many dark hours of this effort.

Much of this work was planned many years ago as background for a volume then in prospect. Highly summarized as these consolidated findings may appear, the whole has required the contacting of many hundreds of specialists and organizations representing the accumulated labors of many thousands of trained and experienced technicians, the larger part of whom must regretfully remain here unnamed.

Appendix B. Background

EVERY SETTING has its subject matter, its background, and its predicaments to deal with. The background comprises the milieu or environmental conditioning media; while its predicaments constitute those categories of logical predications which can best be made to serve as clarifying elements describing the whole.

In other words, the setting must embrace not only its conditioning immediate environs and circumambiences, but the relative possibilities of their consolidation as well, with the whole forming its material for thought.

The setting in this case has been the world, which comprises the planet earth together with its system of created things—including mankind and his institutions, among the general groupings of animal, mineral, and vegetable worlds.

MAN'S WORLD

Man, one of the most recent and the most specialized of all living organisms, has made himself, through his well-meant activities, the somewhat spoiled darling of the whole system. Because he can utilize and more or less control all other organisms, he frequently forgets that he is the beneficiary of a prolonged and delicately balanced development in which he sometimes does more to destroy than to perpetuate its balance.

POPULATION

The human population of the world today is believed to be around 2500 million. In the year 1882 world population, according to the best authorities, was around 1400 million. According to the Biblical life-span of three-score and ten years, this means that within a seventy-year period the world population has increased by 1100 million people—or almost doubled. Population experts now estimate that it will double again within the next fifty years, which means a possible world total approximating 5 billion by the year 2002.

At present over 411,000 persons are born every day, and over 274,000 persons die; thus a net gain of some 137,000 persons daily, or 50 million per year. Seventy years ago the daily net gain was 20 thousand persons, or at the rate of 7 million per year. Hence, world population at present appears to be increasing some seven times faster than formerly.

EDUCATION

Until fairly recent times, the earth was popularly considered the center of the universe. Insofar as mankind is concerned it still is the center of his foremost concerns.

The sun, moon, planets and stars were once considered as hung in the heavens to light the earth for the convenience of man. Navigators still assume the earth to be the center of the universe, with the heavenly bodies revolving around it. They know better, of course, but the assumption is made for the sake of convenience in the compilation and use of their navigation charts and tables.

Those of us born before 1900 were taught that the sun was the center of the universe, and this was viewed as quite an advance in knowledge. Today, as a matter of fact, no one really knows where the center of the universe is, nor have we but a vague and ever-changing concept of its boundaries.

A naval instructor, assigned to instruct newly recruited Naval Reserve officers how to plot ship's movements, has reported that to one leading question he asked, he always got the wrong answer. The question was: "From a point somewhere north of the equator, a ship sails three-hundred miles north, then three-hundred miles east, then three-hundred miles south, then three-hundred miles west. Does she return to the same point from which she started?"

The answer was always "yes"—which is of course incorrect. Yet these young officers were all college graduates, all selected for their brilliance and their adaptability to this kind of work. They were not stupid. They all knew that the world is round; but when they were given a practical job to do with that world—having been accustomed to looking at flat maps—for the moment they forgot the important fact that the world in reality is not flat, and that Euclid's geometry could not apply, for on a round earth you cannot draw a straight line. Further than that, the earth is not standing still, but is revolving and continuously in motion. The direction of this rotation is called "easterly" and the opposite direction "westerly." But since we do not feel the rotation, it appears to us that the sun is revolving in the opposite, or "westerly," direction around the earth. All of which presents problems in measurements, distances, and directions which are very different from problems on a static, flat, plane surface.

We also live in a world of changing civilization, in which many things new are not easily traced or analyzed. Static life, like static theories, can be easily classified and catalogued; dynamic life and exploding theories come near to defying diagnosis. Hence, any attempted analysis of the present can give us but a partial view of existing conditions and problems, with such a picture as a *whole* lacking depth and perspective. And this is the kind of view, this partial single image, most of us get and hold all too often—when what is needed is a sort of stereoscopic comprehensive and comparative image.

Further, the world is a big place, regardless of how fast we can now travel round it. It contains many countries, many peoples, many different ways of living. Nevertheless it does have a coherence of content which certainly entitles the subject to be regarded as an important element in the education of all of its citizens.

A nationwide survey conducted by *The New York Times* in 1951, directed by Dr. Samuel Van Valkenburg, Director of the Graduate School of Geography at Clark University, disclosed an appalling factual ignorance among American college students.

Less than 5 per cent of the college students were taking even one course in geography, with both world and American geography being by-passed by the vast majority of students. In fact, according to the chairman of the Department of Geography at Syracuse University, few other civilized nations are so geographically illiterate. As to population, only one out of four had even a rough approximation of world population, many thinking it might be 100 million or less. And in respect to the world's resources and wealth, by way of example, over 25 per cent of the college graduates were of the opinion that Adam Smith was the author of *Alice in Wonderland,* with another 25 per cent unable to recall ever having heard of him. Regarding resources, they all considered these far too boundless even to venture a surmise.

When one reflects that scarcely 5 per cent of all American voting citizens have ever received education at the college level, and barely ²⁄₁₀ of 1 per cent of these having adequate geographic education (some 261,000 out of 100,000,000 voters), how fearfully appalling must be the degree of such ignorance the world over with nearly 60 per cent of the people being wholly unable to read and write.

Perhaps the most shocking aspect of the replies was the total lack of any concept of big numbers. There was little or no discrimination between "millions" and "billions"; and of "trillions," "quadrillions" and so on, no conception at all. This inability or indifference toward an apprehension of relationships brings us down to the question of intelligence.

INTELLIGENCE QUOTIENT

From the standpoint of international nomenclature the term "intelligence" stems from the Latin *Intellegere,* meaning to understand. The common thread of meaning running through all definitions of intelligence is that it is chiefly a function of the individual's ability to apprehend relationships. Hence intelligence is primarily a problem-solving function of the mind.

In view of the extensive use of so-called "intelligence tests" for all sorts of practical purposes, it would seem to be a matter of some urgency to determine as precisely as possible not only what is meant by intelligence, but its relative extent and use in terms of average mental ability among the peoples of the world.

Despite the fact that educators and psychologists use the term with considerable latitude of meaning and, like a sense of humor, intelligence is something that everybody may think he possesses in abundance, we may secure some measure of it by referring to the standard I. Q. tests for purposes of recording an inventory of intelligence on a comparative basis as it most assuredly is a world resource of utmost importance.

Particularly is this true as at present many world thinkers have come to feel that a satisfactory solution of today's world problems may be beyond our present intelligence capacities. Regardless of the emotional content, it is clear, if not painfully obvious, when we contemplate the requirements for the future, that there is need for considerably greater intellectual power than is now being put to use. This is especially true as it relates to the new factual discoveries about the actual constitution of the world.

There are some thirty or more intelligence tests now in use throughout the world, dating from 1883, which may serve to give us some idea as to both the mass average and comparison to the trends. As the intelligence quotient follows the average age and educational levels rather closely we may gain a fairly good conception from the English, German, French, and American studies relating to both trends and current position. For these results the Tables in Chapter III may serve as indicators of the universal agreement as to the declining rate in points per generation over the past fifty years. A rate, percentage-wise, that seems to follow the decline in the world's top-soil nutrients rather closely.

Aside from the purely biological aspects it will be noticed that in general the higher the economic or social position of the parents, the higher the intelligence quotient of the children. Numerous investigations, other than the example here shown, all point to the same conclusion.

It has been repeatedly shown in all investigations that those families with more than average ability contribute less than the average number of children to the next generation, while the lower the social status the larger the number of surviving children; thus changes in the mental endowment of the population as a whole has tended in the direction of a lowering of the level.

GEOLOGICAL SETTING

Comparatively unknown to most people, the fact long known to geologists, geographers, and geophysicists is that the earth has been shrinking throughout the course of geologic time. According to the geologists the earth has shrunk at least 400 miles in diameter, has lost over 1500 miles in circumference and over 400 quintillion tons in weight, in the course of its geologic age. It is still shrinking.

As a matter of further fact, there are now nearly 800 million acres less land on the earth's surface than there were a mere 70 years ago. There are also nearly 300 million more acres of sea and ocean water area than 70 years ago, with the seas growing ever-larger at the expense of the world's land.

These losses have been due in part to the earth's loss of heat energy into space, and in greater degree to internal molecular change. Even though it has been dissipating its inherited energy and mass for many hundreds of millions of years, it is still far from having attained that internal stability—that "balance"—which will, when finally achieved, result in a featureless world with a universal ocean, and an atmosphere devoid of carbon dioxide.

Erosion, denudation, and weathering keep persistently on and on. Some 13 trillion tons of solid material are washed out of the fields and pastures of the land continents of today's world every year. And with this goes some 2 billion tons of the most important soil nutrients—the principal elements of all animal and plant food—phosphorus, potassium, nitrogen, magnesium, iron, sulphur, and other organic matter.

The above erosion is only the normal geological erosion, and does not include the accelerated erosion and denudation of the man-made variety—which now progresses some three times faster than the normal geologic erosion. Further, this soil nutrient loss alone is also three times that of the vital elements removed by crops and grazing each year. During the past 70 years man has lost over 150 billion tons of these elements largely by his own lack of foresight.

The people of the world today are extracting some 7½ billion tons of raw materials of all kinds from the surface of the earth annually, while over the past 70 years man has used up nearly 1 trillion tons of these irretrievable materials from what he still considers to be his inexhaustible heritage. For every 100 tons he puts back 3.

The implications of today's prodigious waste of irreplaceable resources can best be understood when we realize that the world today—in modern twentieth-century civilization—is squandering its priceless top-soil at the unprecedented rate of 2 inches per year, in the face of the fact that it takes a thousand years to build a single inch of such soil. That amounts to over 2 billion tons of chemical nutrients that go down the drain every year to the inhabitants of the sea, as man plies his quest for "profit." That this is 60 times the available plant food that man returns to the soil, in the various forms of commercial fertilizers, does not seem to fall within the purview of his 96-point intelligence. In terms of annual monetary loss this amounts to over $6 billion in lost productivity alone.

LAND

The land areas of the world, excluding the polar regions, is roughly 33 billion acres, of which less than half was formerly regarded as arable. Taking good and bad land together, it was estimated that 4 acres were required, directly and indirectly, to sustain one human being. At that time it was considered that this would fix the limit of population of the globe to something over 8 billion people.

With these factors in mind it was then thought that by improvements in agriculture, and a diminution of domesticated animals, one could regard a population of 6 billion as approaching saturation for the globe. It was also thought that such a population would never be reached.

SATURATION

Today's estimates of the possible maximum world population vary from 3 billion to as much as 16 billion, with the possible limit lying somewhere between these totals. Over the past decade the term "optimum population" has come into use. While the origin is not clear, nevertheless this conception lies at the base of the position taken by many industrial economists who seem to think that at any given time the population which can exist on any given area of land, consistent with the attainment of the maximum return to industry possible at the time, is definite. Departure from this optimum in the direction of a deficiency they call "underpopulation," and departure in the direction of an excess they call "overpopulation." Regardless of the many past attempts to rationalize the world's population in relation to resources, the ever-increasing march of the world's deserts—natural and man-made—including "built-on" land, has reduced the ratio of arable acres to one-tenth the total available acreage rather than the earlier estimate of one-half. This fact makes a profound difference in all of the previous calculations regarding both the possible saturation point and the optimum desirable for a maximum return to industry.

From the standpoint of four acres per person, we find the present world population to have long since reached the saturation point, with a present overpopulation, man-land ratiowise, amounting to 1750 million. Even on the present accepted basis of two and one-half acres of arable land required per person, the indicated present world over-population approximates 1300 million people.

LAND-SHRINKAGE FACTOR

However, while the world population has increased over 73 per cent during the past 70-year period, the world's total land acreage per person has decreased 43 per cent. The two trends both appear to have accelerated, and both are moving in diametrically opposite directions on what amounts to a single-lane traffic road.

Forty per cent of the industrial world's population live in metropolitan urban centers, where there is seldom more than a 60-day food supply on hand. Even such short-term supplies require a complex organization of farms, farmers, dealers and shippers, truckers and railroads, warehouses, and distributors, with its corresponding technologi-cal dependencies all delicately interconnected and sensitive to far-off occurrences. This facet of modern civilization produces a situation where it can collapse with terrifying speed.

PRINCIPLE OF USUFRUCT IN RELATION TO PERISHABLE THINGS

Mankind in his primitive stage was a part of nature. He still is. There seems to be ample evidence that, as far as future generations are concerned, he has failed to recognize that, if he is to survive, his world is not completely his for consumption and still less for profligate waste. Man may have all the rights and advantages derivable from the use of the world's resources, but the world is his in usufruct alone.

In this sense there is a certain pathos in the helplessness of "civilization" and "race" against the selfish desire to seek today's gain by wasting resources fundamental to man's survival—resources that will stay wasted for a thousand years.

It takes the morphological processes of nature 2 billion years to produce a single ounce of iron and copper, and 4 billion years to produce a single ounce of lead. The people of the world are today using these minerals up at a rate in excess of 100 million tons per year; it would thus appear that we are nearing a period wherein the foundations of modern industrialism may be facing a substantial change.

Over twenty centuries ago Aristotle pointed out that man is prone to pirate when he can, and trade only when he must. In this sense there can be no doubt but that the world's resources have been pirated. And in this same sense the influence of man as a geological agent has become of ever-increasing importance. And by the removal of forests, and the wholesale destruction of woodlands, he has not only increased erosion but has lessened the possible evaporation, with a consequent diminishing of rainfall and an attendant increase in the general temperature. Hence, man has become a destruc-tive meteorological agent as well.

FACT-FINDING, WISHFUL AND OTHERWISE

Irrespective of the great advances in knowledge on an international scale, and of their meaning when applied in attempts to ascertain future probabilities, both the traditional economic theorists and the more unorthodox theorists have presented an outlook more optimistic than the facts would seem to warrant.

Of these, the most recent has been *The Road to Abundance*, 1954, by Jacob Rosen and Max Eastman; here the authors predict the doubling of the world's population every seventy years at present rates. However, there will be plenty of food, and an

abundance of new minerals and energy to support the coming industrial age. Abun
dance, Dr. Rosen assures the world, is all around us—a "dilute abundance" now in the
rocks and in the seas. All we have to do is dig down far enough and process some
4 quadrillion tons of rock, and harvest some 90 billion acres of seas. There is a verbal
abundance based on "resources" not yet at man's command.

Whether such optimistic promises represent man's education beyond his intelligence
we do not know, but it falls well outside the realm of disciplined practical thinking
That an incorrigible optimism is inherent in the human race there can be little doubt
All the predictive studies put out by the various nations and their nationals hew to this
line. The language of science is employed, although the figures and the logic and
casuistry of their analysis may be far from scientific. In any respectable science, any
theory descended from a postulate is not regarded as a final truth, but merely as a
hypothesis to be tested.

As late as 1949, the Ecumenical Institute, in Switzerland, agreed that his
tory is a mystery, and that those who long to know the future, and raise questions of
progress, are showing a lack of faith.

Three years later, in 1952, the President's Materials Policy Commission, in the United
States, issued a five-volume report entitled *Resources for Freedom,* in which they stated
their faith in "the belief of the American people in the principle of growth"; neverthe
less, the report pointed out limits to certain resources.

In the same year a widely publicized report entitled *America's Wealth* was issued
by the Brookings Institution, Washington, D.C. This report concluded the potential
producing capacity, as governed by natural resources and scientific developments, to be
sufficient for the country to support a population of twice as many a century hence
and on a plane of living eight times higher than at present.

In July, 1954, the Minerals Sub-Committee of the U. S. Senate Committee on Interior
and Insular Affairs issued a report stating that those who would have the American
people believe that their mineral resources were nearing depletion, and that the United
States was becoming a "have-not" nation, were perpetuating a fraud upon the Amer
ican people. The report admitted that 80 per cent of the present stockpile of critical
materials was dependent upon foreign sources, but largely at the expense of domestic
producers, which could be corrected by sound legislation.

In addition to the above reports there have been a number of others deserving of
serious consideration. These include a report to the President by the International De
velopment Advisory Board and a report by a group of experts appointed by the Sec
retary-General of the United Nations, both dealing with the world's underdeveloped
countries.

Scarcely two decades ago this sort of "reporting" had taken a form on the order of
propagandized "planning." Europe had its "Geopolitik," "Weltanschauung" (world
view), and "Lebensraum" (living-space), America its "Technocracy," Russia it
"Khozraschet" (business accountability), with Japan and other nations producing their
counterparts in rapid succession. Each relied on statistics to justify their case. Each
stretched representation beyond existing facts. Each engaged in distortion, omission
and casuistic analysis, in attempts to convince people that each was for their best
interests. Each was along the lines of Cromwell's cry, "for the good of the people, and
not what pleases them."

In this setting "Totalitarian" economy and totalitarian economics came into the
march of world event. The political idea submerged under every approach stated that
while autocratic government can exist only on a democratic basis, democracy is justified
only when it has an autocratic superstructure, with the whole operated by a single
party or elite ruling class. In other words, autocracy and democracy are not opposite
which exclude each other, but become effective only when united.

This concept envisages the State as geared to the production of goods which are
ultimately significant in warfare, with the economy becoming adjusted to a state of

perpetual warfare whether or not actual fighting takes place. The entire industrial economy of the world thus becomes not only geared *to* but dependent *on* war as the dominant impulse-factor in the dynamics of modern society. Both quantitatively and qualitatively, wars have become of prime significance to the industrial economics of the world, although traditionally neglected in most orthodox theories of economic development.

In general, governments and public alike are becoming increasingly aware of the importance of having at their disposal unqualified quantitative information on a wide variety of basic essential elements in order to permit intelligent planning, and to serve as a basis for decisions regarding the diverse and complex economic and social problems today confronting them.

This, then, is our background—perhaps on a final frontier of bitter fact—as man becomes increasingly aware of the challenge of his ever-shrinking exhaustible planet Earth.

Appendix C. Procedure

As THIS STUDY was undertaken with several aims in view, its procedures necessarily have been developed in successive stages. At the outset the exploratory assembling of data from widely scattered sources and centers—London, Paris, Rome, Geneva, Washington, New York—proved time-consuming, while the testing for adequacy for our purposes required additional alterations in the original plan as the work progressed.

Although the responsibility for the study as a whole rests with the author, generous assistance in its development has been received from many sources and authorities, as disclosed under "Acknowledgments."

The work consists of an attempt in terms of double-entry accounting to secure such a physical and corresponding monetary-counterpart reconciliation of world resources as the existing data permits.

In this respect the work represents independent studies in the various fields covered, with the first aim being that of ascertaining the fundamental facts within each field as accurately as possible and then presenting them in such systematic and categorical form as to enable thoughtful readers, however divergent their views of public policy the world over, to consider their discussions from a vantage point of objective over-all knowledge as distinguished from subjective single-point opinion only.

Clearly, as the work must be done in broad style, no amount of care taken in working up such data can guarantee precise results. The reader will, therefore, understand that while each study was made by distinct methods applicable to the different collections of data—with the figures used to check and test each other—they represent a composite comparative measurement rather than an enumeration in a final sense.

As most of the large items that enter into each inventory can be arrived at in more than one way, invaluable help has been received from the work of experts in their respective fields. In this manner precaution against gross errors has been taken. Further, as one of the most serious difficulties confronted in working with world data has been the difficulty of definitions; we have included comment on "Nomenclature" separately, as a decisive part in our procedure.

The development of any procedure aiming at a systematic knowledge of the physical or material world, and its correlative institutionalized relationships, cannot escape for guidance reference to the traditional theory of knowledge nor to the more clarified principles and disciplines of recognized modern practical sciences.

In view of the tendency either to exaggerate or to belittle the importance of the collection, classification, and use of numerical data—called statistical procedure—as an independent method of science, it may be well to point out that while it is only one of the methods of science, nevertheless, as any true science rests upon accurate finite measurement, it is always the essential fundamental feature. In the world of practical business operations this is preeminently so. Every bookkeeper, every accountant, when he enters his figures in his record books, is engaging in statistics no matter what he calls his process. *Number,* lest he forget, is the language of both science and business.

THE SCIENCE OF SCIENCE

It has been frequently emphasized by distinguised scholars that the destiny of modern civilization is now inseparately linked with the fate of economic science. It has also been frequently stated by equally distinguished scholars that political economy—economics—has not yet attained the right to call itself a science at all. Most economists have persistently failed to include in their concept of capital the highly vulnerable biotic and geologic potential; yet money and wealth have been *equated* regardless.

224

Popular discussions of economic questions are almost invariably characterized by the fact that only a small and arbitrarily selected part of the world's economic structure and mechanism is taken into account. The most common and the crudest mistakes of popular opinion and political oratory may be traced to this defect.

Man's acquisition of knowledge has come extremely slow. Even the greatest of scientists have sometimes lacked the courage to publish the facts of their discoveries because they were so startling. Nevertheless, a progressive science always finds it necessary, in order to make room for new investigations, to forge ahead fearlessly and leave out such old matters and unproven theories as are no longer essential.

Few people, even today fully realize how big the vaults of present-day knowledge really are, and how much invaluable knowledge they contain. As a matter of fact there is now a shortage of technicians to cope with this mass of data. The presence of a trained personnel in every nation should be the *sine qua non* of a sound world statistical system. This lacking, there may be a tendency to measure a world undergoing swift *dynamic change* with skills and tools designed for measuring a *static* world at *rest*.

Social thinking has thus far suffered an evident disadvantage as compared with scientific thinking. Much of the effectiveness of scientific thinking has rested on the shoulders of a relatively few outstanding individuals. Few individuals ever master the disciplines and technical methods of more than one science, or one group of closely related sciences. In pure science these technical methods are not regarded as an end in themselves, but merely as a means toward the discovery of the nature of the phenomena under investigation.

This is done by drawing observations from data which the technical methods render possible. Sometimes these methods make it possible to observe and measure certain things, events, which otherwise could either not be observed and measured at all, or not so accurately. It has been with all of these factors in mind that the procedural operation of this investigation has necessarily progressed.

Such an approach must seek its guidance from a review of the inherent problems encountered, as well as from the relative degree of validity of the available data. In so doing, however, use can profitably be made of the idea that the world is an organic whole, as a primary heuristic principle to guide us in following the fundamental connections of things with each other.

Therefore this inquiry has considered it advisable to begin with as comprehensive and fundamental a physical quantitative inventory as possible, in order to set a realistic pattern as our basic frame of reference. In so doing the present great advances of the physical sciences—geodetic, geophysical, and others—permit an abundance of authentic data of far greater validity than is yet to be found in any other field.

In so doing we may establish our approach by way of the many "components" representing generally recognized "values," as primary "indicators" subject to a minimum of controversy—and subject also to integration within the existing various national account structures in a way that even a greater mass of fragmentized information could not do.

In today's world of the dominance of science over the lives of all of us, we find ourselves actually living in an area of "knowledges"—composed almost wholly of what we might call the "autonomous" sciences. To join these sciences together in a synchronized unity represents the nature of mankind's present problem. Here we find ourselves confronted with a new frontier—it may be our last—but if we do not approach it too blindly it may offer enormous possibilities. In this sense this work has also been *an adventure* in measuring global resources and their social accounting; an adventure which could not escape trespassing on many related fields regardless of what dangers might be encountered.

Foremost among these binding processes has been the establishment of an adequate physical frame of reference. Next, an institutional frame of reference, and last, such reconciliation as these components indicate.

THE TRIAL BALANCE

In this broad sense the present work represents a first attempt to draft an over-all composite world balance sheet, inclusive of basic elements and covering the world's sovereign national states and the colonial non-self-governing dependencies. As such it is both experimental and *pro forma* in treatment—in fact, a trial balance.

It must be understood that the author is fully aware that no absolute and definitive world balance sheet, satisfactory to all interests, opinions, and factors, can be drafted as of a specific date—either now or at any other time. The sheer physical component of global time and calendar preclude this possibility. But it does not prohibit a funda mental global *mean* approximation—which is far better than no approximation at all.

Econometric, Astrometric, and Physiometric measures are still best expressed in orders of magnitudes and their relations—as in *pi* and the now famous $E = mc^2$—all of which are but approximations. Good enough, however, to lead to the production of both the A- and the H-bombs and atomic energy.

Further, the past quarter century has been replete with evidence that the geophysical world is not only shrinking but is definitely slowing down. In fact even the rotation of the earth and its annual circulation in its orbit is slowing down. Not only slowing down but losing both mass and energy.

It takes but a smattering of geological knowledge to know that the world's land and water resources, its "rocks and rills, its woods and templed hills," are not immutable.

Also, regardless of how well the future world may plan, the competition of countless insects, termites, bacteria, mammals, and a ceaseless accelerated land erosion will incidentally accompany man's operations.

Although ample warnings have been given during the past decade, nevertheless today's civilization, more than any which has gone before, is living visibly and dan gerously beyond its means. The knowledge at our disposal is being used to drain the world's resources, and to borrow from the future as never before.

Regardless of the warnings of the ecologists and economic entomologists mankind merely shrugs his shoulders and, as blindly as his ancestors—who once said, "the Lord will provide," now says, "science will find a way." Thus the busy warring-world of "practical" affairs feels neither the need nor has the time to think of such non optimistic non-go-getter unpopular matters.

Under the circumstances of what its author feels to be today's need, little attempt has been made to "popularize" this study's treatment, as the significance of its funda mental subject matter necessarily calls for a certain amount of sustained thoughtfulness and informed reflection in relatively new areas.

In this respect it is earnestly hoped that the general outline may serve to stimulate honest criticism and constructive suggestion toward the furtherance of more badly needed adventures in its field.

Of course any study of this kind is *a priori* concerned with what is usually referred to as "Commercial," "Physical," and "Industrial" Geography. Nevertheless, in the light of the new scientific epoch we are now entering, it cannot escape an essential enlarge ment into both cosmo- and geo-physical geography as well. Hence, while we are con cerned largely with the existing conditions of interdependence and interactive forces among the different parts and communities of the world, the deeper and more penetrat ing purposes of the study may be described as an exploratory effort to discover, if pos sible, the fundamental causes that have been most active in creating and maintaining these conditions.

TECHNICALITIES

In this undertaking we are immediately confronted with an entire matrix of *complex problems.*

As we are dealing with matters on a global scale, any resolution is immediately confronted with the geometry of the world—past and present, and its corresponding geometric arithmetic—both Euclidian and Riemannian, with such compound reconciliation as to be involved in either approaches.

Again, as this is a "Balance Sheet," a system of components subject to the principles underlying any presentation of accounts in which resolution by geometrical addition and equation-arithmetic becomes necessary, we are compelled to proceed by four principal stages.

1. *Analysis:* or course of procedure, by which the construction of the required basic world may be discovered.

2. *Construction:* by means of international standard units of measure and nomenclature.

3. *Proof:* that our required existing figure of the world satisfies all of these conditions as above mentioned on as authoritative a basis as possible.

4. *Discussion:* of the limitations, if any, within which any solution may be possible.

Such a work, therefore, is *meroscopic* in that it examines one thing at a time, and thus forms the *whole* out of its parts rather than the parts out of the whole; and it is *holoscopic* only as a result of this order of practice.

In other words, we do not start out with an assumption based on things that are *"supposed to be so,"* or that are thought might be *made to appear* to be so, and then proceed to collect all of the factual data possible in order to "prove" the supposition. We proceed first to assemble all of the available fundamental componential data possible, and, after organizing them in their respective correlative categories, we try to discover what kind of *"proposition"* it is with which we are faced. In other words, we are *looking for* rather than *starting with* a proposition.

Fundamental research, as distinct from applied research, can only proceed in this manner philosophically speaking, any order of procedure involves something that is first, something that is intermediate, and something that is last. Thus fundamental research passes from necessary first principles, through intermediate middle terms, to a universal conclusion; while applied research passes from an ultimate hoped-for end, through intermediate means, to an ultimate contingent means.

In modern-day science more resort must be made to the increasing use of the statistical tools of the chemists and geophysical scientists. The economic statistician must learn to work with engineers—or find his statistics engineered.

It is basic that the principal components of the world's physical resources constitute the foundation of all real wealth—in any country, in any language, and under any political system. And *what is done* with these constituent parts out of which the world economy is compounded comprises its assets and liabilities, no matter how they may be expressed in their representative multiple-monetary counterpart evaluation.

OUR CHIEF TOOLS AND THEIR USES

The statistical view has so penetrated modern scientific thinking and *method* that it has gone far beyond anything that Sir William Petty or the Marquis de Condorcet had ever imagined. Also, as Dr. Edward Kasner has stated, the application of statistical methods of physicists in the interpretation of physical reality has been comparable in intellectual importance to the Renaissance.

To be reliable, statistics as factual tools must be honestly gathered and impartially and fearlessly presented. Apart from this, our problem becomes one of the precise definition and the accurate usage of words. As in the old League of Nations and the present United Nations the problem confronting the delegates of nations when talking about the same subject—but in different languages—has been that of making certain that their words and terms have agreed meanings and could be readily translated and understood.

This problem—one of semantics—applies equally to international statistics and particularly to a balance sheet accounting where the terms used by one government must be convertible into terms understood by other governments, and the methods used be similarly understood.

The collection of statistical information by governments for domestic and international use is a highly technical function requiring the services of experts in various administrative and technically specialized positions.

Unfortunately, as the United Nations Statistical Office has pointed out, there is a popular if crude adage to the effect that: "figures don't lie, but liars can figure." Further much of the existing statistical data of the world is far from being in orderly and accurate form. Because of the many organizations involved, it has been necessary to secure coordination of statistical between the United Nations and the many outside specialized agencies.

While this responsibility for such coordination has been vested, by order of the Economic and Social Council, in the Statistical Commission and the U. N. Statistical Office, yet this commission, in no case except for demonstration purposes, permits it staff to undertake the actual collection of national statistics, nor may they engage in auditing the figures supplied them from the various organizations and political government. Further, only eighty-one of the ninety-five nations of the world are now members of the United Nations.

In order to surmount these difficulties this investigation organized the World Asset Audit Association, in 1947, as a nonprofit nongovernmental cooperating corporation authorized by the Department of State of New York to engage in such activities. The services of a trained liaison officer were then employed for direct contact with the United Nation's specialized organizations, the nonmember nations of the world, and other private agencies, as an indispensable requirement of our procedural operations.

It is our conviction that it can be only through such an attempted reappraisal that we may ultimately secure a better understanding of those more significant problems that are today confronting mankind. This, then, has been in broad outline the approach that has set—the standards of our procedure.

Appendix D. Nomenclature
AND GLOSSARY OF TERMS

THE SYSTEM of names and terms employed throughout this work becomes of essential importance in an international study. This is true not only as they relate to the various sciences and individual national communities, but to the accounting terms as well— these not being uniform in all countries.

The fundamental purposes of any study dealing with a large body of facts are, first, that the terminology employed shall be capable of exact understanding and customarily in uniform practice throughout the various sciences and branches of knowledge of the world; and that every descriptive term, technical or otherwise, be rigorously limited to the expression of the precise quality, or mode of action, to which it is applied.

In addition, in order to have an absolute system of reference, the assembled facts must be systematically arranged in conformity with the prevailing knowledge of the physical or material world and its institutionalized format, in a manner which may enable us to determine position and proportions anywhere on the Earth's surface.

In this respect the language of modern science—including that of finance, trade, and economics—in its terminology, signs, and symbols, constitutes the only international language we have. While programs for the unification of scientific knowledge are scarcely more than a generation old, considerable progress has been made during the past decade. In this field the work of the British Orthological Institute, the International Encyclopedia of Unified Science, the Journal of Unified Science, and the reports of the American Institute of Accountants Committee on Uniform Terminology have made outstanding contributions.

SYSTEMATIC REFERENCE

As the term "Nomenclature," meaning a set or system of names or terms used in the various sciences and branches of knowledge by the individual or community, has been adopted by the United Nations and other international organizations, we find it conveniently at hand.

GEOGRAPHIC NOMENCLATURE

The geographic nomenclature has necessarily followed that adopted by the United Nations Secretariat Committee for the Standardization of Geographic Names. This nomenclature is designed to provide a systematic classification of the geographic areas covering the entire world. The designations of territories have been made only for the purposes of establishing a list of names of areas appropriate for the collecting and assembling of statistical data corresponding to the statistics available to the dates given, and do not imply recognition by the United Nations as to the precise political status of the territories concerned or of the names used.

This classification is based on a continental arrangement as long recognized by the International Geodetic and Geophysical Union. The subdivision within each continent is an administrative one, and within the administrative subdivision the names are alphabetized according to their English spelling with the correct name of each area being given in its most convenient form.

This present draft has been revised as of January 1, 1957, and represents a collation of material as obtained from the major authorities in all of the languages concerned.

There are other forms of the names of countries which are acceptable, and in a few cases alternate forms are given enclosed in parentheses. At the present writing, of course, some administrative political relationships remain indeterminate. This is inevitable in the world's present political fluid state.

Nomenclature includes definitions of words and terms in buying and selling in the various industries, and in the technical and general economic literature, as well as the abbreviations and symbols employed in the different sciences.

International nomenclature implies standardization in its broadest sense, as it applies not only to the geodetic and geophysical aspects of the world, but to weights and measures, physical objects, and materials.

In this broad sense, standards of measurement, such as the meter, kilogram, pound, foot, hectare, acre, and monetary units, are as necessary to any national economy as is an alphabet to their language and literature. To meet the needs of modern science and technology these standards have been set up in all fields covered in the present study.

Standard methods of accounting and its corresponding nomenclature have been adhered to throughout.

THE NOMENCLATURE OF MATHEMATICS

Thus far we have been talking about *"sort"* language—the word terms that are used to describe the kind of things in the world. Most civilized societies in this century have, to a degree, democratized the reading and writing of *sort language.*

Consequently, the average person can understand even scientific discoveries if they do not involve complicated measurements. He understands something about evolution, the solar planetary system, geography, geology, etc.

As Hogben has pointed out, the atom and the laws of conservation of matter, mass, and of energy, are safe places to hide—because one has to be familiar with complicated measurements and use "underground" channels concealed from the eye of the people because the average man has not yet been taught to read and write *size language*—which is the language of mathematics; a language not yet fully democratized.

Numbers are finite—not infinite. Some scientists—to this day use the word "infinite" when they mean some "big" number—like a billion billion and so on. *Counting* is a precise operation. It may be wonderful, but there is nothing vague or mysterious about it. If you count something, the answer you get is either perfect or it is all wrong—there is no half way. In counting, no one would say that 1 plus 1 is about equal to 2. It is just as silly to say that a billion billion is not a finite number, simply because it is big. Any number which can be named, or conceived in terms of its integers, is finite.

The known world we live in is a finite world—even though it has taken many centuries for the infinite to be treated as a problem in science, and not as a problem in theology.

In establishing this finite system of reference, essential for scientific measurement, we may further glean an impression of man's place in the material universe. If we are adequately to understand the nature of the world we live in, its resources, and its energy, we have no other scientific alternative.

THE NOMENCLATURE OF THE PHYSICAL SCIENCES

The problem of satisfactory nomenclature meets its most serious difficulties when we enter the field of the autonomous sciences. This is due to the continuous invasions of one science upon another, with their boundaries constantly changing. The physicist views the world in terms of submicroscopic particles, and then proceeds to employ, for convenience, some of the existing mathematical vocabulary which he combines with his own set of algebraic symbols and equations.

As an illustration; while light and other forms of electromagnetic radiation can no longer be described as "waves" only, nevertheless, as there are certain wavelike properties discernible, the physicist still retains much of the old mathematical terminology in discussing the subject. This causes an understandable confusion in the lay public's mind.

For instance, the electronic mathematician is fond of using certain letters in the symbolizing of his equations. He likes to use the letter c to symbolize constants, particularly when referring to the most important constant—the velocity of light. He also likes to use t for time and d for distance. Therefore he is more likely to symbolize the radar formula by $d = \dfrac{ct}{2}$. Whereas the engineer is more likely to employ his own multiplication formula for measuring speed, frequency, and wave length in terms of $z = \dfrac{xy}{2}$, with z for speed, x for frequency, and y for wave length. The main point here is that they are both talking about the same thing. Their method of procedure is identical. The only difference lies in their use of different symbols—a different nomenclature.

THE FUNDAMENTAL DIMENSIONS

In the statements and equations of the laws of mechanics, and hence in all mechanical measurements, only three *fundamental quantities* exist. These are known as the fundamental dimensions, and consist of L for length, M for mass, and T for time.

When Newton formulated the law of gravitation of classical mechanics, first in 1665 from his study of Kepler's empirical laws of the motion of the planets, he used F for the force between two particles of mass, M_1 and M_2 for mass, and d for the distance between them—with G representing the gravitational *constant*. His formula then appeared as $F = \dfrac{M_1 M_2}{d^2}$. In terms of dimensions it was written $L^3 M^{-1} T^{-2}$, and had a numerical value depending on the units used. The foremost thing to remember here is that, although Newton later refined his equations, the gravitational constant became one of the fundamental constants of nature. This, then, was the Newtonian nomenclature.

Mathematically speaking, a *constant* is a quantity whose value cannot change, and therefore cannot be determined by the conditions of the problem being considered. In other words, it is a quantity which never varies, and is completely independent of all the other factors and elements involved. Therefore *constants* are the great measuring rules of science. Due to the fact that no one has yet discovered a suitable economic constant, many economic writers claim economics is not yet and never can become a science. These difficulties, however, should not be confused with the many other so-called practical constants of science, such as π, e, h, and i, which are quite reliable tools.

Then came Planck's famous Quantum Mechanics at the start of our present century, 1900, which considerably upset Newton's once-sacrosanct "laws." Here was a new slant to science and scientific method which could no longer be described in the older classical terms. Here, it must also be emphasized, that while quantum mechanics is really an extension of classical statistical mechanics, it served to introduce what is called the "Uncertainty Principle" in the nomenclature of science, and produced an entirely new kind of arithmetic now basic in all modern physical science.

This was the discovery of the overlooked fact that multiplication of the kind of constant numbers involved, as used in arithmetic and elementary algebra, is not commutative—that is, not interchangeable or subject to substitution and exchange, as is the simple arithmetic of the commercial institutionalized world. In terms of symbols, it simply meant that $a \times b$ does not equal $b \times a$, or $a + b$ does not equal $b + a$.

In this now famous and ultimately world-shaking formula each symbol stands for an entire *matrix* or systematic arrangement of a whole set of numbers, and matrix multiplication has quite a special meaning to physicists, as thereby the ground work for Einstein, relativistic gravitation, and the Atomic Power Age was introduced.

In this study we are not measuring economic event in its present unsettled nomenclature, but physical event in its present systematic terminology. And this is what we mean by the "language of science."

An entirely new world has come into being with all of the startling new meanings that now confront mankind. The next famous addition to the nomenclature of science was $E = MC^2$, startling the world by its incontrovertible fact and by its contradiction of the old principle of the conservation of mass and energy.

Here was the negative of past concepts of the conservation of mass and energy, denying that both are inexhaustible entities.

THE NOMENCLATURE OF ECONOMICS

While the geographical, mathematical, and other scientific terminologies are reasonably clear, and do not call for elaborate explanation, this does not apply to the vocabulary of economics.

Economic terminology is conservative and traditionally formal. Many of its terms have been retained in their original form even after their substance has changed. The highly complex modern world makes use of all the sciences. Because government today has come to play an increasingly dominant part in the affairs of all peoples, and uses science in an attempt to uncover fundamental factors and relationships which are so important that no community can afford to remain in ignorance of them, it would seem that the older term "Political Economy" might better be restored.

Economics has always suffered, as compared with the other sciences, from the inaccuracy of its linguistic equipment. As an example; the term "Land," as used in economics, refers to all natural resources. It is viewed, of course, as a factor of production, and as neither producible nor destructible—as fixed and unalterable—a definition not fully in accord with either the geographer's, geologist's, or geophysicist's concepts.

Also the term "Capital" has, itself, given more trouble to economists in search of an unambiguous definition than would appear necessary in any system of unisignificant terms. This term alone has proven the most difficult in the whole range of elementary economic analysis, and has not yet received any universal unanimity as to its meaning in terms of scope and content.

Again, the very cornerstone of economic analysis depends upon the term "value," a term replete with all sorts of conceptual ambiguities, as well as being difficult of precise universal definition throughout the different languages of the world.

MONEY—THE CONFUSING ABSTRACT MAGNITUDE

Entirely disconnected from and replacing the fundamental values of the world's land and vital natural resources which are inseparable from the life of all peoples, the popular notion of money as the central interest in economic life has created an artificial and fictitious "constant" by which all economic thought becomes plumbed and gauged as either sound or unsound. Hence this idea of money as distinct from and not involving abstractions of value from physical quantities other than metallic or arbitrary quantities intended to *measure* all things economic, supplies a role and power to money transcending theories of both economics and government.

"Money" is a term with many meanings in ordinary speech and five or six meanings in economic discussions. Economists are not always clear as to the exact nature of the connections linking one meaning to another—with results which have proven little short of disastrous in the development of monetary theory and its attendant guide to policy.

Money in economics represents a function, and as such, a storer of values. As a unit of account in commercial arithmetic it becomes a part of capital representing both land and materials—although divorced from the fundamental values of land and its products. In this respect both the arithmetic and terminology of money and finance have become so interwoven with matters purporting to be economic as to be highly confusing to the average person—nor do they correspond in more than a superficial way with the terminological usages in pure economics.

Unfortunately for mankind as well as economists, in place of thinking in terms of the world's depleting physical realities in relation to population, we have been thinking in terms of abstract money—and credit-money at that, chargeable against an unknown future. While abstract money measures all proceed from the weight theories of physics, further than this they do not go. It becomes, therefore, difficult to expect other than perfunctory benefits to accrue from a coalescence of the world's money economy with that of the world's science economy.

These matters have been called to attention, as one of the primary aims of this study has been that of ascertaining, if possible, the relative degree to which the world's monetary values and money have been adequately calculated.

UNITING THE SCIENCES

There can be little doubt that the various sciences are coalescing, and the traditional artificial barriers raised by referring to these sciences by different names are breaking down. Geology uses the methods and data of physics, chemistry, and biology, but not always the same terminology. Today, no one can say whether the science of radioactivity is to be classed with chemistry or physics, or whether economics is more properly grouped with psychology, sociology, finance, geology, or biology.

All of the evidence, however, seems to indicate that it is often just where this coalescing of dual approaches occurs, when some connecting channel between them is opened suddenly, that the most striking advances in knowledge take place. In such instances many questions hitherto insoluble have found answers through such new light cast upon them.

These matters have been taken up in some detail at the risk of boring the reader, but their significance, from a scientific point of view as an integral part of this study, makes it important that they be included in this "Baedeker," for the serious reader who would further pursue and trace through the principal categories of today's World Balance Sheet.

ATOMIC NOMENCLATURE

ATOM: An atom is the smallest primordial part of an element that can exist and still retain the properties of an element. Every atom functions on the order of a miniature planetary system consisting of a *nucleus* composed of *protons* and *neutrons,* with *electrons* rotating in different orbits or energy levels around the nucleus, with the outermost electrons determining the chemical properties of the element.

Elements such as helium and radon are the product of radium disintegration. It is the peculiar nature of radioactive elements to change into something else when they emit beta rays—a radioactive electron particle moving with the speed of light—with that something else always being a heavier element.

PROTON: The proton is a sub-atomic particle bearing a *positive* electric charge. It varies in number in the nucleus of every element. In fact it is the *atomic number* of each element in the international table of *Atomic Weights.* These atomic weights are constant and are completely independent of world geographical occurrences.

NEUTRON: The neutron is a neutral sub-atomic particle, being *neither positive nor negative.* It is approximately the same mass as the proton, and its number varies in the different elements. The neutron was discovered in 1932. It is so small that it can pass directly through all solid matter. In the production of atomic energy the key role is played by the neutrons, as they make possible the self-perpetuating chain reaction.

ELECTRON: The electron is the *negative* electrically charged sub-atomic particle. It is the most agile, fast, and commonest material particle in all matter. There is an *equal number of electrons and protons* in all of the elements.

MOLECULE: A small physical unit of an element or compound originally employed as a unit of reference by chemists, the weight of which is numerically equal to the sum of the *atomic weights* of all of the atoms in the molecule. The molecule may consist of one or more like atoms, or two or more different atoms.

ISOTOPE: Any of two or more chemical elements occupying the same place in the *periodic table* and apparently identical in properties, but differing slightly in atomic weight. The isotope has the same properties of elasticity and conduction in all directions. The term was first applied in 1913. Some 56 out of the 81 known stable elements have been analyzed into these constituent isotopes. In Table IV–9 Chap. IV the relative number of isotopes to protons and neutrons is given. Most all elements are mixtures of isotopes. Isotopes have the same number of *electrons* and *protons,* but differ in the number of *neutrons.*

POSITRON: The positron is a sub-atomic particle of *positive* electric charge, and is equal in mass to the electron. It was discovered in 1932.

MESON: The meson is another sub-atomic particle, intermediate between the proton and the electron. They are the *result of nuclear explosions* in which many particles are ejected from a single nucleus. The meson is said to be 200 times the mass of the electron. It exists in cosmic radiation in the ionosphere of the high upper atmosphere, and was discovered and first measured in 1946.

ATOMIC NUMBER: Represents the number of positive electric charges on the nucleus of a given element, and therefore also the number of electrons normally surrounding the nucleus, or the number of protons within the nucleus. It is the ordinal number of an element in the *periodic system,* and also represents the magnitude of the positive nuclear charge, in terms of the charge on the electrons, as well as the number of extranuclear electrons in the atom. Example: for Oxygen it is written in the molecular system as O_8.

ATOMIC WEIGHT: The average weight of an atom or element in units, each of which corresponds to one-sixteenth of the average weight of the oxygen atom, the international standard of which was agreed upon in 1905 as $O = 16.000$. Atomic weights are quantities of great practical importance, as they are the basis of quantitative chemical analysis and are in everyday use throughout the world.

Example: For Oxygen it is written in the physical isotope system as O^{16}.

ATOMIC MASS: Represents the whole number weight of the atom, and gives the total number of protons and neutrons. It is a fundamental constant, and determines the number of protons and neutrons in its nucleus.

Example: Oxygen atomic weight is 16. Its atomic number is 8, which represents its number of protons. 8 subtracted from the whole number 16, leaves 8 neutrons.

PERIODIC SYSTEM: A system of classification of the elements based on the discovery of a means of establishing atomic numbers by the principle that the properties of the elements are periodic functions of their atomic numbers, and demonstrated by means of a *periodic table.*

PERIODIC TABLE: A systematic table illustrating the periodic system, in which the elements are arranged in order of their atomic numbers and shown in related groups.

The periodic table is the central core around which all chemical and physical knowledge of the elements has grown. It consists in an arrangement of the elements in a unified pattern in such a way as to serve to predict the properties of undiscovered elements.

The entire edifice of modern industrial chemistry and of modern atomic physics has been developed from the periodic table.

The table owes its origin to Dimitri Mendeléev, a Russian chemist of Tobolsk,

Siberia, who produced the table in 1869. It was translated into English in 1905. (Mendeléev died in 1907.)

THERMONUCLEAR: That branch of physics which deals with the breaking down of the nucleus of atoms, and thus releasing heat and energy.

FISSION: Fission is the cleaving and splitting into parts. In nuclear physics, nuclear fission is the breaking down of the atomic nucleus of an element of relatively high atomic number into two or more nuclei of lower atomic number, with the resulting conversion of part of its mass (matter) into energy. This is the principle of the *atomic bomb*.

FUSION: Fusion is the process of uniting, combining, and adding together, as distinguished from division, as in fission. In fusion the energy release is derived from uniting lighter atoms into heavier ones. This process is called nuclear fusion. This is the principle of the *hydrogen bomb*.

FALL-OUT: Radioactive particles emitted by an atomic explosion, which settle back to the earth's surface.

PHOTON: The photon is light itself. Light is a physical quantity, consisting of matter in the form of fast-moving particles, now called photons, and measurable in terms of *energy* of the photons directly proportional to the frequency of the light waves. It is one of the fundamental units of matter along with the proton and the neutron.

GLOSSARY OF OFFICIAL MONETARY TERMS

BLOCKED MONEY: Balances to the credit of exporters covering credit extended to the European Payments Union (E.P.U.) in excess of the country's quota.

CASH: Currency holdings of banks, treasuries, and other officially recognized institutions including postal check accounts and balances with other banks.

CURRENCY: Bank notes and coin in the hands of business, individuals, and foreigners. The equivalent of money in circulation outside the treasuries.

DEPOSIT MONEY: Freely disposable deposits, payable on demand, owned by business, individuals, and foreigners.

FOREIGN EXCHANGE HOLDINGS: Include all foreign currencies, bank deposits abroad, clearing agreement balances, and short-term foreign bills, drafts, securities, and loans; with exchange in each currency valued at its par value, or, in the absence of a par value, at its official or appropriate rate.

GOLD RESERVES: Gold holdings of the various central banks, treasuries, stabilization funds, and other similar officially recognized institutions and banks of the various countries. All gold holdings are valued officially at 35 U.S. dollars per fine ounce.

MONETARY UNION: An agreement between two or more nations to adopt common measures for the regulation of their currencies.

MONEY SUPPLY: The term "money supply" is used to refer to the total of "currency" and "deposit money."

MULTIPLE CURRENCY: Refers to the various currencies in circulation within those countries where more than one currency is freely exchanged. Austria, Bolivia, Brazil, Chile, Colombia, Costa Rica, Cuba, Ecuador, Greece, Iceland, Indonesia, Iran, Israel, Lebanon, Nicaragua, Panama, Paraguay, Peru, Philippines, Spain, Thailand, Uruguay, and Venezuela had multiple currency systems in 1952.

WEIGHT UNIT SYSTEM: A system of accounts, expressed in gold francs in terms of units of 0.29032258.. grammes fine gold, introduced by the Bank for International Settlements to facilitate transfers in gold values of any desired amount. This unit was adopted at the time of formation of the B.I.S., the unit then being the monetary gold franc of Switzerland. The Swiss franc was devalued by decision of the Swiss Federal Council, December 17, 1952, to a gold content of 0.20322.. grammes fine gold; the B.I.S. continues to employ the original standard.

Appendix E. Tabulations of World Religions

TABLE E–1. TOTAL PUBLIC AND PRIVATE PHILANTHROPY OF THE WORLD, 1950

		Amount	% of Total
1.	United States of America	$ 64,000,000,000	43.92
2.	United Kingdom	12,800,000,000	8.78
3.	Germany	11,187,000,000	7.68
4.	India	5,900,000,000	4.05
5.	Spain	5,427,000,000	3.72
6.	France	5,376,000,000	3.69
7.	Japan	5,246,000,000	3.60
8.	Argentina	4,562,000,000	3.13
9.	China	3,780,000,000	2.59
10.	Mexico	2,745,000,000	1.88
11.	Australia	1,943,000,000	1.33
12.	Canada	1,840,000,000	1.26
13.	Sweden	1,792,000,000	1.23
14.	Union of South Africa	1,728,000,000	1.19
15.	Brazil	1,660,000,000	1.14
16.	Italy	1,600,000,000	1.10
17.	Switzerland	1,536,000,000	1.06
18.	Belgium	1,232,000,000	.85
19.	Netherlands	960,000,000	.66
20.	Colombia	806,000,000	.55
21.	Portugal	768,000,000	.53
22.	New Zealand	696,000,000	.48
23.	Norway	640,000,000	.44
24.	Cuba	616,000,000	.42
25.	Denmark	558,000,000	.38
26.	Eire	512,000,000	.35
27.	Chile	500,000,000	.34
28.	Peru	448,000,000	.31
29.	Venezuela	292,000,000	.20
30.	Turkey	250,000,000	.17
31.	Greece	200,000,000	.14
32.	Philippines	195,000,000	.13
33.	Rest of world	3,930,000	2.70
	World total	145,725,000,000	100.00

SOURCES: *The Statistical Atlas,* the *Blue Book of Missions,* the Interpretative Statistical Survey of the World Mission of the Christian Church, the *National Catholic Almanac.*

NOTE: Facilities for collecting figures vary greatly in different countries. Also different standards of valuation are used.

TABLE E-2. A SELECTIVE EXPLORATORY INVENTORY OF MAJOR CHRISTIAN DENOMINATIONS IN THE UNITED STATES

(*Showing Church Bodies possessing over One Million Dollars in Church Property as of 1952*)

	Churches [a]	Membership [b]	Property [c]
Roman Catholic	15,914	31,476,261	$ 2,312,081,000
Eastern Orthodox	1,324	2,129,978	251,176,000
Baptist	87,799	17,990,613	1,569,873,000
Church of Christ Scientist [d]	2,323	295,538	287,782,000
Congregationalist	5,573	1,283,754	500,666,000
Disciples of Christ [e]	8,753	1,963,003	291,150,000
Churches of Christ	16,489	1,250,000	147,056,000
Episcopalian	7,414	2,550,831	746,720,000
Friends	286	113,715	21,317,000
Jehovah's Witnesses [f]	2,905	132,797	2,558,000
Latter-Day Saints [g]	2,577	1,077,285	22,931,000
Lutherans	14,923	6,608,951	355,930,000
Methodists	54,288	11,641,891	1,421,242,000
Presbyterians	14,783	3,635,077	1,068,138,000
Seventh-Day Adventists	2,835	256,583	46,898,000
Unitarians	347	82,420	35,510,000
Universalists	401	62,006	13,900,000
Total above	238,934	82,550,703	9,094,928,000
All other denominations	48,617	12,292,142	1,638,600,000
Grand total	287,551	94,842,845	$10,733,528,000

SOURCE: Basic data developed from an original study made by the author for the American Association of Fund Raising Council in 1936 and brought forward later for the philanthropic department of the Hanover Bank, New York. The primary sources employed being the Census of Religious Bodies in the United States, the *Yearbook of American Churches,* the Official Catholic Directory, the *World Almanac Questionnaire,* and current Reports of the various Taxation and Property Assessment jurisdictions in the United States.

The Census Bureau is planning a countrywide survey of religious organizations covering the year 1956, the results to be published by the Bureau sometime in 1958.

This will be the fifth such census. Previous surveys have been taken at ten-year intervals from 1906 to 1936, as authorized by Congress. The Congress, however, failed to approve a $1,250,000 request for a survey in 1946. No final decision has been reached by Congress for the request of more than $1,000,000 estimated for the 1956 survey.

NOTES: On the basis of an earlier study made by R. R. Doane for the Foundation for Economic Education, the total property account for all U. S. religious denominations stand in round figures approximately as follows:

	Amounts	% of Total
Church edifices and parsonages	$ 3,807,000,000	35.5%
Church land	3,172,000,000	29.6
Endowments and other funds	2,655,000,000	24.7
Inventories and chattels	1,100,000,000	10.2
Total church assets	$10,734,000,000	100.0%

The present status of individual denominational annual reports are far too fragmentary to permit a complete breakdown on a church-by-church basis.

[a] Number of churches refers to church bodies and members of conventions, therefore contains some duplications.

[b] Membership; includes total membership, communicants and adherents, in some cases under 13 years of age, 13 years and over, and age not given, as reported by the various church statisticians. Many church bodies publish total memberships, including members outside the continental United States.

[c] Property; the value of church property as defined by the Bureau of the Census includes edifices, parsonages, and all other land and buildings including furnishings, fixtures, and in-

TABLE E–2. A SELECTIVE EXPLORATORY INVENTORY OF MAJOR CHRISTIAN DENOMINATIONS IN THE UNITED STATES (Concluded)

ventories normally used in connection with church services and religious activities. In addition the figures here given are inclusive of church endowments and other funds.

ᵈ Church of Christ Scientist; the By-Laws of the Church of Christ Scientist, for recent years, specify that membership figures are not for publication. However, as the total number of churches and societies together with their memberships were given in the Religious Censuses of 1926 and 1936, with only the number of churches and branches reported in later years, it has been possible to construct an approximate estimate.

ᵉ Disciples of Christ; founded by Thomas Campbell and formerly known as the Campbellite Church. The denomination comprises the International Convention, the United Christian Missionary Society, and several cooperating associations and boards.

ᶠ Jehovah's Witnesses; a membership role is not kept, but there are 2,905 "companies" (congregations) in the United States with 132,797 missionary ministers and a world total of 456,265 reported for 1952. In addition to the congregational assemblies in regular meeting halls, 91,842 weekly Bible Study groups assembles regularly in private homes.

ᵍ Latter-Day Saints; contains 692 churches of the Reorganized Church of Latter-Day Saints.

The National Council of Churches of Christ in the U.S.A., a protestant organization; Dr. Louis Kenedy, publisher of Roman Catholic Books, and the Jewish Statistical Bureau in New York have backed the proposed survey. Among reasons advanced for such a survey were the following:

It would show the world that the U.S. democracy has a strong spiritual base.

It could be used commercially by manufacturers of religious items in marketing their products.

It would be a guide for the various denominations in determining how much of a following they have and in what areas.

Adventist Bodies (1954 membership)		% of Total
Seventh-Day Adventists	260,742	87.68%
Advent Christian Church	30,737	10.34
Church of God (Abrahamic Faith)	5,295	1.78
Primitive Advent Christian Church	476	.16
Life and Advent Union	117	.04
Total bodies	297,367	100.00%

TABLE E-3. CHANGES IN NUMBER OF AFFILIATES OF THE PRINCIPAL RELIGIONS OF THE WORLD, 1882–1952

	1882	1952	Change	% Change
Non-affiliated	4,047,470	519,658,969	+ 515,611,499	+12,739.1%
Roman Catholic	230,866,533	421,340,901	+ 190,474,368	+ 82.5
Mohammedan	176,834,372	315,699,103	+ 138,864,731	+ 78.5
Confucian	256,000,000	300,289,500	+ 44,289,500	+ 17.3
Hindu	190,000,000	255,715,506	+ 65,715,506	+ 34.6
Protestant	143,237,625	193,014,595	+ 49,776,970	+ 34.8
Buddhist	147,900,000	150,300,000	+ 2,400,000	+ 1.6
Eastern Orthodox	102,976,000	127,629,986	+ 24,653,986	+ 23.9
Primitive	117,681,000	121,150,000	+ 3,469,000	+ 2.9
Taoist	43,000,000	50,053,200	+ 7,053,200	+ 16.4
Shinto	14,000,000	25,000,000	+ 11,000,000	+ 78.6
Judaism	7,186,000	11,303,350	+ 4,117,350	+ 57.4
Zoroastrian	75,000	124,890	+ 49,890	+ 66.5
World total	1,433,804,000	2,491,280,000	+1,057,476,000	+ 73.8%

SOURCES: 1882; Dr. M. Fournier de Flaix, world authority, Quarterly of the American Statistical Association, 1902. The Blue Book of Missions, 1905. From the Encyclopaedia of Social Reform, Bliss edition, p. 922, 1908.
1952; Encyclopaedia Britannica Yearbook, 1953.

NOTE: Data covering the world's religions are, by their nature, rough approximations only. Aside from Christianity, few religious organizations attempt to keep statistical records; and different methods are employed in counting members between the Catholics and Protestants.

All persons, of whatever age, who have received baptism in the Catholic church are considered members, while in most Protestant churches only those who "join" the church are numbered.

COMMENT: Considerable critical examination of the various figures covering membership in the Roman Catholic church may be called to attention here, as there does not seem to be complete agreement from data released by the various original sources. These world figures vary, by sources for the same year, as follows:

Source	Membership
British Catholic Directory	398,277,000
Official Orbis Catholicus	350,000,000
World Almanac	338,386,000
Encyclopaedia Americana	294,583,000
McCabe International	180,000,000

Countries which, from geographical and historical conditions never accepted officially the Reformation are still commonly referred to in some quarters as Catholic countries, with the entire population usually included in the Catholic total. There appears to be considerable evidence that the Catholic world total data, as corrected on this basis, would appear as follows:

	1882	1952	Change	% Change
Roman Catholic	122,820,996	190,446,087	+ 67,625,091	+ 55.1%

TABLE E-4. A HALF-CENTURY OF RELIGIOUS CHANGE IN THE WORLD, 1900–1950

	% Change
North America:	
Roman Catholic	+ 425
Protestant	− 26
All other	+1,870
South America:	
Roman Catholic	+ 63
Protestant	+ 47
All other	− 68
Europe:	
Roman Catholic	+ 23
Protestant	+ 15
All other	+ 66
Africa:	
Roman Catholic	+ 469
Protestant	+ 232
All other	+ 8
Asia:	
Roman Catholic	+ 68
Protestant	+ 458
All other	+ 44
Oceania:	
Roman Catholic	+ 135
Protestant	+ 120
All other	− 85
World total:	
Roman Catholic	+ 83
Protestant	+ 35
All other	+ 56

TABLE E-5. CHANGES IN THE WORLD'S SPIRITUAL INVENTORY, 1882–1952; MEMBERSHIP CORRECTED FOR AGE COMPARABILITY

	1882	% of Total	1952	% of Total	Change	% of the Change	% Change
Confucian	206,000,000	14.4%	313,046,000	12.6%	+ 107,046,000	10.1%	+ 52.0%
Hindu	190,000,000	13.3	255,716,000	10.3	+ 65,716,000	6.2	+ 34.6
Mohammedan	176,834,000	12.3	315,699,000	12.7	+ 138,865,000	13.1	+ 78.5
Buddhist	147,900,000	10.3	150,480,000	6.0	+ 2,580,000	.2	+ 1.7
Primitive & Anamist	102,976,000	7.2	121,150,000	4.9	+ 18,174,000	1.7	+ 17.6
Taoist	43,000,000	3.0	50,053,000	2.0	+ 7,053,000	.7	+ 16.4
Shinto	14,000,000	1.0	25,000,000	1.0	+ 11,000,000	1.1	+ 78.6
Jews	7,186,000	.5	11,303,000	.4	+ 4,117,000	.4	+ 57.3
Sikh	3,994,000	.3	6,340,000	.2	+ 2,346,000	.2	+ 58.7
Zoroastrian	75,000	.01	125,000	.01	+ 50,000	.01	+ 66.7
Total [a]	891,965,000	62.3%	1,248,912,000	50.1%	+ 356,947,000	33.7%	+ 40.0%
Protestant, Christian	123,238,000	8.6%	193,015,000	7.8%	+ 69,777,000	6.6%	+ 56.6%
Roman Catholic, Christian	122,821,000	8.5	190,446,000	7.6	+ 67,625,000	6.4	+ 55.1
Eastern Orthodox, Christian	117,681,000	8.2	127,630,000	5.1	+ 9,949,000	1.0	+ 8.5
Total Christian	363,740,000	25.3%	511,091,000	20.5%	+ 147,351,000	14.0%	+ 40.5%
Unclassified & none [b]	178,099,030	12.4%	731,277,000	29.4%	+ 553,178,000	52.3%	+310.6%
World total	1,433,804,000	100.0%	2,491,280,000	100.0%	+1,057,476,000	100.0%	+ 73.8%

[a] Predominantly Eastern religions; it is difficult to get accurate data covering these faiths, particularly because in China one may be at the same time a Confucian, a Taoist, and a Buddhist. In Japan one may be both a Buddhist and a Shintoist. In India one may be at the same time a Buddhist, a Sikh, and a Hindu.

[b] The "Unclassified and none" contains largely the various Fetishisms: Astrologists, Spiritualists, Druses, Shiites, Yezides, other miscellaneous cults, and those who have not yet joined any faith.

241

Appendix F. Bibliography

1882 PERIOD:

Accounts and Papers of Parliament, 1865–1886.
Board of Trade Reports, Committee of Privy Council for British Trade, 1876–1896.
British Trade Book, Schooling, John Holt, 1901
Dictionary of Commerce, M'Culloch, John Ramsay, 1832.
Dictionary of Statistics, Mulhall, Michael G., 1892–1899.
Digest of the Census, Booth, Charles, 1886–1892.
Growth of English Industry & the Commerce of Nations, Cunningham, William, 1882.
Historical Statistics of the United States, 1789–1945.
History of British Commerce, Levi, Leone, 1872.
Industrial History of Free Nations, Torrens, William T. M'C., 1846.
Journals of the Royal Agricultural Society, 1828–1890.
Journals of the Royal Statistical Society, 1828–1890.
Population, Wealth, Power & Resources of the British Empire, Colquhoun, Patrick, 1884.
Reports of the British Board of Internal Revenue, 1841–1881.
Royal Commission Reports, Blue Book, 1882, 1884, 1885.
Statesman's Yearbook, 1882–1883.
Statistical Abstract for the British Empire, 1878–1882.
Statistical Abstract of the United Kingdom, 1880–1893.
Surveys, Historic & Economic, Ashley, William James, 1900.
The British Empire, Dilke, Charles W., 1890.
The Condition of Nations, Social & Political, Kolb, George Friederick, 1880.
The Economist, 1882–1883.
The Growth of Capital, Giffen, Robert, 1890.
The New Encyclopedia of Social Reform, Bliss edition, 1908.
The Progress of the Working Classes, Giffen, Robert, 1884.
Whitaker's Almanac, 1882.
World Balance Sheet, Mulhall, Michael G., 1895.

READINGS:

Bohm-Bawerk, Eugene V., *Capital & Interest,* A Critical History of Economic Theory, 1889. English translation, Macmillan & Co., London & New York, 1890.
—, *Karl Marx and the Close of His System,* The Macmillan Co., 1898.
Gunton, George, *Principles of Social Economics,* G. P. Putnam's Sons, N. Y. 1891.
List, Frederick, *The National System of Political Economy,* 1885. Longmans, Green & Co., London, 1928.
Marx, Karl, *The Critique of Political Economy,* original edition, 1859. Translation from the second German edition, Kerr & Co., Chicago, 1911.
—, *Das Kapital,* 3 volumes.
    Vol. I, The Process of Capitalist Production, 1867, Kerr, 1908 and 1926.
    Vol. II, The Process of Capitalist Circulation, 1885, Kerr, 1907.
    Vol. III, The Process of Capitalist Production as a Whole, 1894, Kerr, 1909.
—, *Selected Works,* 2 volumes, Marx-Engels-Lenin Institute, Moscow, 1933.
—, *Capital;* 2 volumes; G. D. H. Cole translation from the German ed. of *Das Kapital,* Vol. I, J. M. Dent & Sons, London, 1946.
—, *The Poverty of Philosophy,* 1846, International Publishers, N. Y.

Mill, John Stuart, *Principles of Political Economy*, 1848. Colonial Press, N. Y. 1890.

Ricardo, David, *The Principles of Political Economy and Taxation*, 1817. Dent & Sons, London, 1911.

Rodbertus, Johann Karl, *The Formation of Political Economy* (Entstehung der Volkswirtschaft), 1850, 14th edition, 1919.

Smith, Adam, *An Inquiry into the Nature & Causes of the Wealth of Nations*, 1776. Edwin Cannan edition, The Modern Library, N. Y. 1937.

INTERMEDIATE PERIODS: (For inter- and extra-polation checking.)

Countries	*Sources*
Argentina	Bunge
Australia	Knibbs
Austria	Fellner
Belgium	Stuart
Brazil	Mirando, Stamp
Canada	Bankers' Association
Chile	Simon
China	Lieu, Sino-International Economic Research Center
Denmark	Gini
Ecuador	Yearbook of Ecuador
France	Pupin, Thiery
Germany	Helfferich
Hungary	Fellner
Italy	Gini
Japan	Stamp
Mexico	Patino
Russia	Neymarck
Spain	Barthe
Sweden	Flodstrom, Fochlbeck
Switzerland	Gini
United Kingdom	Giffen, Milner, Money, Crammond, Stamp
United States	King, Doane, National Bureau of Economic Research

NOTE: For a full description of the above works see *Encyclopaedia Britannica*, 1948 ed., vol. 23, pp. 450–451; and *Studies in Income and Wealth*, vol. 10, National Bureau of Economic Research.

1952 PERIOD:

Annual Abstract of Statistics, British Statistical Office.

Annual Reports of the Bank for International Settlements.

Annual Reports of the Bank for Reconstruction & Development.

Annual Reports of the International Monetary Fund.

Balance of Payments Yearbook, International Monetary Fund.

Business Statistics, 1953 ed., Statistical Supplement to the Survey of Current Business.

China Information Bulletin, Chinese News Service.

Czechoslovak Economic Bulletin, Ministry of Foreign Trade.

Demographic Yearbooks, United Nations.

Direction of International Trade, Joint publication of the I.M.F. and the I.B.R.D.

Focus, Monthly publications of the American Geographic Society.

Foreign Policy Bulletin, Foreign Policy Association.

Headline Series, Foreign Policy Association.
Index Svenske Handelsbanken, Stockholm, Sweden.
International Financial Statistics, International Monetary Fund.
Magyar, Külkereskedelmi Zserbkönyv, 1938.
National Income Statistics, Statistical Office of the United Nations, 1938–1952.
Norway Digest, Royal Norwegian Information Service.
Resources for Freedom, 5 vols., The President's Materials Policy Commission.
Spain, Spanish Information Bureau.
Statesman's Yearbook, 1952–1954.
Statistical Abstract for the British Commonwealth.
Statistical Abstract of the Netherlands.
Statistical Abstract of the United Kingdom.
Statistical Abstract of the United States.
Statistical Yearbooks of the League of Nations.
Statistical Yearbooks, United Nations, 1951, 1952, 1953, 1954.
The Official Journal of the Union of South Africa.
Yearbooks of Food & Agricultural Statistics.
Yearbooks of Labor Statistics, International Labor Office.

SPECIAL REPORTS:

Bulletin of Political, Economic and Cultural Information, Palocio Foz, Lisbon, Portugal.
Comparability of National Income Statistics, Economic & Social Council, United Nations.
Danish Foreign Office Journal.
Documents & Reports on Poland, Polish Research & Information Service.
Economic Conditions in Denmark, Danish Statistical Office.
Far East Data Books, Division of Statistical Reports, U. S. Office of Desearch & Reports.
First Memorandum on the Central Economic Plan, Netherlands Central Planning Bureau.
Forest Resources of the World, F.A.O., Division of Forestry & Forest Products.
General Headquarters, Supreme Commander for the Allied Powers, Japan.
Industrial Reparations Survey of Japan, Overseas Consultants, Inc.
Inter-Allied Reparations Agency First Report, 18 signatory governments.
International Population Problems (Restricted), Population Commission, United Nations.
International Reference Service Reports, Bureau of Foreign & Domestic Commerce, U.S.A.
Italy's Economic & Financial Position, B.I.S., Monetary & Economic Department.
Nationalization of Key Industries in Eastern Europe, Foundation for Foreign Affairs.
On the World Economic Situation, Dr. A. A. Arutiunian, U.S.S.R.
Organ of the Information Bureau of the Communist Parties, Belgrade, Yugoslavia.
Report of the Economic Survey Mission to the Philippines.
Report of the U.S. High Commission, Military Government of Austria.
Report of the U.S. High Commission, Military Government of Germany.
Reports 1 and 2, Reappraisal of the Forest Situation, U. S. Forest Service.
Stalin Five-Year Plan, Embassy of the U.S.S.R.
Statement on War Losses & Damages of Poland, Bureau of War Indemnities, Warsaw.
The Sudan, The Sudan government.
World Wealth Reports:
   National Debt & Income of 11 Nations, Institute of International Finance, N. Y. University.
   National Income of 64 Nations, U. S. Bureau of Statistics.

Public Debt, Income & Expenditure of 38 Nations, Stock Exch. Official Year Book, London.

Wealth, Debt & Income of 49 Nations, Redmond & Co., N. Y.

World Economic Conditions (Confidential), Economic Dept of the Chase National Bank, N. Y.

World Wealth Estimates, 48 Nations (Confidential), Economics Div. I.T.&T. Corporation.

READINGS:

A Treasury of Science, edited by Harlow Shapley, Harper & Brothers, N. Y. 1943.

Analysis of Nationalism in Southeast Asia, Emerson, Rupert, 1946.

Beyond Supply & Demand, Gambs, John S., Columbia University Press, N. Y. 1946.

Capitalism, Socialism and Democracy, Schumpeter, Joseph A.; Harper & Brothers, 1947.

Economic Problems of War, edited by George A. Steiner, John Wiley & Sons, N. Y. 1942.

Economics in the Modern World, Thompson & Probst, University of Chicago, 1949.

Essays on Nationalism, Hayes, Carlton, J. H., American Foundation for Political Education.

Germany's Master Plan, Borkin & Welsh, Duell, Sloane & Pierce, N. Y. 1943.

Historical Geology, Schuchret, Charles, John Wiley & Sons, N. Y. 1924.

International Economics, Harrod, R. F., Cambridge University Press, 1948.

Land Economics, Ely & Wherwein, The Macmillan Co., N. Y. 1946.

Mainsprings of Civilization, Huntington, Ellsworth, John Wiley & Sons, Inc., N. Y. 1945.

Natural Principles of Land Use, Graham, Edward H., Oxford University Press, 1944.

Power Politics, Wight, Martin, Royal Institute of International Affairs.

Races, Lands, & Food, Mukerje, Radhakamel, The Dryden Press, N. Y. 1946.

Religion and the Rise of Capitalism, Tawney, R. H., Harcourt, Brace & Co., N. Y. 1937.

Richland, Poorland, Chase, Stuart, Whittlesey House, N. Y. 1936.

Science and Sanity, Korzybski, Alfred, 2nd edition, The Science Press, 1941.

Science & the Modern World, Whitehead, Alfred North, The Macmillan Co., N. Y. 1939.

Soil Conservation, Bennett, Hugh Hammond, McGraw-Hill Book Co., N. Y. 1939.

The Economic Recovery of Germany, Guillebaud, C. W., Macmillan & Co., Ltd., London, 1939.

The Economics of War, Menderhausen, Horst, Prentice-Hall, Inc., N. Y. 1940.

The Evolution of Earth & Man, ed. by Baitsell, George A., Yale University Press, 1929.

The Meaning of Evolution, Simpson, George Gaylord, Yale University Press, 1950.

The Mind & Society, Pareto, Vilfredo, 4 vols., Harcourt, Brace & Co., N. Y. 1942.

The Modern Democratic State, Lindsay, A. D., Oxford University Press, 1949.

The Origin of Life, Oparin, A. I., The Macmillan Co., N. Y. 1938.

The Revolt of the Masses, Ortega y Gasset, W. W. Norton & Co., N. Y. 1932.

The Theory of Capitalist Development, Sweezy, Paul M., Oxford University Press, 1942.

The Theory of Economic Progress, Ayres, C. E., University of N. Carolina Press, 1944.

The Trade of Nations, Heilperin, Michael A., Alfred A. Knopf, 1947.

Towards World Prosperity, edited by Mordecai Ezekiel, Harper & Brothers, 1947.

Vanishing Lands; A World Survey of Soil Erosion, Jacks & Whyte, Doubleday, Doran, 1939.

World Agriculture, an International Survey, Oxford University Press, 1943.

World Economic Survey, 1942–1944 (11th issue), League of Nations.

World Politics, Nelson, Levit, & Probst, University of Chicago, 1948.

SPECIAL ATTENTION:

Human Breeding and Survival, Burch, Guy Irving, Pelican Books, N. Y. 1947.
Human Fertility: The Modern Dilemma, Cook, Robert C., William Sloane Associates, N. Y. 1951.
Industrial & Commercial Geography, Smith, J. Russell, Henry Holt & Co., N. Y. 1947.
Our Plundered Planet, Osborn, Fairfield, Little, Brown & Co., Boston, 1948.
Population on the Loose, Pendell, Elmer, Wilfred Funk, Inc., N. Y. 1951.
Population Roads to Peace or War, Pendell, Elmer, Pelican Books, N. Y. 1947.
Publications of the Population Reference Bureau, Washington, D. C.
Road to Survival, Vogt, William, William Sloane Associates, Inc., N. Y. 1948.
The Challenge of Man's Future, Brown, Harrison, The Viking Press, N. Y. 1954.
The Limits of the Earth, Osborn, Fairfield, Little, Brown & Co., Boston, 1953.
The Principles of Human Geography, Huntington, Ellsworth, John Wiley & Sons, N. Y. 1949.
World Resources & Industries, Zimmermann, Erich W., Harper & Brothers, N. Y. 1933.

ATLASES:

Ambassador World Atlas, C. S. Hammond & Co., Inc., New York.
American Oxford Atlas, Oxford University Press, New York.
Atlas of the World's Mineral Resources, Department of Geography, University of Maryland.
Atlas Ziem Odzyskanych, Central Statistical Bureau, Warsaw, Poland.
Century Atlas of the World, 1897–1911, The Century Company, New York.
Cosmopolitan World Atlas, Rand McNally, New York.
Encyclopaedia Britannica World Atlas, Trade ed., C. S. Hammond & Co., Inc., New York.
Encyclopaedia Britannica World Atlas, Unabridged.
Modern World Atlas, C. S. Hammond & Co., Inc., New York.
Odhams New Atlas of the World, Odhams Press Limited, London.
Our World from the Air, Internat'l Survey of Man and His Environment, Doubleday & Co., N. Y.
Oxford Advanced Atlas, 7th ed., Bartholomew, Oxford University Press, England.
Oxford Economic Atlas, 8th ed., Bartholomew & Lyde, Oxford University Press, England.
Pictorial World Atlas, C. S. Hammond & Co., Inc., New York.
Ready Reference Atlas of the World, Weber-Costello Co., Chicago.
The Fortune Atlas for World Strategy, Alfred A. Knopf, New York.
Times Atlas of the World, 5 Volumes.[1]

TAX AND ASSESSMENT SYSTEMS OF THE WORLD:

1882 Period:
  Reports of the Commissioners of Inland Revenue, United Kingdom.
  Board of Trade Reports, and Statistical Abstract, for the British Empire.
1952 Period:
  Tax Systems of the World; 6th, 11th, 12th, and 13th editions.
    The Tax Research Foundation, Mayne S. Howard, editor. Prepared under the direction of the New York State Tax Commission; Commerce Clearing House, Inc., publishers, Chicago.

[1] Vol. III, Modern Europe, ready later this year, 1955. Complete Atlas available in 1959. The project will have required more than half a million man-hours of skilled work and will have cost about two million dollars.

Appendix G. Conversion Factors

METRIC UNITS AND THEIR BRITISH AND U.S. EQUIVALENTS

Metric Units	British or U.S. Equivalents
Length:	
1 centimetre	0.393700 inch
1 metre (100 cm)	3.280833 feet
	1.093611 yards
1 kilometre	0.621370 mile
Area:	
1 square centimetre — cm²	0.155000 square inch
1 square metre — m²	10.76387 square feet
	1.195985 square yards
1 hectare (10,000 m²)	2.47104 acres
1 square kilometre — km²	0.386101 square mile
Volume:	
1 cubic centimetre — cm³	0.061023 cubic inch
1 cubic metre — m³	35.31445 cubic feet
	1.307943 cubic yards
Liquid measure:	
1 litre	0.87990 Imperial quart
	1.05671 U.S. quarts
1 hectolitre (100 litres)	21.9975 Imp. gallons
	26.4178 U.S. gallons
Weight:	
1 kilogramme (1,000 grammes)	32.1507 Troy ounces
	2.204622 avdp. pounds
1 quintal (100 kg)	220.4622 avdp. pounds
1 metric ton (1,000 kg)	1.102311 short tons
	0.984206 long ton

BRITISH AND U.S. UNITS AND THEIR METRIC EQUIVALENTS

British or U.S. Units	Metric Equivalents
Length:	
1 inch	2.540005 centimetres
1 foot	0.304801 metre
1 yard	0.914402 metre
1 mile (1,760 yards)	1.609347 kilometre
Area:	
1 square inch	6.451626 centimetres carres
1 square foot	0.092903 metre carre
1 square yard	0.836131 metre carre
1 acre (4,840 sq. yards)	0.404687 hectare
1 square mile (640 acres)	2.589998 kilometres carres
Volume:	
1 cubic inch	16.387162 centimetres cubes
1 cubic foot	0.028317 metre cube
1 cubic yard	0.764559 metre cube
Liquid measure:	
1 Imperial quart	1.13649 litre
1 U.S. quart	0.946333 litre
1 Imperial gallon	0.045460 hectolitre
1 U.S. gallon	0.037853 hectolitre
Weight	
1 Troy ounce	0.0311035 kilogramme
1 avoirdupois pound	0.453592 kilogramme
1 cwt (112 lb.)	0.50802 quintal
1 short ton (2,000 lb.)	0.907185 tonne metrique
1 long ton (2,240 lb.)	1.016047 tonne metrique

SOURCE: *United Nations Statistical Yearbook*, 1954, page 555; also pages 556, 557, **and** 558 for other units of measure.

General Index

Index of Countries